music of the spheres

BY GUY MURCHIE

MUSIC OF THE SPHERES

with illustrations by the author

HOUGHTON MIFFLIN COMPANY BOSTON

THE RIVERSIDE PRESS CAMBRIDGE

BOOKS BY GUY MURCHIE

MEN ON THE HORIZON

SONG OF THE SKY

MUSIC OF THE SPHERES

SECOND PRINTING

The Riverside Press

CAMBRIDGE · MASSACHUSETTS

PRINTED IN THE U.S.A.

TO MY BROTHER

DONALD

who loved the waves and
the spangled sky

There is geometry in the humming
of the strings. There is music in the
spacings of the spheres.

PYTHAGORAS
5th century B.C.

acknowledgments

During the six years of full-time study and labor I have put into this book, I have had assistance and inspiration from hundreds of sources — most constantly of all from my wife Käthe, who distracts me from distractions while working as best she can to keep the grass greener on our side of the fence. And among many others no one has helped me more than Professor Mael A. Melvin, now in Argentina, who gave me a brainstirring, concentrated course in atomic physics, and Per Lowdin, professor of chemistry in Uppsala, Sweden, who cleared up many a cloudy paradox with his beautiful articulation.

Likewise I have been assisted by Astronomy Professor Samuel Herrick of the University of California (who answered questions about space and stars), by Professor Harlow Shapley (who looked over my astronomical illustrations and discussed the universe) and other astronomers of Harvard Observatory (who read or criticized various chapters on moons, planets and stars), by astronomer Seth B. Nicholson (who was hospitable to my proposed names for the eight nameless moons of Jupiter, four of which he himself discovered), by Professor Aage Bohr of the Copenhagen Institute for Theoretical Physics, by Professor Gerald Holton (who helped my chapter on relativity without approving of it) and other physicists, mathematicians and philosophers at Harvard and Massachusetts Institute of Technology, by Giorgio de Santillana, professor of the history of science at M.I.T. (who read the whole manuscript with a constructive eye), by Michael Powsner, a rare and generous science teacher of South Shaftsbury, Vermont (who gave books, time and ideas), by Daniel Comstock, an engineer with imagination (who gave me my first lesson in relativity), by Mervin J. Kelly, president emeritus of Bell Telephone Laboratories, by Willy Ley, authority on space travel, by R. Buckminster Fuller the geometric philosopher, by Isaac Asimov the science writer (who criticized the manuscript in detail), by Gerald Brenan the historian of Spain, who told me the story of ancient Sybaris (pages 363–365), and by several highly competent editors, particularly Betsy Pitha who made many constructive suggestions while gently working her fine-toothed comb through both the text and illustrations.

Of course none of these generous persons can be held responsible for the errors that must still be lurking somewhere in these pages. The authorship of all surviving boners, alas, must remain mine alone.

Among periodicals my most consistently valuable source has been *Scientific American*, with occasionally useful gleanings also from *American Scientist*, *Main Currents*, *Navigation*, *The New York Times* and the science section of *Time*. And the following books have contributed significantly: *A History of Science* by George Sarton, *Introduction to Astronomy* by Cecilia Payne-Gaposchkin, *Earth, Moon and Planets* by Fred L. Whipple, *The Stars* by H. A. Rey, *Frontiers of Astronomy* by Fred Hoyle, *Concerning the Nature of Things* by Sir William Bragg, *The Physical Basis of Things* by John A. Eldridge, *General Chemistry* by Linus Pauling, *Matter, Earth and Sky* by George Gamow, *The Strange Story of the Quantum* by Banesh Hoffmann, *Light and Colour in the Open Air* by M. Minnaert, *The Analysis of Matter* by Bertrand Russell, *Space, Time and Gravitation* by Sir Arthur Eddington, *The Principle of Relativity* by Albert Einstein, H. A. Lorentz, H. Weyl and H. Minkowski, *Physics and Philosophy* by Werner Heisenberg, *Philosophy of Science* by Philipp Frank, and many others, the more important of which are mentioned by name in the text.

Monte Miramar, Malaga, Spain   G. M.
1961

contents

moons of rock
and suns of fire

1. out from the breathing earth

THE STARS BENEATH MY FEET stare upward, strange and bold. They do not twinkle. They burn steadfastly in the black, bottomless sky.

My watch says 02:40 Universal Time. But it is not really night. That searchlight glaring at us is the sun. That toenail of crescent beside it the new moon, bright as snow, even its dark side illumined so clearly I can recognize Mare Imbrium without using the telescope.

Most conspicuous of all is the great pale-blue ball that fills a third of the void: the earth, by far the most positive thing outside our ship within reach of my senses — a matriarch of gravity leaning out at us from ink-black space — a somethingness rolling through nothingness. Its dappled surface, here crisp and clear-grained, there soft and filmy, is pure blue between the curved storms and lesser suds of white cloud areas, while on one side a fiery highlight of sunshine reflects off the glassy Pacific Ocean.

If I must admit to feeling a little giddy right now perhaps it is just the break-off, sometimes called "space dumps," that the satellite pioneers used to complain of — a sort of apprehensive loneliness that no amount of friendly banter with the rest of my crew seems really able to shake. With conscious casualness I stoop to wipe the floor port with my magnetic rag and gasp again at my incapacity to comprehend those stars below as well as above me. Or are they really not below me but just over there and out here or this way and that way?

Although I have read about space all my life, nothing I've learned could begin to prepare me for the reality. The utter and soul-draining blackness of that gulf that drops away and down and down to infinity! I am as a mosquito lost at night over the Pacific Ocean. And the real Pacific that was once so endless — I can see it still down there as but the shining cheek of a world that has fallen from my feet. My aloneness is breath-taking.

But I think I am already getting used to the relaxation, the weightlessness of space — it is like swimming, only more so — though the lack of a definite up or down will take longer. Not that that alarms my mind, which can consciously adjust, but it does provoke a hollow corporal insecurity somewhere beyond the reach of the will.

Time will soon reply to these questions, of course, especially if time up here in space is part of time on Earth. So far it seems to be — but one should not be hasty in such matters. Time changes with speed, and every vortex of gravity may have its own. Besides, I am trespassing on the future here. I mean that I am really *not* here yet in the common terrestrial understanding for, at the present writing, men have not quite attained to habitable stations in space — although as surely as winter is followed by spring they will have done so shortly after this book is published.

Nonetheless, for all my inability to be here in flesh at the earthly moment I am still inevitably here in the truer larger sense — in future body almost as surely as in present mind. For robot space stations are already in our local sky and bigger and better ones abuilding on Earth and who knows in how many other places in both ancient and future days? Thus my presence in this borrowed space is a symbolic certainty and a true part of the very time-space continuum I am venturing to explore.

I say "venturing" advisedly, for if you don't think this passage through the boundless unknown is a venture I humbly wish you would just try it yourself sometime — whether or not you have a body fit to accompany you as, we shall presently see, may not much longer be so very important.

"Why?" you may ask. "Why should I stir from my accustomed ways for the risks and trials of space? What could be my motive? Have I not trouble enough already on the earth I was made for?"

Yes, you have trouble on Earth all right, I admit. But who told you you were made for Earth trouble alone? Space is part of the world — your world if you have the stuff to make it yours. Did anyone warn the birds that the air was only for bees and bugs? Do you suppose God put the stars here just to look at? Did He draw a boundary to your piece of sky?

I say space and time are as inevitably yours as the wind and the sea and you cannot refuse them. Man must respond to his destiny. He has already knocked on the upper door and it is opening. The hinges will not be stayed.

As if this were not reason enough to be here riding an intangible orbit with faith in Newton for my fuel, I have a world of other reasons. The earth has been rolling blindly through the void for some five billion years, slowly developing an organ of consciousness, and it is just now arriving at the stage where it is capable of seeing and understanding itself. Its stones and rivers have begun to speak and its winds at last have found their tongues in the mind of man. The very layers of the soil, the grain of glaciers, the rings of trees, even the sea bottoms have become living pages of our world's diary that she may read back to herself for the first time.

Thus you and I have been appointed to a greater consciousness than our own. Man has become the Self of the material earth — in a larger symbolic sense, perhaps potentially a cell of the consciousness of the whole time-space universe. So I say it behooves him to enlarge his view, to accept life's new dimension when it is offered — to adopt the perspective of space.

Indeed, there is a greater nature up here, a nature that does not abhor a vacuum or trust a parallel line. Space is where heat no longer rises, where things fall not down but along, where gravity can push as well as pull, and even the straightest lines are curves. It is where you begin to happen to events instead of just letting events happen to you. It is where you must be on constant guard against the dangers of "common sense." It is where scientists and philosophers will be finding not only deeper answers to their questions but deeper questions for their answers. It is the home of unworldly dreams and undreamed-of worlds, of globes of fire and clouds of spinning gas, of emptiness impenetrable, of planets inhabitable, of moons incredible. It is the major reality of the material world, the first vantage place for outer knowledge. I have come here with open eyes to see the unseen. I have come with open mind to listen for the music of the spheres.

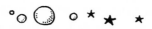

To understand what this fantastic world is all about — to see its basic pattern and meaning — I must crane my soul to examine it deeply and, in so far as is possible, independently. I must seek a perspective far beyond the traditional, beyond the safe and proper, even beyond the human. I must see not only out of my own eyes here and now but out of lenses and soul-ports on the undiscovered planet Umkrid 22 in the dry spring of the year 47,909! It is an ambitious aim for a book of twentieth-century earthly publication.

Since one must begin somewhere, let me begin with the most familiar, our home sphere, then branch outward to the moon and sun and stars. Then inward to the dazzling cosmos of the atom — to space, to time and their relations — deferring until later a close look at life, at the mind and the spirit — yet essaying, if it be permitted me, a humble muse upon the meaning of it all.

One of the first things to be noted about our home sphere, the earth, is that it is not a sphere. Instead, although the eye alone cannot detect it, it is more exactly what a geometrician would call an oblate spheroid with a faint tendency toward the pear shape, a sort of fat doorknob gently flattened at the spindle poles, worn from long handling in some places but in need of sandpapering in others — perhaps a little on the warped side or, if you'll pardon my saying so, slightly skewed. In fact, one could never define its shape precisely, for it is not only hopelessly irregular in detail but constantly changing. In a very real sense it is alive. Like an animal it stirs in its sleep, it "breathes" air, it grows, its wounds heal, its juices circulate, its skin metabolizes, its nerves crackle quietly with vital messages. It even rumbles with internal gas and dreams and itches a little and (through its inhabitants) feels self-conscious.

This living aspect of the earth is something you don't hear much about in geography classes, but it is hard to miss from my new space-eye view. Beside the obvious rhythms of the swirling waves of weather folding over and over each other, the steady advance of the soft twilight edge of night and the ever-changing atmospheric colors, the solid flesh of Earth itself where visible seems to blush and glow with the hours. The great western plains of wheat reflect light differently after a wide shift of wind. The green of shallow seas deepens toward blue with the rise of tides. The Gulf Stream and the jet stream change courses in the heat of an afternoon. Looking at large mountain chains, one can even sense the slow lateral movement of continents steadily pinching the loose skin of the planet.

Of course, geophysicists know that this life rhythm of the globe does not stop at the surface but continues right through its middle, that not only the sea and the air have regular tides but the very rock gently nods to the beck of the moon, and waves tuned to the sun literally pierce the planet's heart. A single stone or a granite cliff naturally seems too brittle in human eyes to have any springiness in it, yet a crystallized rocky crust the size of the earth proves to be more flexible than steel and molds itself almost perfectly to the flows of the material below, which is increasingly fluent with depth. The black basalt yields to what is deduced to be pliable greenish olivine in the first fifty miles; within a few hundred more this becomes a plastic mantle of silica or magnesia or perhaps iron oxide, turning completely liquid halfway to the center (as is proved by seismic waves); and there is almost surely some sort of alloy of molten nickel-iron at the core.

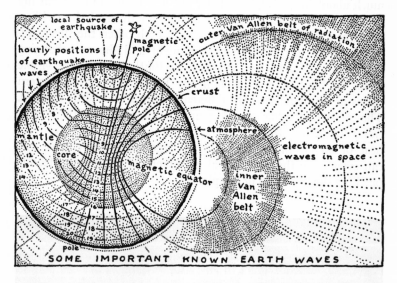

SOME IMPORTANT KNOWN EARTH WAVES

Although the pressures are so great in the earth's depths (up to four million times the greatest atmospheric pressure) that even "liquids" may be twice as "solid" as steel, there is definitely some free flow of substance. Indeed, shock waves that reach the surface as earthquakes and mysterious slow tides involving magnetism and gravity and modulating the actual shape of the planet continue to pulse through it like bile and adrenalin in the body.

The earth's magnetism, for example, evidently has a strong primary field geared to its axis of rotation with various overlapping lesser components that shift continuously. These residual magnetic fields recently were measured to move irregularly westward at an average rate of more than a mile a month, completing a full revolution about every 1,600 years — thus suggesting that the earth's moving core and mantle exert a force upon each other comparable to the armature and field coils of an electric motor. The poles of the earth, both geographic and magnetic, have likewise been deduced to shift, in this case only a few inches a year. The calculation goes back to the year 700,000,-000 B.C., when the North Pole seems to have been in what is now Arizona, then probably a swamp or a shallow area of the great world sea.

The flowings of earthly materials of different densities also create cryptic patterns of subnormal and supernormal gravity on the surface, like the recently discovered sinuous band of low gravity in the East Indies, where everything weighs a little less and a champion javelin thrower has an advantage of nearly a foot over some of his rivals in higher latitudes.

A beginning of conception of the temperature increase with depth into the earth can be had by visiting the "world's deepest well," an old borehole of the Continental Oil Company near Wasco, California, where you can cook your coffee just by lowering it 15,000 feet or less. For rocks reach the boiling point of water in the first two or three miles below the solid surface practically everywhere on Earth, and there is an increase of something like 50° F. with every mile of descent from then on (assuming pressure is the determining factor and not mainly the radioactivity of the earth's skin as some think). The rate gradually diminishes until the temperature levels off, according to present estimates, somewhere around 10,000° F. at the center.

The long-range effect of this cauldron of moiling, boiling rock and metal of course has been to brew a surface slag of earth just such as we know today, but which has by no means yet finished cooking. In fact, if the phases it has already gone through are any indication, it will look and be startlingly different in a mere hundred thousand years and in a few million you will scarcely know it as the same world. The present mountains, for example, are just a momentary frown on the earth's face — passing wrinkles that have only at long intervals appeared before and will never be the same again. During almost all of her five billion years of life the earth's face has been much smoother than we can remember it, the oceans shallower, the continents lower, smaller and swampier. In fact, much of the time since the oceans first appeared they have covered the earth so evenly that there were scarcely more than a few strange-shaped islands (such as the primordial Labrador) in the single world ocean and much less contrast of climate between the equator and the poles, the seasons unnoticeable, and most winds trade-winds that blew all through the shorter days and nights and years and under the heavier clouds that seldom parted to let the fish and crabs and insects see the bigger, faster moon.

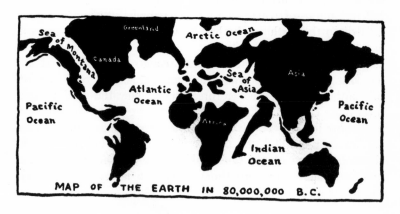

MAP OF THE EARTH IN 80,000,000 B.C.

It has only been now and then during relatively brief periods of shrinkage that the earth's crisp skin has had to wrinkle much to fit the cooling, contracting mantle beneath it. Between times the mantle may well expand, splitting the surface along seams known as rifts, while the wrinkles are quickly worn down to gentle plains by the constant grindstones of rain and wind and sand that have been measured to erode away all exposed parts of the land at the average rate of about an inch a century. Naturally this wear is hundreds of times faster on mountain crags or in the beds of rushing streams, but in settled valleys (as in the oceans) there occurs the reverse of erosion, a piling up of sediment and vegetable and animal matter and debris of civilization, preserving history for the archaeologists. Also, the average erosion pace is naturally slowed down in the gentler ages when there are no mountains. But still there has to be an over-all net erosion gain on land else the mountains would get out of hand, and all geological evidence shows that the intermittent swelling and crinkling of the mantle — which has altered the earth's circumference by amounts probably as great as 100 miles since the oceans formed — has been more than matched by the smoothing out of wrinkles faster than they came. In fact, nearly two miles' depth of solid granite has been washed and blown off the land's entire face, counting pinnacle and plain alike, just during the oceanic ages. This is shown by the fact that the salt now dissolved in all the oceans, if spread out uniformly over the land, would make a layer 450 feet thick — 450 feet being 5 percent of "nearly two miles" — while practically all of the salt has been traced to granite rock of which it also forms 5 percent.

Naturally, it is an effort of imagination to visualize this crimping and grinding, this rhythmic roughening and polishing of the earth. But the evidence of it is not out of reach. I need little more than to shift to a coarser time-gear in my sense of perspective to see the fleeting flesh in what poets used to call the "everlasting hills," the surgery of rivers, the chewing of rock by invisible jaws of air, the rasping hoofs of glaciers, even the now-rough, now-gentle uplifting of whole continents. Consider the placid Buena Vista oil field in California, which looks like the epitome of *terra firma* but which geologists find is rising steadily half an inch a year, four feet a century. This dull rate ceases to be dull the instant you multiply the centuries ahead to notice that, if it holds its pace, Buena Vista will be two miles taller than the present Mount Everest (likewise rising) before even a million more years have fled. And of course, a million-year-old mountain is just a shoulder-shrug to an earth that already counts her years in the billions.

Like matter itself, *terra firma* thus reveals her illusory nature. Every peaceful cornfield becomes a potential Paricutin of smoke and brimstone, every little fissure a San Andreas Fault of threatening earthquake catastrophe. Of such are mountains born and raised — too slowly for mortal eye to see — too slowly to be noticed by the full sweep of human history — yet literally bursting and buckling and boiling in the view of the patient moon, who has reason enough to know the meaning of violence as anyone can see in her pitted face.

If creation of mountains needs a long view for appreciation, the building of continents needs a still longer one. Yet both are essentially the same process on scales of differing magnitude. All the earth's crust, including the seas, is floating on the molten basalt and olivine some ten to fifty miles down and, like icebergs in water, all parts of the solid crust displace volumes of the sub-liquid exactly in proportion to their weight. Thus the continents, being made of relatively more of the lighter granite,

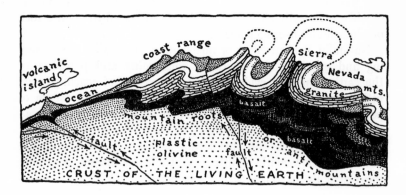

float higher than the heavier basalt ocean floors, and every mountain must balance its height with a similar depth reaching unseen far into the dark fluid beneath. This is so literally true, say geologists, that removing mountains will have the same kind of difficulty for future atomic engineers that eliminating old willows had for our forebears: no sooner will they get the mountain leveled clean than the lightened "stump" will start to rise again, floating on olivine, and this resprouting will likely continue in diminishing degree until the last stubborn root has been painstakingly dug away.

What is true of rock applies in less degree also to rock's shifty burden of ice in the form of glaciers crawling on the floating rock and of pack ice drifting on the sea that rests on floating rock. Looking over the earth carefully, I notice that a full tenth of all its land is covered with glacial ice, mostly in Antarctica and Greenland, with a slight sprinkling in the warmer zones. And if I thumb back through the pages of geologic time, it is apparent that these glaciers are the remains of the last ice age, which covered about a third of the land some twenty thousand years ago. The ice age was the fourth in the current series of ice ages which, according to the most plausible present theory, was caused primarily by the aforementioned wandering of the earth's axis of rotation, which only a few million years ago brought the North Pole from the Pacific to the Arctic Ocean. Although the cooling effect of oblique and reduced sunlight in the polar zone had previously been offset by the relatively free circulation of the vast Pacific waters, this source of warmth was left behind as the axis swung farther into the Arctic confines. And after the water evaporating from the cooling Arctic Ocean had produced so much snow and therefore such a volume of glaciation that the earth's sea level ebbed nearly three hundred feet (exposing much of the undersea ridge that joins Iceland to the British

Isles), the Arctic became so dammed up and isolated that it froze over. By this time, however, the ice age had reached a maximum. The crust over the Arctic Ocean cut off evaporation, humidity and snowfall so drastically that the glaciers were reduced to a slower growing rate in winter than their melting rate in summer with the result that they gradually dwindled down toward nothing. This net melting in turn raised the sea level again, restoring circulation and warmth to the Arctic until it was once more an open sea and could release enough humidity to trigger a new ice age.

With the South Pole also moving into the interior of a continent at the same time the North Pole penetrated the enclosed Arctic, the earth's normal polar-tropical circulation of surface juices was restricted to an extreme degree — producing an effect similar to widening the spread of a thermostat switch until the furnace turn-on and shut-off temperatures are so far apart that the house (in this case, the earth) alternates between being too hot and too cold.

Such a complex state of temperature-humidity oscillation, of course, may well continue until the earthly poles, prodded by weight shifts between glacier and sea, work their way back into ocean regions of larger circulation. For obviously all it takes to start a glacier is a slight unmelted residue of spring snow at the time of the first autumn flurries in an average year. As long as there is just that slight net gain of the white patch from one year to the next, the glacier will grow, and precipitation out of humid air is surely as vital a factor as coolness in creating it. This is shown by the presence of glaciers on the equator in humid spots like Ecuador, New Guinea and even around Lake Victoria in hottest central Africa, while dry northern Alaska, northern Siberia, and the northernmost tip of Greenland, where it now seldom snows, have no glaciers at all.

But the largest lag factor affecting ice-age rhythms seems to be the amazing insulation of the terrestrial oceans as a whole — oceans which today still retain much of the coolth of the last glacial period in their depths, being sometimes below the freezing point of fresh water along their bottoms and averaging close to 32° F. throughout, despite much greater warmth at most places on the sunny surface, to say nothing of the immense heat of the underlying basalt. This present oceanic coldness inevitably inhibits salt-water evaporation, thereby retarding worldwide precipitation including snowfall, the raw material of glaciers. So in natural consequence, most ice areas are now waning. Yet in another twenty or thirty thousand years, when glaciers will presumably be only museum pieces, the ocean will have warmed enough so that evaporation will be faster, the skies cloudier, and — if man has not interfered too much with his dense population and chemical, atomic, space, solar, and other technologies — snowfall may have increased to the point of tipping the balance and launching the next ice age. Other factors like sunspots and volcanic dust in the atmosphere, the rise of mountain chains and anomalies of global motion undoubtedly have their effects, but geophysicists still seem unable to establish their relative importance.

The circulation of the oceans, of course, like the freer, faster flowing of the atmosphere, is one of the great components of earthly environment. Like a vast engine driven by the thermodynamic need for exchange between the cool polar condenser regions and the warm equatorial boiler belt, the oceans circulate partly in vertical fronts of different tempered water masses and partly in great revolving horizontal gyres wherever they find room, the centers of their surface whirls, like the semistagnant Sargasso Sea, being displaced toward the west by the torque effect of the earth's turning, thus intensifying currents on the western sides of oceans: the Gulf Stream, the Japanese Current, the Brazil, the Agulhas . . . And these currents are much more complex than they used to seem, not only changing their courses daily but habitually sloughing into separate filaments, some of which form loops that tear completely loose and roll off to the sides as capricious eddies hundreds of miles in diameter. Other

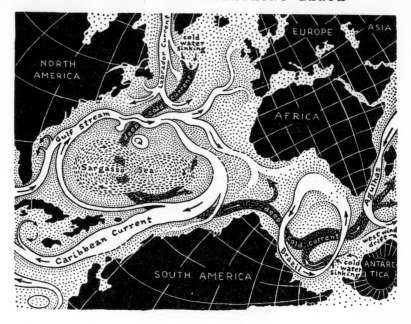

cooler currents from the Arctic and Antarctic slink some two miles under the better-known surface streams, carrying icy glacier run-off water toward the equator, bearing rich microscopic nu-trients to deep, black "deserts" where fish would starve without them, carving great subsea valleys, in some places cutting steep canyons a thousand miles long like the one running south from Greenland, in others indenting great plains studded with 20,000-foot submarine volcanoes. More than five hundred examples of a weird variety of such volcanoes have been recently discovered on the Pacific floor in the form of truncated cones called guyots. These have internal veins like plants through which they once sprouted slowly with lava sap, but they are now dormant and flat-topped, perhaps from surf-action during some intermediate atoll stage before the elevation and draining of the present con-tinents deepened the oceans to their existing levels.

The reason for the somewhat greater total flow of ocean water toward the equator than toward the poles seems to be the excess of evaporation over precipitation in the earth's doldrum belt of greatest heat as contrasted with the reverse condition in the cloudier temperate latitudes. But if rain can thus stir the seas, how much more does the wind influence the water below it, pushing and sucking the waves along, especially the little ripples that oceanographers have lately discovered are far more efficient than the bigger waves in absorbing energy from the sky — like the atoms, making up in coordination and numbers what power they lack as individuals.

The total circulation of the atmosphere is also more important than sea motion in giving life, for it refreshes the entire world, bringing aeration to the oceans and breath and drinks to mosses, mosquitoes, muskrats and men. But like the earth's more solid parts, the air too shares in evolution. It was not always fit for breath. Chemical deduction suggests that when our home globe was very young and hot, the atmosphere was mostly ammonia fumes mixed with wild gassy compounds of bromine, chlorine, fluorine or sulfur. The blend was, in fact, too violent to last. The atomic fury of the temperature could not be held down by earthly gravity, and almost all this primordial witches' brew escaped, to be slowly replaced on the cooling surface with milder volcanic gases that belched from the simmering rocks: preponderantly carbon dioxide, water vapor, and nitrogen.

While the earth cooled enough to condense its water vapor into oceans, oxygen was increasing through the chemical impact of sunlight upon the water (containing oxygen) and later upon green plants that had absorbed carbon dioxide from the pristine air. And thus evolved our present atmosphere, continually spooned with warm updrafts and centrifugal momentums into the yeasty pattern of jet streams, rolling frontal storms, monsoons, tradewinds, hurricanes and cells of circulation that we are beginning to know today. Only "beginning" to know, because the terrestrial atmosphere with its incomprehensible currents, its sporadic domes and dales of pressure and humidity, its chemical and magnetic layers, is far too big to be adequately observed while the ratio remains of two million tons of air to each man, woman and child on earth.

Yet significantly, if not forebodingly, man has already had an influence on this great gassy envelope — as indeed on the solid surface beneath it — an influence largely inadvertent but in cumulative effect unmistakable. In fact, this human influence must presage something deeply fundamental to the earth, being an event suddenly and utterly new on a planet that has seemingly tried everything in its five billion years. Perhaps it does not look like much to you down there in the traffic and bustle of Earth, but I assure you any detached scholar can see it with half an eye from up here. And it has become clear as space itself in the past fifty years.

Before that, one might have shrugged the manprints off as just a passing phase of old-fashioned earthly nature: the forests of China that suddenly looked moth-eaten a few millenniums ago, then almost completely vanished as from the plague; the valleys of Mesopotamia and the Nile that began to break out in specks of spring green; the strips of harvest yellow that have slowly spread like a creeping moss over the fertile plains.

But now look what is happening. The dots of cities have begun to accelerate outward and many a newly green valley has already been swallowed whole by masonry and twinkling lights! It looks as if concrete and electricity are more alive than vegetation and new lakes are appearing like blue blossoms in every continent, great rivers changing their courses, wide deserts receiving water where such luxury has not been seen in ten million years, and more and more strange arterial lines being scratched each year across the plains. Certainly this is a startling jolt in the leisurely pace of natural evolution.

Even the color of the air is changing, along with its chemistry, as smoke and carbon dioxide pour into it in tiny but multiplying streams. I can see the smoggy wisps floating in a hundred valleys where they were unknown before this century. I've even noticed unnatural rain clouds suddenly sprouting as if man at last had really learned to sow the seeds of weather. And what is this: this unprecedented volley of explosive fury, these potent

flashes in the desert and on lonely ocean isles followed by mush-
room clouds a hundred miles across? Whose are these new darts
of life rising completely out of the air to challenge the meteors of
black space? Even a few rash upstart rivals of our ancient
moon, like the very sky station I am riding?

Is it a disease that has come to our good earth? Is mankind
a virus bred to conquer his host organism in a fever of delirium,
or is he just part of a healthy mold that must flower on all
suitable planetary clay? Is he a fluke of fate or a phase of life?

I am here to seek the answer. I too sprang from that world
down there, and am still part of it, even as this fleeing space
station — even as the devoted moon. I am of the race that dwelt
in Karnak and Jarmo and Jericho and Chichen Itza and Cnossus
— in Olduvai Gorge and the Dragons' Mountain. My body
was shaped in the rivers where vertebrates developed and the lung
was born. My apprenticeship was in the trees where I grew my
hand. I was once Proconsul, the pre-man. After the uplifting of
the continents produced the grassy fields, I learned to stand
up and look far and to outthink the lion.

In this day I have walked on the shoulders of the Pharaohs
as they walked on the shoulders of the apes, for each page of
history along with its cities must sink literally beneath the pav-
ings of the future, even as I in my turn will lie buried under
the scriptures of rocks today unformed.

If my honored ancestors once arose from sea to land and into
the air, is it not my turn now to move onward beyond air
into space? For I am also the creature that learned to weigh
stars. I have seen the world in a puddle dry up one day and
begin elsewhere the next. I know that any world may die and
be born and that my own world has shown signs of being the
cell of a greater life. I accept as man's normal business: to reach
for the sun, to build things reachable out of things unreach-
able. Yet before reaching out with my hand I reach out with my
mind — a human mind which can pass through the hottest fire
and the blackest space — a mind which has never been taught to
shun the moon or to fear the stars — and which has, for a reason
still unknown, been endowed with a swiftness greater than light.

2. into the stomach of space

AT FIRST THE BLACKNESS OF THE VOID that swallows us out here seems empty — a clear crystalline vacuum. Yet acquaintance steadily endows it with a certain tangibleness, a mysterious and subtle palpability that hardly touches the senses while deeply penetrating the mind.

This it may be that the young physicists are excited about when they say space is "chuck-full" of things: of waves and fields and magnetic properties, of energy both positive and negative, and even of hard-to-measure "particles" mingled with hard-to-believe "antiparticles" acting along lines of invisible curvature.

We will be looking closely at the texture and inner nature of such things in the second part of this book, but first we must just learn to use space a little, to live with it as a medium of travel into the great outside world, to savor it as a frame of material existence and as the surround of our floating home which it somehow harbored long before we earthbound bar-

barians ever came to recognize it as the newest frontier of our provincialism.

As Goethe once said of the institution of marriage, "The possible will be attempted only because we have postulated the impossible." So, I think, must the enormous possibilities of space be dared for the very reason that "flying to the moon" has been proverbially impossible through all history up to now. Certainly one need embrace this burgeoning age of rocketry with heart as well as mind, just as did the ancient Phoenicians and Greeks accept the advent of great ships along with harpies and sea monsters and boiling maelstroms — as later Henry the Navigator launched the age of organized discovery upon downhill oceans and islands haunted with dangerous simurgs and werewolves and mermaids. If Columbus somehow succeeded against all the vaunted hazards and superstitious yarns of sailors, so must we. If Galileo be remembered longer than the threats of the vested and the scoffings of the orthodox, and after him Fulton, Pasteur and the Wright brothers, so yet may we too accomplish deeds that are bigger than doubts.

Science fiction is obviously today's legend of space and in its turn is being overtaken by research scientists and hard-headed engineers who, like Ulysses, have firmly bound themselves to the mast of fact against the worst wiles of the sirens of fancy. Although the austerity of their lives on the stark deserts of White Sands, Alamogordo, Muroc, the steppes of Russia or the beaches of Canaveral may be relieved in some cases by reading about the magnetic, methane-breathing nereids of Neptune, today at last the inventors are filling out our ancient dreams with tangible hardware. And common people, no longer snickering at literal moon rockets or vehicles for Venus, are now urging the engineers to hurry, anticipating an accelerating success with "space suits" for their children, even devouring a whole new wave of literature on the already classic subject.

This literature had a beginning at least as far back as the second century A.D. when Lucian of Samosata wrote about a man whose ship sailed beyond the Pillars of Hercules and at the edge of the world was picked up by a waterspout and carried to the moon. In Lucian's second book, the now experienced hero borrowed two wings, one from a vulture, the other from an eagle, and took off for the moon from Mount Olympus. It was a day in which flying through the air was considered the same thing as space travel and some people believed it logical that birds could really migrate to the stars.

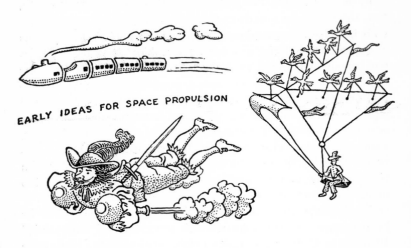

EARLY IDEAS FOR SPACE PROPULSION

So far as I am aware, the next book on space — appearing 1,500 years later — was written by the greatest astronomer of his time, Johannes Kepler, who realized that wings needed air, which probably did not extend all the way to the moon, and therefore used demonic propulsion as a less implausible means of getting his hero there. Since his own mother had been indicted as a witch and magic was still popular science even among the educated, demons seemed real enough. But Kepler's description of the moon, at least, was based on his own startling observations by telescope and had a profound influence on later writers (including Cyrano de Bergerac, whose *Histoire comique ou Voyage dans la Lune* was published in 1650) right up to the present century.

It would be almost impossible to read or even count the vast writings, mostly fiction, that have appeared about space travel since the development of aviation brought us to its threshold. But now actual accomplishment in current news reports is crowding fiction into the background. Earth-built rockets are part of the celestial firmament. They have become satellites of the earth and the sun and have landed on the moon, while man himself is following closely, having accepted this ultimate vehicle as easily as the balloon, the parachute or the airplane. In point of fact, the rocket far antedates them all. For it is actually an ancient Chinese invention, was used against the attacking Mongols in the siege of Kaifeng in A.D. 1232 and incidentally contributed the famous "red glare" to American skies in the War of 1812. But it remained little more than a psychological weapon and a plaything until World War II. Then it suddenly zoomed into rapid development. Although 1940 had seen no man-made rocket ever move as fast as 1,000 m.p.h., by 1950 several had exceeded 5,000 m.p.h. and before 1960 had reached an astounding 25,000 m.p.h. in outer space, demonstrating the possibility of crossing the Atlantic in half an hour, seeing sunrises in the west, sunsets in the east, stars by day, sunshine by night, and other miracles of wind, temperature and light. The highest altitude achieved by man-made devices increased still more rapidly: from about 10 miles in 1940 to 250 miles before 1950 and, by 1960, with the conquest of earthly gravitation fully attained, there seemed no limit whatever.

This explosion of material progress has been too fast for average human intuition, however, so that missile firings are hard to believe even when you see them, and all rocket doings still seem to me like staged drama. Before a major shoot, the launching site is alive with scurrying jeeps and trucks and figures clad in chemical-proof abas, some with earphones or walkie-talkie radios, some on servicing towers pumping hydrazine or giving rocket "brains" their final intelligence tests while radar mirrors sweep the sky with pulsed electronic beams, and the glassy eyes of cameras, telescopes and theodolites look on coolly from neighboring beaches or mountainsides. The dozens of human jet-age stargazers waiting around for the zero hour of launching then always remind me of the faithful shepherds of similar deserts in the ancient Holy Land who have long had an equally great faith that the world can be changed. Even though on the face of it the two kinds of change are different, I think they are also profoundly related in a way that will one day be made manifest to all.

Those who think man is becoming overbold in this rash tampering with physical evolution have, of course, a powerful argument in the extreme and multiple dangers of such a change of worlds for which the human body is obviously not genetically prepared. Certainly the artificial haste of man's leap is far from precedented anywhere in earthly history. Biologists point with trembling fingers to the contrast between it and the way the fish so successfully colonized the land against similar difficulties. During many painful and frustrating eons of struggle to conquer a deadly new medium, the air, inevitably the fish suffered frightful losses as their heroic pioneers were stranded by receding tides and suffocated or baked alive in marshy deltas, trying to keep their vital juices from drying up in the blistering, blinding outer sunshine — just as space doctors are now trying to design space suits that will protect men's blood and lungs and skin and brains against the glaring vacuum and radiations of space. But little by little, through relentless genetic variation and selection, the fish developed a tough air suit that not only enabled them to carry their own traditional sea environment to land with them but filtered out the dangerous parts of the spectrum of sunlight and stabilized their temperature sea-fashion within narrow limits despite the fickle winds and the daily and seasonal freezes and roasts of the cruel airy world. The sudden and unexpected load of a full G (earthly gravitational unit) of unsupported weight in "empty" air of course left the soft-muscled ones flattened helplessly on the beaches, as jellyfish often are marooned to this day, but gradually the most elite of the elite new breeds grew powerful antigravity muscles and air gills called lungs and held themselves up off the ground and at last even shifted into high gear with legs and wings.

Thus laboriously and extravagantly did nature accomplish in millions of years the equivalent of what man now seems bent on accomplishing in one generation. No wonder there are few responsible scientists who are optimistic about a full-scale conquest of space in this century. The only tolerable space suit now in prospect for more than brief use is a solid walled chamber with full insulation, air conditioning and mechanical limbs, for no body-contour suit yet developed seems able to provide adequate flexibility without serious risks of loss of pressure, to say nothing of insufficient insulation. The human body demands at least three pounds per square inch of air or oxygen pressure around it, which the space suit must unfailingly provide. Any leak threatens immediate death. Moisture and carbon dioxide given off must somehow be disposed of and oxygen and temperature maintained — these being services which for only a few hours require more apparatus than a man alone can practically handle, especially if he is expected to be able to concentrate on a dangerous and unfamiliar world outside his clothing.

But do not think this tough problem will not be licked sooner or later. If the fish could do it, who are we to quit? As surely as we are the cousins, if not the descendants, of the very most successful of all the most daring of fish, space is within human reach. Man knows it in his soul. None of the rocket scientists has expressed doubt about ultimate victory, even though the cost in lives and heartbreaks and years cannot be foreseen, nor the many losing and winning combinations of devices and techniques.

Out of the legions of engineers and researchers every year new prophets of space arise to point the way in confident voices — sensationally successful young men like Wernher von Braun of V2 fame, who has been compared to Peter the Hermit and who explains his faith in words Peter might have used in defending the visionary paupers' crusade: "Prophets have always been laughed at, deplored and opposed, but some prophets have proved to be following the true course of history."

If this be mystical, at least von Braun's expressed ambition of going as far as the moon in person before he is through is human and natural. And his specific plan for constructing a fleet of three-stage ferry rockets, each as big as a sixteen-story building, with which to reach a satellite orbit and there put together a permanent settlement of dwellings, observatories, shops and assembly plants, has a practical earthy realism about it — even though it adds up to being a blueprint of the first space town in human history (very likely in solar-system history as well) and which is to drift blithely along at more than 4 miles a second some 1,075 miles above the earth. Admittedly, the work and expense involved in teaching these 180-foot rockets to fly and fly with precision and reliability, each carrying eleven tons of payload high enough to lay the cornerstone of a brand-new "moon" and safely return, amount to a major national project. For as surely

as Mount Everest required a hundred men to get two men to the top, the conquest of space requires many thousandfold more.

Indeed, such a thing grows by geometric progression. Just as elephants are more complicated than fleas because they are larger, not larger because they are more complicated, so a three-stage rocket (large because it must contain a hundred tons of fuel for each ton of cargo) has its special motors to work its large controls, its little fuel pumps that pump fuel to drive its big fuel pumps, its hydraulic systems and electronic feedbacks, its radar recorders and gyro potentiometers and servo motors and assorted safety gadgets and accelerometers and pressure gauges and governors *ad confuseam*.

Von Braun has worked out a full-dress invasion of Mars which at present would cost about the same as fighting a fair-sized war and, he thinks, will be a welcome substitute when wars are "a thing of the past." Several dozen of his destroyer-size (1,410-ton) three-stage rockets must make about 400 ferry trips up more than a thousand miles from the earth to build and stock the large satellite assembly plant and service station there, from which a squadron of two 1,870-ton "orbit-to-orbit" space ships (a passenger vessel and a freighter) will be prepared and sent to Mars with fourteen men. Arriving at the gravity gate of the red planet after 260 days of high-speed sailing, the astronauts will build a Martian mooring and service station (perhaps on one of Mars' tiny moons) and equip it with "landing craft" for taking nine men down to the planet itself for a full year of exploration.

The scientific know-how for accomplishing this is already at hand, says von Braun. Gravity is no longer an uncontrollable or monstrous force. Man is already big enough for interplanetary travel and is definitely committed to it with appropriations already provided. The plan is actually in process as part of the American man-in-space program (called Project Mercury) with a prime goal date of 1971 when Mars will next be in most favorable proximity to the earth. Now it is largely a matter of making more tests, getting better organized, cooperating more closely with the Russians if possible, building large stocks of high-quality equipment and doing a lot of unprecedented human engineering.

As for gravity, although it is still one of the great mysteries of nature, man has learned how to use it to his advantage just as he has learned to use steam, electricity and the atom in varying degrees. To be sure, gravity has opposed his departure from Earth with a stubborn terrestrial jealousy, but he has discovered it is not so fierce as it used to seem and that once gravity is about to be breached it relaxes into an amazing docility. In fact, of all the realms of scientific progress "nothing succeeds like success" in the sky. At 12,000 miles above the earth a "pound weight" weighs only an ounce. The higher you go the easier you go, even though gravity never disappears entirely in the known universe.

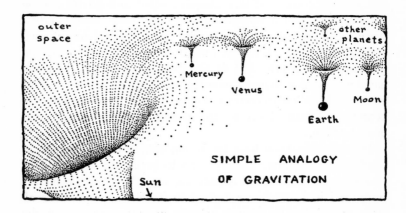

SIMPLE   ANALOGY
OF   GRAVITATION

Perhaps the most helpful analogy about gravity from the viewpoint of rocket crewmen venturing into space is to think of gravitational fields as remote whirlpools in the calm ocean of emptiness that lies between the stars. On the mirror-smooth "surface" of space there is virtually no strain nor turbulence nor friction — just clear sailing in any direction — except in those rare maelstroms created by the moon, the planets and the stars.

Space journeying, in fact (as far as gravitation is concerned), would be as simple as a calm sea voyage on earth did we not live in the very center of one of these gravity whirlpools. The space engineers describe ours (which is typical) as funnel-shaped and 4,000 miles deep, because "the work of getting away from the earth is exactly the same as would be needed to climb vertically through a distance equal to the radius of the earth" if gravity all the way up were just as it is at sea level.

Of course this analogy is an oversimplification, because gravity is not everywhere the same, nor is it whirling literally, and it extends upward far beyond 4,000 miles — in fact, never ends entirely, according to Newton's famous law or Einstein's refinement of it. The reason for describing the gravity field as having a funneloid or (more precisely) helicoidal-trumpet shape is only that such a form approximately expresses the change with altitude, and is easy to visualize — though actual gravity is something much more profound, as we shall see later on in this book.

The climb is naturally very tough up the nearly vertical walls at the bottom of any large gravity whirlpool but, when you have built up enough impetus to reach the gentler slopes above, it takes only a little more to come out completely onto the flat ocean surface where you can just relax and coast indefinitely. If you can't quite make it straight out of the whirlpool, however, you need not give up. There is still the alternative of changing your course to a spiral, an ellipse or a circle — of at least holding your own against gravity by going rapidly around and around the maelstrom instead of directly up it. That is exactly what you would probably do if caught in a real whirlpool, and that is what the captive moon does in the whirlpool of earthly gravity. It is the principle of the "Wall of Death," the old carnival sideshow stunt in which a motorcyclist defies gravity by riding fast around the almost vertical walls inside a cylindrical tower built like a silo with a bowl-shaped bottom.

The specific value of this trick to defeat gravity is that although an initial speed of about 25,000 m.p.h. (about 7 miles a second) is needed to coast from the earth straight up, you can

do with much less by taking off eastward from the equator, thus
gaining a free boost from the earth's horizontal spin of 1,000
m.p.h. at that latitude and continuing to slant up eastward until
clear of air friction. At about two hundred miles up, as the
satellite rockets have already demonstrated, a horizontal speed
of a mere 5 m.p.s. is enough to keep you from falling back
to Earth — and you have thus become a private "moon" on a
"free orbit." At an altitude of 25,000 miles, you can stay up at
only 2 m.p.s. and your orbit can be even freer. It may be a
swooping orbit like a comet's or a nearly circular orbit like
the moon's. It makes little difference so long as you stay above
air and have attained the necessary angular momentum. Getting
completely out of the whirlpool is, relatively speaking, a push-
over from here. The rule is that from any orbit that holds you continuously above the earth (or above any other gravitating body)
all you need do is multiply your velocity by the square root of
2 to escape the body altogether. Thus, if any satellite with
an average velocity of 2 m.p.s. increases it to $2\sqrt{2}$, or 2.8 m.p.s.,
it will just sail off never to return.

Of space's many weird problems, the navigation or astroga-
tion one is particularly interesting to those of us who have so
long flitted about the easy earth. Have you ever wondered how
you would find your way between the worlds? Or what it might
feel like to be "lost" while in plain sight of your destination because of doubt as to which way either you or your destination were
going? Earth maps are mostly in two dimensions, even though
some of them attempt to portray the contours of the land as well as
suggest the curvature of the sphere. But space is definitely at
least three-dimensional. How does a space navigation chart look?
    The answer is that, strictly speaking, charts will not be used
for space navigation, mainly because plotting on a chart is much
too crude a procedure for the fine precision that is essential

in outer three-dimensional space. As my friend Professor Samuel Herrick, astronomer and founder of the Institute of Navigation, puts it, "Whereas navigating to the nearest minute of arc is adequate for sea and air navigation, in space we shall have to take account of the second of arc, or even smaller fractions of it. That will require six or seven decimal places in calculation, and . . . you may be sure that all space navigation will be done with calculating machines instead of charts."

The basic reason for such a standard of accuracy in space of course is not alone the obvious one that the tiniest error in aim at departure from Earth may amount to missing a planet such as Venus by many thousands of miles five months later unless corrected, perhaps at great expense, but also that space ships (like all celestial bodies) follow orbits, not straight lines. For it takes six mathematical quantities to define the position and velocity of the ship at any moment: the three coordinates of its location in three-dimensional space and the three components of its velocity in the same 3-D frame of reference, every one of the six being subject to constant change even when the ship is just drifting.

If you don't think this is complexity requiring electronic help, you need only consider it carefully in relation to more familiar situations like flying an airplane about the earth. Down there in the terrestrial atmosphere, if you know your location accurately even in only two dimensions (latitude and longitude), you have practically solved your navigation problem, for your position in the third dimension (altitude) is confined within narrow limits and easy to determine, and your velocity components are also so restricted and normally so controllable that you hardly need know them except to help in reckoning your latitude and longitude.

But here in space there is no kind of surface constantly available for reference in finding your bearings, and your cruising speed may vary not just fifty percent from, say, 400 to 600 m.p.h., but can range many thousand percent from a fraction of a mile per second up to more than 50 m.p.s., without even considering the much greater speeds needed for travel beyond the solar

system. Groundspeed as well as airspeed rapidly loses its meaning as you rise above the atmosphere, for you soon realize in space
that different parts of the earth's surface are moving not only in
different directions but at different speeds in relation to the
rest of creation. Earthspeed (motion relative to the center of the
earth) naturally becomes the new criterion of movement. Then,
in turn, moonspeed, sunspeed, Marsspeed . . . The same goes
for space coordinates, altitude inevitably growing into radial distance, rate of climb or descent into radial velocity, and latitudinal and longitudinal direction from the earth into solar or
galactic latitude and longitude, and so on.

It is a relief not to have to worry any more about wind, a
purely atmospheric phenomenon so far as we know, but, before
you have time to sigh over this bounty, you realize with some
shock that the curvature of space more than replaces wind as a
navigation variable to contend with. And even though it is
true that space distortion is more regular and predictable than
any earthly gale, it is also more insidious and pervasive. In
fact, space turns out to have a kind of geometric "pressure
pattern" that is invisible, impalpable, immensely subtle and the
very devil to keep track of.

While we must wait until Chapter 13 to go deeper into the
basic nature of space, I can say here that space ships coasting
along in what is called a state of "free fall" must always follow
either an elliptical (closed) orbit or, if they are going faster,
perhaps a hyperbolic (open) orbit for a brief time. In either case,
it is literally true that there are no straight lines in space and it
is not possible to steer a space ship in any ordinary sense. It is only

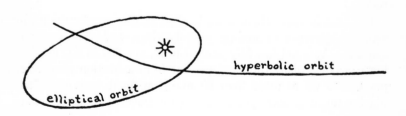

possible, by applying rocket thrust, to change it from one orbit to another. As astronomer J. G. Porter of the Royal Greenwich Observatory puts it, "even with unlimited supplies of fuel, in a ship which is constantly driven, it would still be impossible to travel in a straight line" — that being a course which does not exist.

Curves, then, must be accepted and dealt with as inevitable, like women in a man's world, tantalizing or troublesome though they may be. A way of easing the trouble, however, is to pre-compute your intended orbit along with a few substitute or emergency orbits and their appropriate conjunction seams of spheroidal surfaces of position (a calculation Dr. Porter says "is not going to be a nice job") while you are still on Earth with the best electronic computers at hand, so that in space, if all goes reasonably well, the navigation problem will be largely a matter of checking angles between sun, planets, moons and asteroids to see how closely they conform to the precomputed values.

This vital work will be done with instruments now under in-tense development which presumably will combine the functions of the filar micronometer, the electronic star tracker, the gyro-stabilized octant and the telescope. Obviously the traditional sextant, calibrated only to the minute of arc, is not nearly pre-cise enough in reading, say, Jupiter (85,000 miles across) as a point of light. Even the cross hairs of a good telescope, if aligned with the wrong part of Jupiter, might permit an error of 10,000 miles. Radio and radar instruments, of course, will supplement the visual ones, probably with elaborate bearing and range-measuring techniques similar in principle to the newest systems being installed in terrestrial airways to keep pilots constantly informed of the direction and distance to all stations around them — hence, by electronic transposition, of their own location.

While operating within a hundred thousand miles or so of a planet, moon or other body, such systems are particularly valuable and, when doppler radar is perfected to the point of making it possible to measure exact intervals between impulses, spacemen will also be able to read on a dial their speed of approach toward, or recession from, any substantial object within range. This is by no means the same thing as reading their "true velocity," but it can be at least an important clue at the crucial beginning and end of a journey.

And then, by feeding all the information obtainable into the space ship's miniature electronic brain, including the vital but hard-to-get data of velocity, the discrepancies between the pre-computed values and the observed values can be digested and translated into terms of exact corrective maneuver — such as .58 G of thrust in the direction of galactic latitude 49°50′33″.6 south and longitude 12° 11′21″.0 east applied April 18 from 21:30:00 until 22:35:15 U.T.

Such a correction, of course, would mean a relatively small change of orbit, which would not appreciably reduce the fuel supply. But in a long interplanetary voyage, the big problem will be to keep corrective maneuvers small without letting them become frequent, since an error as tiny as 0.001 miles (five feet) per second in speed on a trip to Mars could make you miss the red planet by an embarrassing 50,000 miles.

And, even apart from errors, there are inevitable and drastic changes of orbit required in space travel, not only in accelerating away from a home space station at the start (partly to save travel time), but also, and more so, in matching velocities with your destination at the end. Some people seem to think space travel can be very economical as well as swift, but they probably fail to realize the enormous momentum possessed by a small space ship (weighing a few dozen tons) when it has built up a reasonable cruising speed of, say, 30 miles a second. Even though the space ship would weigh only a thousandth as much as an ocean liner like the *Queen Mary* it would still have the same momentum the *Queen Mary* had if she could move just one thousandth as fast as the space ship, or 108 miles an hour. If you can visualize now how much rocket fuel it would take to stop or turn the *Queen Mary* while she was hurtling through space at 108 m.p.h., you will know something of the basic problem of velocity blending which many astrophysicists believe must remain practically beyond the fuel capacity of any space ships at least until atomic or solar energy is fully developed as the power source for space. The strict relationship between maneuverability and weight is indicated by a missile engineer's recent calculation that chemically propelled space ships on heliocentric orbits must consume about 3 percent of their total weight in fuel every time they change their orbits by as much as five minutes of arc.

The difficulty here is inherent also in the varied order of the celestial orbs which, like the earthly oceans before them, still show little sign of having been created for the purpose of simplifying the struggles of humanity. The orbits of even our nearest planetary neighbors, for example, are not in the same plane as the earth's. And even though a space ship could be put into an "optimum" orbit that is roughly tangent to those of both the earth and, say, Venus at opposite ends of its elliptical shape, its velocity would require about as much fuel and power to match the velocity of its destination at either end as it had consumed in climbing away from the earth in the first place — and this assumes very accurate timing throughout and no errors.

There is obviously only one time a year (not an earth year but a composite year averaged from those of the two planets) when this optimum orbit is obtainable: the time when one planet overtakes the other on their way around the sun. When a circus rider jumps from one horse to a passing one while they gallop around the ring, he naturally leaps just before the moment of greatest proximity and lands just after it. So will the space navigators plan a journey to Venus: departing when Venus is almost a sixth of a turn behind the earth and arriving after she has passed it by almost the same margin, their chosen optimum orbit bringing their ship from aphelion (the orbit's farthest point from the sun) as it leaves the earth through 250 million miles and 146 days to perihelion (closest point to sun) at Venus in such a natural manner that were it to just miss Venus through engine trouble at velocity-matching time it would coast onward like a boomerang, circling around to the departure point on the earth's orbit again in another 146 days, another 250 million miles.

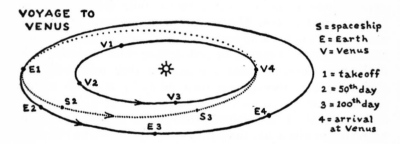

VOYAGE TO VENUS

S = spaceship
E = Earth
V = Venus

1 = takeoff
2 = 50th day
3 = 100th day
4 = arrival at Venus

Of course, its navigator could not expect to find the earth there this time, for you Earthians would then be some 120 million miles behind the space ship (having traveled a longer path) and still going away. In fact, he would not come within ten million miles of Earth again until his fifth time around, 5 spaceship years after departure (4 earth years or 6⅖ Venus years). If he had enough air, water and supplies to hold out that long, he could have taken another crack at Venus at his third perihelion, though more likely he would be saving everything for what would probably be his last and only chance to get back to — you guessed it; there's no place quite like it — home.

Of course, if a space ship had efficient atomic motors and no problem about running out of fuel, it could overcome almost any difficulty of a missed rendezvous by just turning on the power and chasing its destination until it caught it. Or it could take a short cut home, not by the slow, economical elliptical orbit route but by the daring hyperbolic course of a plunge downward past the sun and out on the other side. This would be very extravagant in fuel, involving the radical maneuver of almost complete cancellation of lateral planetary motion, but it would save a lot of time because the ship would pick up enormous speed in its drop toward the sun just as a comet does. Although such an unconservative course might be likened to crossing from one skyscraper tower to another in New York by direct cable instead of by the more leisurely route of taking an elevator to the ground level and walking across the street, then up in another elevator, the method may some day become very important in voyages to the outer planets such as Jupiter, Saturn and Neptune, which would otherwise consume much if not most of the passengers' lifetimes. It has been calculated that if the space ship adds still more to its speed past the flaming sun by using up most of its remaining fuel, this will not only give it tremendous momentum but, lightening its load, make it shoot upward toward Neptune with such great rapidity that its crew can forget their problem of how to pass the weary years, occupying themselves instead with the urgency of slamming on their brakes before it is too late.

The long-range space and time relationships in all such voyages are quite satisfactorily found by solving the equations used in what is known in space mechanics as the "two-body problem." That is the relatively simple consideration of how two bodies move while influenced by nothing other than their own mutual gravitational attraction, the two bodies normally being the space ship and the sun.

But of course the near approach to another planet will require answers from the much more difficult "three-body problem" and, where even this closer approximation to reality is insufficient, from "perturbation theory" (which treats all gravitational influences beyond the third body as "perturbations"), integrating larger influences by Cowell's method, smaller periodic ones by

Encke's, and so on. Most of such more advanced "astroga-tional" work will probably be done as part of the electronic precomputation on Earth from where, in emergencies, it may prove helpful as a special "trouble-shooting service" that will forward key corrections by radio or heliograph to the naviga-tor in space.

In any case, one does not need to get bogged down with more details of space navigation at this elementary stage of as-tronautics. If we must be swallowed by space, let us not succumb to its bile before we have even noticed the contents of its stomach. Let us attend to the near at hand and take nature in digestible doses — one world at a time — so that we may hope to know at least where we are.

3. invitation to the moon

THAT PALE ORB OF ROCK swinging around the earth seems to me to have significance beyond what humanity has generally accorded it. Although only an incidental decoration to many, a sky festoon to the romantic, the moon is nevertheless a lucid example of natural law beyond our home world, a daily demonstration that a stone weighing 81,000,000,000,000,000,000 tons can be made to float indefinitely 240,000 miles overhead without visible means of support.

She is also the earth's closest relative, high arbitress of Easter and an unmistakable celestial personality who invites candid comment. Though not extremely old, neither is she young. Even from here, one can plainly see her history written in wrinkles. Yet we must admit that she is rounded and beautiful, clear-cut of character, and faithful in many such time-honored duties as accompanying the terrestrial traveler on long journeys despite his passing of trees and houses, hills and clouds. And she is always punctual in appointment, ever facing the earth directly — in fact, amazingly regular once you understand her devious ways.

This is not to say she is without mystery either as to the un-documented features of her past or the enigmatic present hidden within her countenance and behavior that are at once familiar and unearthly. How often I remember from my days with the airlines, cruising under a broken overcast to see the moon stealthily shouldering her way between cumulus masses — a tigress skulking in the jungle. Or when she was crescent, watching her cleave the cirrus with her scimitar blade. Or gibbous, becoming a bowl of porridge under the nimbus steam.

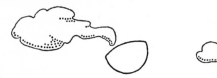

Sometimes it is hard to realize, when the moon seems un-imaginably far away, that there are cars on the roads of Earth that have been driven farther — that in space 240,000 miles is only arm's length. Yet obviously, at 240 m.p.h. that distance is covered in 1,000 hours of flying time. At 2,400 m.p.h. in 100 hours. Some airline pilots have done twenty times as much: the full equivalent of ten round trips to the moon.

If the moon is not literally arm's length away, she is actually within the stretch of your body. Someone has calculated that the average human arteries hold about 24,000,000,000,000 red blood cells which, laid edge to edge, would stretch 116,000 miles. If you added all your white corpuscles and, if necessary, stored up some extra blood in a personal bank, you could expect the blood of your own body to be easily enough to reach the moon.

The moon might appreciate some new blood too, for her future never looked less secure. Not only has she already felt the rude jab of an earthly missile, without so much as a per-functory "May I?" but growing numbers of eager Earthians down there, who like to talk about being good neighbors, have already filed claims to sections of her land and begun arguing about carving it up to their personal ends.

Besides, millions of men have long been reading their private superstitions and pet "man in the moon" meanings into the suggestive markings of the moon's bright mountains and dark plains. Did you know that from India people see in the moon not a man but a little gray rabbit with long ears and outstretched paws? Perhaps this is nearly the same as the moon goblin Puritan mothers used to show their children, which had a wart on its nose and held scissors for snipping off the tongues of those who sassed their parents. In Samoa they see a moon lady who sits up there eternally weaving a nebulous cloth into clouds, while other South Sea natives see moon trees laden with fruit for eternal feasting of departed souls. The Indians of the American northwest envision a horned toad that hopped to the moon to get away from a wolf. Other tribes see a duck there. Still others, a spread eagle. In Australia some see a staring cat's eye, while the French recognize the wicked face of Judas Iscariot. And Irish maidens, after drinking white wine and rose water, look at the moon through silk handkerchiefs to see the faces of their personal fates, murmuring,

> I prithee, good Moon, declare to me
> This night, who my husband shall be.

In olden terrestrial days the moon was mainly a divine feminine influence, a glamorous goddess of fertility, often a very down-to-earth personality. Take Selene, the Greek moon, who was wooed by King Zeus and by Pan in the shape of a white ram, and who loved Endymion so much that she put him to sleep on Mount Latmus so she could kiss him secretly as she set each night. The result of the latter lunar indulgence over many years was the birth of full fifty moon daughters — thirty of whom have already been converted from legendary figures into actual planetary satellites as they were discovered by Galileo, Cassini, Herschel, Nicholson (four each) and other recent astronomers, variously circulating in moonly devotion around Mars, Jupiter, Saturn, Uranus and Neptune. (See the moon table on pages 62–63.)

Our modern moon, of course, outshines all ancient ones a

hundredfold in wonder and romantic potential. She was our earliest celestial destination. She was the first outside world to echo radio impulses sent from the earth into space. She is a mirror who reflects both sunlight and earthlight to our sight just as our world returns moonshine along with sunshine to her, so that one glance at the dark side of the new moon apprises us of the weather for thousands of miles westward where the whiteness of wide cloudy areas is earthshine's main source. She is the place where all of us see morning during the night, where her slow afternoon stretches into our dawn. She holds the power of appearing paradoxically larger when she is rising or setting than when she is 4,000 miles nearer overhead.

Astronomers think of the moon as a kind of clock — an ancient timepiece that helped eighteenth-century navigators check their longitude, a clock that moves reliably before the stars at the rate of about one diameter (32' of arc) every forty minutes of time, a clock whose face is the map of history telling the story of a violent youth and of a sterile maturity — up till now. Rocket men see in the moon a way-station to the solar system, a future refueling base for satellite tankers, a navigation check-point after takeoff for the planets.

The moon is all of these things — and more. If you look at her through a telescope you can pick out an amazing landscape, its meaning in part instantly obvious but also in part inscrutable even after careful study. Her face may remind you first of a smallpox victim. Or an old artillery ground. You can make out crater heaped upon crater, in some places tiny craters showing in larger craters which in turn rise out of still larger ones. One peak of the Leibniz mountains soars four thousand feet higher than Mount Everest and is located near the northern lunar pole amid the so-called "mountains of eternal light" which never withdraw from clear sunshine no matter how the moon's face is turned. Clavius, the largest crater of all on the visible moon, has been measured at 146 miles across, making it bigger than Massachusetts, Connecticut and Rhode Island combined. In fact, it is so big in relation to the tight curvature of the moon that if you stood in the middle of Clavius it would appear as an endless plain receding in all directions, for the 20,000-foot mountains surrounding you would be hidden well below the horizon.

Astronomers and selenographers (who study the moon as geographers study the earth) do not all agree as to whether moon craters are meteorite scars or ancient volcanoes or perhaps even rings left by bursting bubbles of gas, but the best present opinion is that almost all of them were made by meteorites. The volcanic theory was based largely on the weak gravity of the moon, which not only can attract relatively fewer meteorites than the earth but would allow bigger volcanic eruptions from which the lava would be hurled much higher and farther than on earth.

MOON CRATER   MT. VESUVIUS

Opposed to this idea, however, are the enormous sizes and depths of the craters, some of them a thousand times larger than any known terrestrial volcanic cones and many of them two miles deeper than the surrounding plains. There is also their unvolcanolike encroachment upon each other and their resemblance to artillery shell holes which similarly often have a small peak rising out of the center. In any case, the impact of tremendous ancient meteorites weighing many millions of tons or even small asteroids could explain just as well as volcanoes the pale marks radiating for thousands of miles outward from some of the craters, obviously produced by much more spectacular explosions than we have any record of on Earth. Lava flooding, of course, seems the likeliest explanation for the extensive dark "moon mares" where no craters are visible but which should also have received their portion of large meteorites throughout the earlier years of moon history. One theory has it that some of the last of the meteorites themselves released the lava by smashing the moon's crust, thus effectively flooding and concealing their own scars.

The earth also may have been as pocked as the moon in its early days with similar huge craters which have long since been eroded out. There is definite suspicion of a trace of just such a crater in a recent geological survey of northern Quebec, known as one of the most ancient parts of the dry earthly crust. And the very shapes of Hudson Bay, James Bay and Ungava Bay are highly suggestive.

But naturally, scars on the moon remain much longer than on the vegetating, restless earth, for without air to produce wind or clouds or rain or trees or streams there is almost nothing to change the moon's mountains. About the only possibility of erosion there that selenographers have figured out so far is the destructive expansion and contraction caused by the 400° F. temperature change between roasting day and deep-frozen night. The vacuum of course produces neither twilight nor insulation, and the coming of the first shadow at sunset brings an abrupt drop in temperature. And even more drastic is the effect of the swooping earth shadow when the earth passes exactly between the sun and moon — suddenly eclipsing the sun as seen from the moon, the moon as seen from the earth — producing a temperature plunge of 270° in one hour followed by a corresponding rise on the return of sunshine, an occurrence frequent and violent enough to cause major exfoliation of the moon's rocks over billions of years. Obviously, this eclipse-caused erosion can happen only on the one side of the moon that faces the earth, so, by deduction, we assume the other, less-eroded side is still rougher — as indeed the Russian photographic rocket of 1959 confirmed it to be.

It takes a little effort of imagination to think realistically of walking about on the moon— although it is not as hard as actually walking about on the moon — for the moon obviously cannot approach the earth in human-oriented hospitality. Much moonscape, in fact, is probably as bad as the Badlands of South Dakota or worse, though the lower levels are likely covered with gravelly dust, perhaps many inches or feet thick, that has worked down there from the crumbling cliffs and slopes. The feeble gravity would make up for some of the obstacles, of course, and crevasses no more than a hundred feet wide might be jumpable or sheer fifty-foot crater cliffs vaultable with practice. Tiny grain-sized meteorites may hit the ground intermittently like stray bullets out of the black sky, their velocity of dozens of miles per second virtually undiminished by atmosphere. The odd splashes of dust raised by these particles naturally do not form puffs and float as in air but fall downward with slow, steady acceleration. Nor do they make any noticeable sound, for silence prevails in the moon's vacuous calm of sublime desolation without weather, animals, birds, insects or vegetation visible anywhere. And overhead for fourteen earth days the sun blazes like a searchlight in the night surrounded by dazzling unblinking stars, while the great blue-white earth sits perpetually in one spot (never moving more than 7 degrees from its mean position), appearing fifteen times as big in area as the moon does on Earth and a hundred times brighter, yet never rising nor setting, just slowly revolving and, more slowly, going through its monthly phases from crescent to gibbous to full, ever exactly opposite and in perfect time with the moon's own corresponding changes.

The earth thus viewed through the refraction-free vacuum of space is always an awesome sight: its seas a darker, slightly greenish blue, its land pale-blue with tints varying from dull green to umber, from gray to red, and dramatically streaked in white around the equator with brilliant patches of stormy areas halfway to the dazzling poles. Certainly it is unique among planets in our solar system, being more than three quarters covered with water, a substance about as rare in the universe as a whole as emeralds are rare on earth. This general water scarcity is due both to the fact that oxygen forms much less than one percent of the total bulk of universal elements and to the fact that H_2O exists as water only in the narrow temperature range between freezing and boiling, while it remains ice throughout some 492 degrees (Fahrenheit) below freezing and steam for thousands of degrees (depending on surrounding pressure) above boiling before it splits into its separate elements.

It is therefore only the rare combination of chemistry and precise distance from a heat source (the sun), plus size and gravity sufficient to keep the elements from escaping into space, that permit the earth its dainty air and jewellike oceans — oceans that glisten in the sun as on no planet our telescopes can see, often showing that blinding highlight at some ocean spot where the sun is reflected with mirror clarity. As the clouds also constantly circulate with the winds, so our unique gem must slowly wink and blink as its lights dance from sea to cloud to forest to desert to cloud to sea, adding the magic of uncertain mood to the regular fluctuation of its revolvement.

If you wonder why only one face of the moon always looks toward the earth, which is also why the earth must hang almost stationary in the moon's sky, making the moon's day equal to its "month," it may be interesting to review the work of Sir George Darwin (son of the discoverer of earthly evolution), who has made more precise calculations of moon history (a beginning of celestial evolution) than anyone else I know of. The origin of the moon is still a matter of speculation, the leading theories favoring the idea that she either grew up with the infant earth separately from a common nebulous beginning, or that she burst from the earth just after the earth condensed into a globe — the expulsive force being one combination or another of centrifugal, tidal, volcanic and vibrational influences. Darwin's own calculations point to vibration as the key propellant. According to his theory, since the earth's longest natural vibration rate is about two hours, some four billion years ago when the day was only four hours long and solar tides in the earth therefore two hours apart, the sympathetic vibration naturally greatly amplified the tides. At one critical period of nearly perfect resonance that lasted some five hundred years, these tides presumably crescendoed to such overwhelming size that at the bulg-

ing molten equator of the then dizzily whirling earth enough
material lashed out into space to form the moon.

Other authorities, particularly Sir Harold Jeffreys, have since
shown by careful mathematics that such tides could have reached
a maximum height of not more than a couple of hundred miles
which would not have been enough to expel the moon — and
that therefore the moon must have been born before the earth
herself had entirely formed — at least as early as when they were
both in their primordial nebulous state of gas and dust. In which
case the moon was originally just the condensation of a gassy
filament extruded from the thin mother earth cloud by the tidal
force of the sun at a time when our planetary orbit was so
elongated that the mother cloud swooped like a comet, now
close to the sun, now way out toward the distant stars.

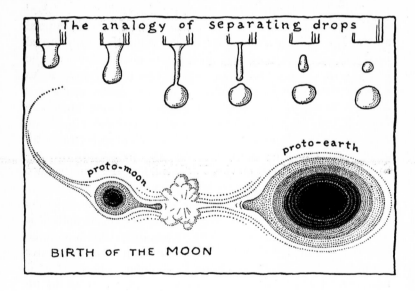

The analogy of separating drops

proto-earth

proto-moon

BIRTH OF THE MOON

On some such swing when the tidal period chanced to combine harmonically with the natural oscillation of the cloud, the
resonance must have reached a climax that plucked the tidal

wave of filament like a harp string, straining it beyond its elastic limit so that it snapped free and stayed just out of reach, revolving around and around the main cloud — a separate but still captive drop of Earth.

In basic accord with this idea was also that of Henri Poincaré, the mathematician and savant who, investigating the dynamics of spinning liquid spheres half a century ago, concluded that if such a ball accelerates "it must first distort itself doorknobwise, then develop a lop-sided equatorial bulge which at some magnitude of centrifugal force will finally extrude tangentially into a separate smaller body."

Whatever the actual facts of the moon's nativity, after she collected herself into a molten ball and settled into an orbit around the earth, her gradual development has become calculable backward from present observation to a reasonable nicety. Darwin thus found that the moon once upon a time evidently revolved less than 3,000 miles above our steaming skies as she whipped around her orbit in a four-hour month while the earth turned in its four-hour day, each keeping the same face toward the other, each daily eclipsing the other and raising tremendous stationary tides in material memory of the then fairly recent accouchement. But as the moon receded, she could not continue to keep up with the earth's turning and slipped behind, separating the month from the day while each period lengthened, also probably rotating slowly on her own axis independently — thereby setting up huge moving Earth tides on the lunar surface to match the great but lesser moon tides on earth.

It is of course these tides that have caused the moon to recede to her present remoteness, a result of the *push* of gravity that is hard for humans to understand while they remain so materially intoxicated with gravity's *pull*. For what you may have noticed as an apparent lag in the tides behind the moon as it moves across the sky is seen from our space-eye view as the rotation of the earth carrying the tides beyond the moon so that the tide crests stay just ahead (east) of the line joining the centers of earth and moon. This naturally tends to urge the moon perpetually onward (to the east) and, by thus increasing centrifugal force, to drive it outward — thereby creating a component of push induced by the tides of gravity!

But the same tides that urge the moon ahead, by the law of reaction, tend to hold the earth back, the friction of water against land over billions of years gradually absorbing some of the earth's energy and braking its rate of spin down to our present day. The very large tides on the moon have long since braked the moon's spin to the point where she cannot turn independently. The astronomers calculate that this taming of the moon was accomplished so gradually that each million years made scarcely any difference, only the accumulated billions having a really dramatic effect. Yet even now while the moon's dry face is anchored by gravity to the earth, and the earth still turns and turns but more and more slowly, we can sense, abstractly through mathematics, the slight changes in the balancing forces that are almost unbelievably delicate but are still steadily pushing the moon and proportionately lengthening the month. According to Darwin's reckoning, the moon must stop going away when the month reaches 55 of our present days in length, for by then (assuming man has not tampered with it) the earth's rotation will have slowed down so much that the day will also be as long as 55 present days. In other words, the earth too will hold one face toward the moon as both bodies slowly circle each other like tired dancers, and with the moon standing still in the sky our lunar tides will cease to flow or to push the moon any further.

The date for this remote event has been tentatively set by various astronomers as somewhen between the years A.D. 10,000-000,000 and 50,000,000,000, and the moon is approaching it now by receding from us at the dainty pace of only three fifths of an inch a year. If you have trouble believing that anyone could compute a fraction of an inch of annual shift 240,000 miles away, remember that it is average motion over a long period of time and that the moment the moon's edge blocks out a star can be measured with great precision, allowance being made for the exact altitude of whatever lunar slope or valley actually snips off that tiny beam of light. When you use equations involv-

ing both time and space, exact determination of the time factors
enables you to solve for the space factors with comparable exactitude.

Then sometime before the dry summer of the year A.D. 50,000-
000,000, the spinning of the earth may be so slowed down by
the remaining solar tides that the day will begin to be longer
even than the elongated month of that scarce-imaginable time —
the same earthly day that is now lengthening to the merry tune
of a thousandth of a second every century — and the lunar tides
will gradually begin again, this time in the reverse direction as
the moon rises in the west and sets in the east, and will pull Earth
and moon together instead of pushing them apart — something
you may understand abstractly (if you've ever studied physics) as
an inevitable consequence of the "law of conservation of angular
momentum."

Thus, almost imperceptibly, if moon and Earth should still
exist in such an inconceivably remote age, the moon may begin
its long journey back to the earth again. And thus at last the
stretch from sunrise to sunset will literally approach a coon's
age and each night become an occasion for hibernating. Whatever intelligent beings remain on Earth then will be able to
live in daylight, or darkness or twilight as long as they choose
just by moving occasionally in the appropriate direction. Women
(if evolution has preserved them) may actually be able to order
a time of day to fit a mood or a dress instead of having to
adapt themselves to the daily schedule as we do now.

If all this (which is based on but one of many theories)
seems a mite strange, consider Mars, whose moons are so fast
they can be read almost as easily as the hands of a clock. The
Martian day already is three times as long as his inner month
as defined by his nearer moon, Phobos, which thrice rises in
the west and zips across to set in the east before Mars can rotate
once. Meanwhile, the Martian outer month (four times longer)
lasts so little more than his day that his midget farther moon,
Deimos (5 miles in diameter), hangs above the horizon for more
than two of its months (61 earthly hours) and passes through
all its phases twice between rising and setting.

No one seems to have calculated just when our moon will

come home to roost, but it will definitely be long after the cows come home, if ever, and the manner of such coming has been worked out considerably — a dramatic show indeed, this spectacle that's in store for our descendants — all provided, of course, that we have any and that the sun is still burning then and that the earth and moon have been left to their natural courses.

It is hard to describe such a tremendous thing as the moon's descent with factual realism. How will she make the landing? Will the earth and moon first face each other fixedly while the round moon slowly settles upon one spot? Could we choose the spot — say, our largest ocean (if we still have any ocean) — and direct the moon there? Would our oceans and atmosphere (if atmosphere remains) be partially sucked up by the moon and flow all around it and around the contact place, leaving our old seas half dry and new continents exposed? Or would the moon come spiraling in at speed and land slantwise on the equator to roll around the earth many times before coming to rest? Would any of us have a chance to survive the terrific earthquakes and transcontinental tidal waves and unimaginable hurricanes, the thunderous tornadoes, the black dust storms thousands of miles deep? Which way will be up when the moon roosts on the earth, and what sort of life will be possible to any survivors?

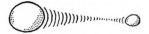

The actual event, as forecast by modern astrophysical knowledge, finesses many of these fearful questions in a surprising manner. The first thing that will be noticed, say astronomers, is that the approaching moon will have developed a protrusion toward the earth. Viewed from space, the moon will be growing more and more egg-shaped, an invariable trait among large nonspinning secondary bodies which get close to their primaries. And the small end of the egg will always aim at the earth, ever reaching out nearer and nearer under the eternal "come hither" of gravity.

The moon is even today slightly eggy. She is, after all, a

large nonspinning secondary, and her paunch aimed toward us has been measured as 3,000 feet higher than the average lunar surface. This is sixteen times as much Earth tide as the moon should have at 240,000 miles, and astronomers explain it as a "fossil tide" that froze that way when her distance was only 90,000 miles. But by A.D. 100,000,000,000 or so the reapproaching moon may be literally as ovoid as a hen's egg. And as gravity eggs her on still nearer (to about 5,000 miles' distance), astronomers say she will inevitably crack and great rifts will open up her interior and she will rapidly separate into two, then three, four, and more pieces, each of which will tend to disintegrate further as it continues to circle around the earth.

The fundamental reason for this is that at about 5,000 miles the gravity of the earth must begin to affect the moon's material more than the moon's own gravity does, so the material will spontaneously fall away from the moon system to form itself into a new equilibrium in more intimate partnership with the earth. The experts do not agree on exactly how successive steps of this extraordinary process will take place, but they are largely united in their opinion that such a break-up is a natural development, one which, under critical circumstances of satellite proximity, must happen. In fact, they can see it happening in our own solar system right now. Not every stage of it, of course, is visible in this twentieth-century instant of slow astronomical time, but Jupiter's inmost moon is deduced to be egg-shaped and headed for the break-up point, while Mars' fast moon, Phobos, is so ripe it could pop almost any millennium now. Indeed, Phobos circles so close above the Martian equator that, like a fat man's middle button, it cannot be seen from either pole. On the other hand, the rings of Saturn are believed to be the strewn debris of a moon that has already broken apart and become pulverized — this fairly recently, astronomically speaking, in fact perhaps during the hundred million years just past.

One tends to think of moons as rigid spheres like stone cannonballs, for most known moons seem to be made of stone or solid material of comparable mass. Yet a stone as big as a moon behaves in many ways more like a liquid than a solid. Not only does any solid body larger than 60 miles in diameter melt in its center in about a billion years, according to astronomer Gerard P. Kuiper of Yerkes Observatory, but even the unmolten outer parts have elastic qualities and flow under the influence of gravity, gradually assuming whatever shape conforms to the net dictates of equilibrium. Just as a compact bucketful of water emptied out a tower window quickly turns into rain, so there is a definite range of nearness to its planet through which a moon cannot pass without disintegrating — without becoming, in a manner of speaking, unmoonly. This range, discovered in 1850 by Edouard Roche, a French mathematician, is called Roche's limit. For a satellite of the same density as its planet, the disintegration distance has been calculated at 2.44 times the planet's radius between the two centers. Saturn's rings, for example, are wholly within Roche's limit, while all known moons of all planets remain outside, including even Phobos by the slim margin of 660 miles. In fact no exception to the law has yet been observed anywhere.

So the astronomers can judge with considerable confidence the life expectancy of any settling moon as it spirals closer and closer to its planetary disintegration zone until the strain of its paunch tide becomes unbearable and it snaps in two — like a rubber band. Such a forecast, far from guesswork, is the result of careful calculation. The elasticity of stone and other materials in astronomical masses has indeed been figured out closely enough to give a table of the break-up radii for different substances. A gaseous moon, for instance, comes apart where a liquid satellite would be safe, and a molten moon, moving farther in, must burst where a solid moon need never fear to tread.

Although Phobos' ten-mile diameter may be too small to give it a Roche's limit outside Mars' atmosphere, all the larger moons seem destined for eventual disintegration, whereupon all of their pieces that don't somehow fall into the planet must continue on their orbits, distorting themselves eggwise, bursting again and again from tidal stress till they become small enough to lose their elasticity, when probably only the friction of occasional collisions will continue to wear them down from boulders to stones to gravel to sand to dust as they revolve endlessly around the sky. Thus we should expect one day to witness the great rings of Jupiter!

Eventually Uranus and Neptune will sprout rings the same way when their inner moons break up. And almost exactly the same thing is bound to happen to the earth if celestial nature is left to its own devices long enough. Gerard Kuiper, authority on the solar system, thinks the earth has got rid of one such "sediment ring" already, mostly by having our newborn moon plow through it on her way out toward her present orbit. In any case, the accompanying shower of huge chunks and moony meteorites could be terrifying, not to say devastating, if not countered in some way. But somehow I don't think the problem need be depressing to an enterprising species like us with billions of years to plan in.

A key to ultimate moon undoing, of course, is tidal action, so it is helpful to look at the tides if we are to understand the fullness of moon history, past or future. The ancient Arabs made a beginning when they deduced that tides were caused by the expansion and contraction of the sea under the heat of moonlight, while the Chinese thought of the ocean as the earth's actual blood that was pumped rhythmically by some yet undiscovered terrestrial heart.

Only in modern times have we learned that all tides result from the fact that the gravitational pull on the near side of a body is stronger than the pull on its far side. Thus oceans on Earth become distorted as parts nearest the moon (and, to a lesser degree, the sun) pull away from the less responsive solid earth, while the solid earth in turn pulls away from the still less respectful sea on its far side. This difference in moon influence between the two sides of the earth now amounts to 7 percent,

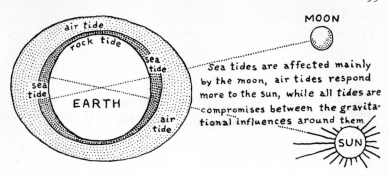

Sea tides are affected mainly by the moon, air tides respond more to the sun, while all tides are compromises between the gravitational influences around them

and in the case of the distant sun to about 2 percent. Ocean tides on Earth, however, are not as simple as they would be if just the moon and sun thus influenced them, for in practice near-by mountains also have a ponderable effect and sea-bottom friction and wind rubbing and coastal contours all exert various lags which, in view of irregular natural oceanic rhythms and the moon's own meandering orbit, make such complications that tide tables are of different "establishment" in every port.

In Tahiti and parts of the Irish coast, for instance, sun tides are stronger than moon tides. In many places, there are four tides a day; in others (called amphodromic points), virtually none. In still others, the morning and evening tides are of very unequal size, or they lag many hours behind the lunar transit.

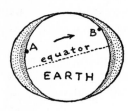

The tide at A is greater than at B because tides rotate somewhat in latitude as well as in longitude

MOON

Almost everywhere high tides increase with the full or new moon (when the sun adds 30 percent to the moon's pull) or wane to neap strength at the quarters (when the sun's effect cancels 30 percent of the moon's pull). And when the moon is at perigee (closest to the earth) another 30 percent factor is added to tidal strength, as compared to apogee (point farthest from earth).

The tides extend to the water under the ground far from the sea, to the solid earth itself, and even up into the high ionosphere where sun tides are generally stronger than moon tides and rise and fall several miles twice a day probably because they are in closer harmony with the natural elastic rhythm of air. And now we find that tides extend throughout the solar system as a function of its gravitational field, that there are majestic galactic tides of stars and space dust surging through the Milky Way, and probable supergalactic tides between the remotest and largest organizations of galaxies.

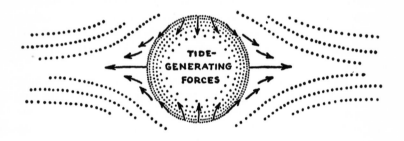

Among the earliest of moon prophets, I have heard, were the ancient Chaldeans, who may have discovered the mystic eclipse interval called the Saros, the regular period of 18 years and 11⅓ days between similar crossings of the sun by the moon, which (some historians think) enabled them to predict eclipses. But most people of their time still considered eclipses the warnings of moody gods and when, as happened to Nicias' Greek army at Syracuse, Sicily, on August 27, 413 B.C., "the sun perished out of the sky," they sometimes disregarded urgent expediency in order to appease the celestial powers, only to get attacked and wiped out by a less scrupulous enemy.

Even the Egyptians did not suspect the complicated irregularities of the eclipse pattern that, we now know, leapfrogs around the earth in spirals, Saros by Saros, working from the poles to the equator every 1,200 years. Nor did the astronomers of the seventeenth century who tried to pin down the moon's schedule with impartial accuracy see any clear path out of their growing confusion. The "synodic month" (period required for the moon to return to its same position in relation to the sun) came out as 29 ½ days, while the "sidereal month" (period of her return in relation to the stars) turned out to be only 27 ⅓ days and the "draconitic month" (period in relation to her nodes) 27 ⅕ days. It was not easy to decide which was the proper month nor how any of them should be fitted into the year.

The movement of the moon, in fact, proved even harder to keep track of than the gyrations of the planets, traditionally known as the "wandering stars," because its relative nearness to Earth made its apparent motion (including its seeming irregularity) many times greater. And such details as precession and the discrepancy between axis of turning and axis of symmetry taxed the genius of Newton, inventor of the calculus, so heavily he once admitted that his "head never ached except when studying lunar theory." Even as recently as thirty-five years ago when E. W. Brown of Yale completed his great work on the orbit of the moon, which stands today (despite our new age of electronic calculating machines) as a culminating achievement of mathematical astronomy, the scientific world gaped to realize he had spent a quarter of a century devising, correcting, checking and polishing a single equation for the moon's motion that covers some 250 large pages!

A simpler way of looking at the moon's inextricable behavior is to analogize her intimate relationship with the earth as a kind of dependency between a mother and grown daughter who live together. For not only does the moon move about the earth; the earth also moves about the moon. Putting both motions together, Newton found, as he had hoped and expected, that there was a common center of gravity for the combination. It was as if the two were joined by an invisible rod from the

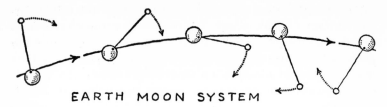

EARTH MOON SYSTEM

center of the earth to the center of the moon, a rod ever twirling like a baton in the hands of an aloof drum major, the sun, around whom the common center of gravity (axis of the twirling rod) moves in a smooth ellipse. The marvelous perfection of this system has been remarked by many great thinkers from Kepler to Einstein. Exact measurement of the location of the common center of gravity (about 3,000 miles moonward from the center of the earth yet still 1,000 miles below our land and sea) has enabled us to "weigh the moon" after filling in Newton's basic equation with the gravitational constant. As the distance of the centers of the two bodies (from the common center of gravity) is inversely proportional to their masses, and the common center is about $\frac{1}{82}$ of the way from the earth's center to the moon's, the moon can weigh only $\frac{1}{82}$ as much as the earth, or a mere 81,000,000,000,000,000,000 tons.

From this follows the deduction that the moon's specific gravity is 3.3, that she is made of much lighter stuff than the earth with its interior of olivine and iron, that she may well be of just ordinary granite all the way through. But if our moon is lighter than Earth, she is of much sterner material than some moons like Jupiter's Callisto, the biggest of all known moons, who, with specific gravity only 0.6, is literally buoyant enough to float on a watery ocean.

All things considered, ours is far from an average or common moon. Not only is she the nearest to the sun of all the thirty-one known moons, but she is much the largest in proportion to her mother planet. Some astronomers even consider the earth-moon combination a double planet. No other such partnership is to be found in all the solar system, perhaps because, as one theory suggests, satellites that exceed about one fiftieth the mass of their primary tend toward instability and do not long survive.

In any case, there are only five moons bigger than ours in the solar family (Jupiter's Io, Ganymede and Callisto — all named after Jupiter's illicit loves — Saturn's Titan and Neptune's Triton), and none of these is as heavy as one thousandth the weight of its planet. Most of the others are less than a millionth of their primaries, though in other respects they vary to a surprising degree. Mars' little Deimos, for instance, which is smaller than Mount Everest, has such weak gravity that, according to Fred Whipple of Harvard Observatory, a man on it "would weigh only a few ounces and would be capable of jumping several miles, if not completely off the satellite." Mars' west-rising moon, Phobos, might seem to nonmathematical Martians a withershins moon, moving "against the sun" in accord with the definition of that Scottish adjective. But Phobos is really not contrary but just over-eager in an orthodox direction since he revolves to the east even faster than Mars turns eastward behind him.

We have almost everything somewhere in our solar system, however, including several truly contrary moons that move opposite to the spin of their planets. The first of these was discovered in 1898 and named Phoebe. It is Saturn's most remote moon, moving in a retrograde orbit of eight-million-mile radius and counter to Saturn's eight known inner moons, to her rings and to herself! Later, a large satellite called Triton was observed going withershins around Neptune. And four small retrograde moons have been found moving contrariwise about Jupiter, tiny rebels who seem to be thumbing their noses at nature in general. But although at first all of these renegades appear to defy the harmonic order of creation, making a law unto themselves, astronomers believe that at least the Jovian ones are likely to be former asteroids that overtook the big planet from inner (solar) orbits and were thus caught going against the main traffic in a gravitational field that was too much for them. Once captured, they have just not been able to get away, though evidence of their struggle remains visible in most cases in their wild orbits, which form a kind of permanent celestial record analogous to the rings of trees. This sort of record is probably at least as eloquent and durable as any history written in the rock strata of Earth and may even be comparable in principle to human memory stored in patterns of atomic orbits in the brain.

We are by no means, however, at the end of the amazing variety among our known moons. One of Jupiter's is three-quarters frozen water by volume, which practically makes it a snowball. Another Jovite that appears as faint as a candle three thousand miles away got lost for thirteen years on its eccentric orbit and had to be rediscovered by electronic computer at a range of 500 million miles. One of Saturn's, named Titan and a good deal bigger than our own, is the only moon in the whole solar system known to have an atmosphere. Although the titanic "air" is far from the humanly breathable kind we are used to and is certainly very cold, it just conceivably could support some sort of life.

And the oddest moon of all may be Saturn's piebald eighth satellite, Iapetus — this one less than half the size of ours and, like it, holding one face always toward its planet. Yet as Iapetus moves around Saturn, its brightness varies by a factor of five, showing that one side is five times as light in shade as the other and presumably smoother in texture by a like amount. One can speculate that Iapetus may have been disfigured on one side by some great explosion on Saturn, or perhaps it happened at the time of the creation of the rings, or in some collision with another moon or asteroid or comet. Or could Iapetus be just a lopsided piece of some earlier moon? Or possibly the result of a billion years of eclipse erosion — erosion on one face only through abrupt temperature drops during eclipses?

One does not hear any talk about submoons in modern observatories but I cannot help but wonder whether there may be a few submoons about too — tiny natural satellites of satellites some-where in our system. None has yet been discovered. But that does not prove their nonexistence. Since most moons themselves have been hard to find and Jupiter's outer moons could not be seen with the naked eye even from Jupiter, submoons would naturally be almost impossible to detect — even in the systems of the nearest planets. The bigger moons of the giant planets would be the most likely hosts of submoons, of course, though a submoon (probably a small fraction of a mile in diameter) would be invisible even to the 200-inch reflecting telescope at this great distance. Our own moon, on the other hand, could hardly have any submoons much larger than a meteor without their being detected by now, for her first artificial submoon (the Russian rocket that photographed her back side) is definitely within the realm of detectability.

Another trait of moons that has long fascinated me is their tend-ency to rock back and forth, and I used to think that when our own moon finally settled one face toward the earth it might have reached equilibrium like a well-oiled but slightly uneven wheel spinning on a shaft, at last ceasing its full rotation to rock pon-derously like a dying pendulum to and fro over millions of years. But astrophysicists say there is too much tidal viscosity for that. In effect, the moon's oil contains a soupçon of glue. And the only rocking it can do is the 12 ° of arc it is now seen to swing through each month, showing us one cheek at first quarter, another at the third. This so-called libration is caused by the fact that, although the moon rotates (on its own axis) at the same average rate that it revolves (around the earth), the *even*ness of the *rotation* is not quite matched by the *uneven*ness of the *revolution*, which, being elliptical rather than circular, speeds up at perigee, slows down at apogee, rocking earthwise to the rhythm of a particular kind of slow lunar lullaby known only to the boundless cradle of the sky.

That there are more than moons to occupy the astronomers these nights seems evident from the strange fact that eight of Jupiter's moons, discovered over the past two thirds of a century, have not even yet been named. And as I float through my bottom-less garden of stars and watch our own solitary moon swinging slowly onward, I ponder the significance of such pointed neglect.

Parent planet	Proposed name for nameless moon*	Name of named moon	Density	Designation or order of discovery	Discoverer and date	Miles from center of planet	Diameter in miles	Period of revolution around planet days	hrs.	mins.
EARTH		Moon				240,000	2,160	27	7	42
MARS		Phobos			Hall, 1877	5,800	10		7	39
		Deimos			Hall, 1877	14,600	5		30	18
JUPITER	Iodama ("heifer calf of Io")			V	Barnard, 1892	112,700	100?		11	57
		Io	2.7	I	Galileo, 1610	262,000	2,320	1	18	28
		Europa	2.9	II	Galileo, 1610	417,000	1,960	3	13	14
		Ganymede	2.2	III	Galileo, 1610	665,000	3,200	7	3	43
		Callisto	0.6	IV	Galileo, 1610	1,170,000	3,220	16	16	32
	Carmanor ("servant of moon goddess")			VI	Perrine, 1904	7,140,000	75?	250	17	
	Arion ("high moon creature")			VII	Perrine, 1905	7,290,000	30?	260	1	
	Psylla ("the flea")			X	Nicholson, 1938	7,300,000	12?	270		
	Cyrene ("mistress of the bridle") — retrograde orbit			XII	Nicholson, 1951	13,000,000	13?	625	10	
	Antiphus ("contrary") — retrograde			XI	Nicholson, 1938	14,000,000	15?	692		
	Autonoë ("with a mind of her own") — retrograde			VIII	Melotte, 1908	14,600,000	25?	739		
	Hecabe ("moving far off") — retrograde			IX	Nicholson, 1914	14,900,000	13?	745		

(Moon Table continued)

Parent planet	Direction of orbit	Name of named moon	Density	Designation or order of discovery	Discoverer and date	Miles from center of planet	Diameter in miles	Period of revolution around planet days	hrs.	mins.
SATURN	normal	Mimas	0.5	VII	Herschel, 1789	115,300	270?		22	37
	normal	Enceladus		VI	Herschel, 1789	148,000	300?	1	8	53
	normal	Tethys		V	Cassini, 1684	183,000	700?	1	21	18
	normal	Dione		IV	Cassini, 1684	235,000	650?	2	17	41
	normal	Rhea	3.5	II	Cassini, 1672	327,600	1,000?	4	12	25
	normal	Titan		I	Huygens, 1655	760,000	2,850?	15	22	41
	normal	Hyperion		VIII	Bond, 1848	920,000	250?	21	6	38
	normal	Iapetus		III	Cassini, 1671	2,212,000	800?	79	7	56
	retrograde	Phoebe		IX	Pickering, 1898	8,040,000	200?	550	10	
URANUS	slightly retrograde	Miranda		V	Kuiper, 1948	81,000	100?	1	9	55
	slightly retrograde	Ariel		I	Lassell, 1851	119,000	300?	2	12	29
	slightly retrograde	Umbriel		II	Lassell, 1851	166,000	250?	4	3	28
	slightly retrograde	Titania		III	Herschel, 1787	272,000	600?	8	16	56
	slightly retrograde	Oberon		IV	Herschel, 1787	365,000	550?	13	11	7
NEPTUNE	retrograde	Triton		I	Lassell, 1846	220,000	3,000?	5	21	3
	normal	Nereid		II	Kuiper, 1949	3,350,000	200?	359	10	

* Of these proposed names, Seth Nicholson, discoverer of four Jovian moons, writes the author: "The names you suggest ... are good logical ones." But skeptically, he adds, "I think that, like Pullman cars, they will be known by their numbers, not their names."

I scrutinize my moon table (q.v.) and dream a little and meditate and muse on names for nameless worlds.

It may be just my own private form of lunacy in this trackless void, but I can't help but wonder how long such celestial pathos must continue — how long will neglected satellites go mooning onward in their lonely dudgeon — how long can the tentmaker's son go unheeded:

> Yon rising moon that looks for us again—
>   How oft hereafter will she wax and wane;
> How oft hereafter rising look for us
>   Through this same garden — and for one in vain!

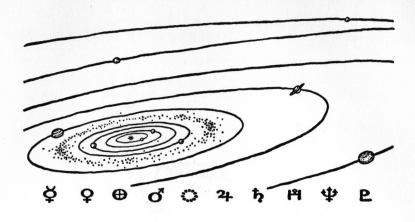

4. OUR SISTER planets

I FIND IT RATHER HARD TO REMEMBER, out here in trackless space, just how those mystic, sibling worlds called Venus, Mars, Jupiter and Saturn appeared from Earth. And even harder is it to recover much perspective on how they seemed in ancient times — say, in the dim dawn days of Greece when Anaximandros of Miletos expatiated upon creation in the sixth century B.C., opining (I've read) that "something capable of begetting hot and cold out of the unbounded was separated off at the origin of the world. And from this arose a sphere of flame encasing the earth as the bark around a tree. When this had been further compassed by certain rings, the sun, moon and stars were born." As for the earth itself, he went on, it "swings free, held in its place by nothing. It is fixed by its equal distance from everything. We are on one of the surfaces, and the other is on the opposite side."

Half a century later, Pythagoras of Samos, who has been called the patron saint of science, intuitively divided creation at the level of the moon into a *super*lunar sphere, containing all the regular stars, all ascended souls and immortal gods, and a *sub*lunar sphere, where dwelt all bodies that could be classed as irregular, mortal or dead. He was the most influential western philosopher of his time, and his appointment of the moon's range as the borderline between regularity and irregularity, arbitrary though it now appears, carried great weight. The wandering stars, called planets (from *planētēs*, a vagabond), were already understood to be higher than the moon, which made them superlunar and eternal — and this raised the difficult question of why they did not move with more regularity. Their confusing movements had even been compared by Anaximenes (also of Miletos) to "the gyrations of leaves falling off the tree of stars." Yet Pythagoras resolved the dilemma with his profound and contagious faith in divine order expressed in a law of universal harmony under which the planets would be found to revolve in circles upon invisible spheres if only one could measure them in true perspective.

Pythagoras is said to have played the phorminx, a seven-stringed

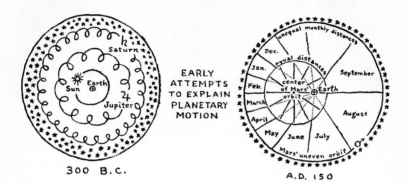

EARLY
ATTEMPTS
TO EXPLAIN
PLANETARY
MOTION

300 B.C.

A.D. 150

harp made of tortoiseshell — reputedly invented by Hermes, god of science and eloquence. Instrumental music in those days was generally considered a form of religious ritual, but Pythagoras seems to have been so fascinated with the mystical abstraction of numbers that he experimented mathematically with the harmonics of the vibrating string and became impressed with the remarkable similarity between musical intervals and the spacings of the planets, which then included the wandering sun and moon. For, according to Hippolytos (c. 400 B.C.), "Pythagoras maintained that the universe sings and is constructed in accordance with harmony; and he was the first to reduce the motions of the seven heavenly bodies to rhythm and song."

This is undoubtedly the origin of the music of the spheres in which the seven classical planets symbolized the seven notes of the scale, and the heptachord in turn founded the seven-day week and perhaps the seven vowels of the Greek alphabet upon the same seven spheres. Certainly this is such a reasonable derivation of our common hebdomad that it is hard to imagine how else the entire civilized earth could have accepted the basic septimal rhythm of the calendar with its Sun day, Moon day, Tiw's (Mars') day, Woden's (Mercury's) day, Thor's (Jupiter's) day, Frigg's (Venus') day and Saturn's day.

The Greeks soon seemed unable to imagine any planet without its orbital sphere, upon which it moved in a perfect circle, any other orbit being obviously less than godly. And for them, each of the seven celestial immortals exerted its particular mood upon the temper of the central earth — giving us the corresponding moody adjectives of sunny, looney, martial, mercurial, jovial, venereal and saturnine — while the less-specialized Greek tragedies became *dis-asters* (against the stars), each wanton barbarian raid *ex-orbitant* (out of orbit) and anything beyond the normal four world ingredients of earth, water, air and fire, a *quintessence* (fifth element). And so forth.

Ptolemy of Alexandria later placed an "eight sphere" outside the original seven to hold the fixed stars and the Milky Way, and he and other mathematicians added still more spheres to the celestial scale in efforts to account for all the apparent eccentricities of the planets, including the puzzling but recurrent figure-eight-shaped *hippopede* (horse-fetter) maneuvers of Mars, Jupiter and

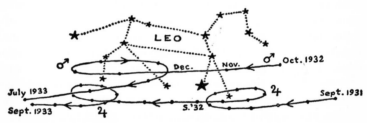

APPARENT TRACKS OF MARS (ABOVE) AND JUPITER (BELOW), MONTH BY MONTH, THROUGH THE CONSTELLATION OF THE LION

Saturn. Out of these spheres developed the famous concept of the epicycle, a small rapid orbit whose center revolves slowly around a larger orbit which may swing in turn about a still larger one, brilliantly explaining the most baffling of planetary motions better than they had ever been explained before. But somehow it seemed forced and unnatural, and successively closer measurements of the planets kept calling for more spheres embellished with more epicycles until, by the sixteenth century, it took more than eighty spheres to account for the observed movements, and even that number did it very imperfectly.

Opposing this lamentable trend toward complexity, a few daring visionaries had conceived of simpler explanations, such as Heraclides of Pontos' rash idea in the fourth century B.C. that "since Venus and Mercury are never observed at any great angular distance from the sun, they may revolve about it" or the even more startling and probably original proposal of Philolaos of Croton a century earlier that "the earth circles around the sun."

Unfortunately, few people had thought of keeping systematic records of the positions of the planets in those days, so there was little evidence for decisively proving or disproving any theory. With the possible exception of a 360-year series of Chaldean star measurements begun under King Nabonassar in 747 B.C., and to a lesser degree the Babylonian and Egyptian efforts, observing had never been regarded as particularly important. Noble concepts of the mind were rated much higher. But the intuition of Heraclides and the inspirations of Philolaos and, later, of the great Aristarchos of Samos (who held that the earth not only revolves around the sun but spins daily on its own axis) seemed more blasphemous than noble — and where was there any solid datum to contradict the obvious fact that the great earth is fixed in the middle of creation while the dainty little stars and parasitic planets swing respectfully around it? How could any devout astrologer take seriously the wild conjectures of such later philosophers as Nicholas of Cusa that the earth cannot be central because the universe is infinite and infinity has no center?

It was not until a German (dwelling in Poland) named Nikolaus Koppernigk, better known by his Latin name of Copernicus, got exasperated at the ridiculous numbers of spheres and epicycles required to patch up the heavens that Philolaos' and Aristarchos' old ideas (which Copernicus had read about) were revived and published in A.D. 1543. I am referring, of course, to Copernicus' famous work De Revolutionibus Orbium Coelestium, On the Revolutions of the Celestial Spheres, which included the startling hypothesis (of Ecphantos the Pythagorean, Hicetas of Syracuse, Heraclides and Aristarchos) that the earth rotates daily about its

COPERNICUS

own axis. This idea had been made much more plausible by the recent exploits of Columbus, Balboa and Magellan. But Copernicus could find only fourteen observations to support his argument that the sun is the center of a system of revolving planets, a number that, he admitted, was far too small on which to claim a proof. So his concept was offered mainly on the strength of its simplicity. That seemed reason enough to his orderly mathematical mind, which still saw no need to question the orthodox Pythagorean uniformity of circular orbits in a basic machinery of spheres. Yet almost despite his own efforts, as in the case of his older contemporary, Columbus, Copernicus opened up a world so unbelievable that he himself did not live to recognize it.

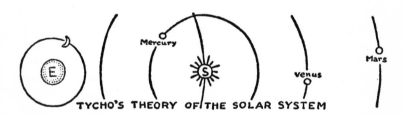

TYCHO'S THEORY OF THE SOLAR SYSTEM

Strangely enough, the complete acceptance of Copernicus' new celestial order was to come in large measure from a colorful and arrogant Danish nobleman named Tycho Brahe, who not only did not believe in much of it but supposed he had practically disproved it because his pre-eminent instruments could not detect sidereal parallax, or the difference in apparent direction of a body (say, the North Star) as seen from different places (say, opposite sides of the earth's orbit). He insisted, quite reasonably, that at least a slight bit of parallax must be revealed if the earth were really swinging around the sun — for, in those days before the telescope, no man had ever heard or dreamed of such a fantastic thing as the since proven distance of the nearest star at 25,000,000-000,000 miles.

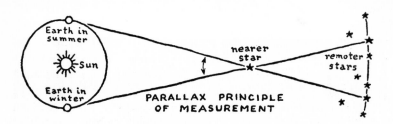

Tycho Brahe was different from the usual playboy son of an aristocrat. Although he lost his nose in a duel at twenty and had to wear a false one the rest of his life, he was such a serious student of astronomy, reverently putting on his finest robes to measure and honor the stars, that King Frederick II of Denmark presented him with the island of Hveen near Copenhagen and financed the erection there of the fabulous Uraniborg ("Castle of the Heavens"), complete with printing press, paper mill and running water, where Tycho and his staff made systematic observations of stars and planets for more than twenty years. Indeed, Tycho is considered the first modern scientist in that he not only built instruments of remarkable accuracy, including a quadrant 37 feet high calibrated to the minute of arc and a clepsydra which kept time through a steady dripping of mercury, but he repeated every measurement four times, made precise allowance for the errors of all his equipment and even worked out a refraction table to correct altitude angles for the bending of light rays that had passed through the thick lower air. Using as many as nine assistants at one time, he insisted that every fact be checked and rechecked before it was recorded with unprecedented and scrupulous care. A clue to the quality of his results is his successful measurement of the length of the year to within a second of the modern figure, and construction of a five-foot globe of brass to represent the sky on which he engraved the positions of 777 stars and planets so exactly that they and his paper records later formed the main basis of Kepler's discoveries and, to only a slightly lesser degree, made possible Newton's great work on the laws of gravity and motion, which has been the plinth of science and engineering ever since.

Johannes Kepler, the thirty-year-old German assistant who succeeded Tycho after his death in Prague in 1601, was almost exactly opposite him in temperament. Poor, gentle, sickly and weak in eyesight, he had little stomach for monotonous nightly observations but preferred searching for some clear law in the bewildering whirl of moody planetary motions. That he was meticulous in the popular horoscope service he ran in his spare time is suggested by his calculation of his own conception as having occurred on "16 May, A.D. 1571, at 4:37 a.m.," followed by "a pregnancy lasting 224 days, 9 hours and 53 minutes." That he was a mathematician to the heart is shown by his very logical and successful method of finding an optimum wife by classifying all the ladies of his acquaintance in the order of their eligibility, then proposing down the list to ensure that the first who said "Ja" was automatically the best obtainable.

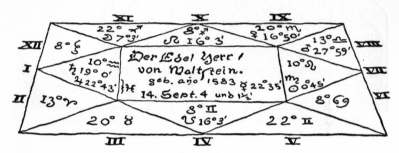

WALLENSTEIN'S HOROSCOPE CAST BY KEPLER - 1608

Although he enthusiastically accepted the Copernican theory for its convincing simplicity, Kepler was so steeped in astrology and mysticism that he was a virtual Pythagorean and never ceased looking for harmonies or unsuspected relationships between the motions of the several planets. Why were there exactly six planets, now counting the earth but not the sun or moon? Was it because six was a "perfect" number, the product as well as the sum of one, two and three?

One of Kepler's most serious projects was circumscribing the "sphere" of each planetary orbit with a different one of the five regular solids (tetrahedron, cube, octahedron, dodecahedron and icosahedron) to see if they would exactly fit between the spherical surfaces as he devoutly presumed they should if the heavens were really divine. The fits, however, turned out to be only "fairly good" — definitely not perfect — so Kepler turned to music as the mathematical function that might yield a better clue to planetary intervals. He actually transcribed the music of the spheres, evidently having accepted the tradition that each planet was alive and be-

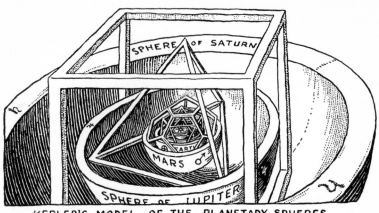

KEPLER'S MODEL OF THE PLANETARY SPHERES

souled if not presided over by its individual guardian angel who alone could hear its harmony. He was so poor at this time that he must have wondered whether his own terrestrial angel was really listening but, transposing from relative velocities in various parts of their different orbits, he somehow came up with basic melodies for each planet, the earth's notes being simply "mi, fa, mi" repeated over and over, which could be interpreted as "miseria, famina, miseria" — misery, famine, and more misery — the prevailing doleful theme of Earth. Little Mercury's tone was soprano, Venus' appropriately contralto and, continuing outward from the sun, Mars' a falsetto tenor and the voices of the giants Jupiter and Saturn both deeply bass.

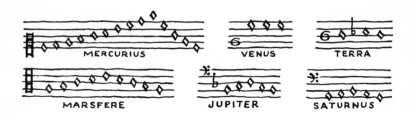

Yet always the beautiful abstractions of mathematics nourished the exuberant patterns of Kepler's reasoning. In an age when almost no one believed in the reign of law in nature, he had faith in ultimate divine justice, which meant order, which meant law. And no matter how deep his frustration, he kept on trying and rejecting, plotting and measuring, one after another the geometric forms and combinations that might explain the weird motions of Mars so painstakingly pinpointed by old Tycho — Mars, who seemed to offer a particular challenge with his apparent "horse-fetter" gyrations whenever he passed close to the earth — Mars, whose distance away (therefore his position in space) could not be seen, but only his direction from an earth which was itself moving in an invisible, unknown manner around the sun.

Reluctantly Kepler soon had to abandon the circle as the divine orbital shape. Even with the help of elaborate epicycles, it just could not be made to fit reality any closer than eight minutes, about one seventh of a degree. Though another astronomer suggested that a discrepancy of only 8' of arc might easily have resulted from a slip in a planetary observation without the aid of a telescope, Kepler firmly replied that it was "quite out of the question for Tycho to have made an error of that magnitude." After he had also rejected the egg-shaped orbit and was anxiously but carefully plotting out all the other forms of the oval he could think of, Kepler suddenly discovered to his unbounded delight that the simple ellipse with its off-center foci (originally rejected as ungodly) was what he was looking for. Perhaps only then did he remember Tycho's careful description of a comet's elliptical orbit in 1588, the first such ever known!

At any rate, Kepler could almost feel Tycho's proud smile of

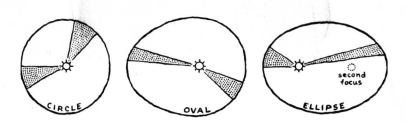

CIRCLE   OVAL   ELLIPSE   second focus

admiration when, in 1609, a few months before Galileo Galilei in Padua built the first astronomical telescope, he started writing out his three great laws of planetary motion: (1) *The orbit of every planet is an ellipse with the sun at one focus.* Which stands to this day a pillar of celestial mechanics.

With the orbital shape thus at last cleared up, it was relatively easy to define the manner of planetary movement, irrevocably uniting time with space: (2) *The straight line joining a planet and the sun sweeps over equal areas during equal times.*

And finally, after another nine years of hard struggle to tune in more closely to the elusive music, he noticed a striking similarity in the last two columns (below) of one of his many tables of periods and distances

PLANET	RELATIVE DISTANCE FROM SUN	PERIOD IN YEARS	SQUARE OF THE PERIOD	CUBE OF THE DISTANCE
MERCURY	0.387	0.241	0.058	0.058
VENUS	0.723	0.615	0.378	0.378
EARTH	1	1	1	1
MARS	1.524	1.881	3.538	3.540
JUPITER	5.203	11.862	140.707	140.851
SATURN	9.539	29.458	867.774	867.977

from which he immediately derived his now famous harmonic law: (3) *The squares of the periods of revolution of the planets are proportional to the cubes of their respective mean distances from the sun.*

If all this seems fairly simple now that we have been shown

the way, remember that Kepler was the first man in world history able to define the actual movement of the spheres. And if he had lived beyond the age of fifty-nine he very well might have found the answer to his final quest for a unifying principle to explain his by then famous triad of laws — something which it took no less a genius than Isaac Newton, the great English mathematician, to accomplish half a century later with his epochal definition of gravitation: *Every particle of matter in the universe attracts every other particle with a force proportional to the product of their masses and varying inversely as the square of the distance between their centers.*

We will meet Newton again in the second part of this book. Here we are dealing with those sisters of Earth, the planets, which were Kepler's particular concern as the most challenging celestial beings of his day. And their fascination for modern astronomers in their variety and alien mystery is not likely to diminish while they draw rapidly closer to our reach.

Mercury, nearest planet to the sun, is also the swiftest and smallest — in fact, smaller even than Ganymede and Callisto, Jupiter's largest moons. Although the Greeks named him Mercury when they saw him setting just after sunset, some of them also called him Apollo when he rose at dawn, even though the better educated among them were well aware that he was one and the same. Probably the name Mercury finally stuck because of his mercurial temperament as expressed in his fickle elusiveness. His year is only 88 Earth days, and he spends them moving at speeds ranging from 23 to 36 miles a second, swooping now within 29 million miles of the sun, now way out to 44 million miles. This eccentric orbit makes him invisible most of the time, yet early in this century it provided one of the most important proofs of Einstein's theory of general relativity, as we shall later see.

Not much more is yet known about Mercury, because he is so small and hard to observe, and at best he is hardly an inviting destination for an exploratory voyage. His sunny side is hot enough (770° F.) to melt lead and tin and has long since cooked his atmosphere completely away, while his dark side, never warmer than around 400° F. below zero, is colder than midnight on Pluto, a hundred times farther from the sun. The reason for such extreme cold so near the sun, of course, is that Mercury, like our moon, keeps only one face toward his primary, leaving his back side in perpetual darkness and, being atmosphereless, without effective means of acquiring heat from his front. Even his three-week-long seasons, mainly produced by his frenzied tempo of spiraling in and out from the sun, cannot much atone for the fixed climatic extremes of his lit and unlit iron mountains.

VENUS AS
SEEN FROM EARTH ♀
as the evening star
as the morning star

Venus, the second planet from the sun and twin sister of the earth, offers a gracious contrast. And, I'm glad to say, much more hospitality, even if, as befits her name, she is well shrouded in feminine mystery. Her veil is not just a figure of speech either, for the obvious brightness of Venus does not come from anything so firm as flesh but rather from her flowing sari of white clouds.

Like Mercury, Venus is a moonless planet who, swinging regularly between us and the sun, has lunelike phases of her own. Thus we have known her shady side ever since Galileo first caught her in his glass and saw that she must circle completely around the sun — strong evidence in support of Copernicus. And we have recorded her extraordinary changes in appearance from a remote gibbous peach beyond the sun to a close crescent of pale pumpkin six times greater in diameter as she overtakes the earth every nineteenth month on her inside track — these being the first tele-scopic revelations of the mysterious Hesperus of the evening and Phosphorus of the morning from Greek antiquity.

Her crescent indeed is a unique sight and different from anything else known to the heavens, being not at all the sharp sickle of our young moon's blade but a kind of soft pearly sash encircling more than half her body with the enchanting haziness imparted by a lush atmosphere. And when the sun is almost directly behind her, Venus does not vanish completely like a new moon, for a delicate negligee of filtered light lingers around her silhouette in a complete ring — actually a halo of pure gloaming bestowed by her radiant sire.

Yet for all her dainty charm, Venus stands no less than champion in visual magnitude among all the fixed and wandering stars to be seen from Earth. And when she is at her maximum brilliance, between two and three weeks before and after her synodic rendezvous with the sun, she is easily visible on earth in full daylight and will cast distinct shadows on any clear moonless night.

One is apt to forget, moreover, that since her almost circular orbit never permits her to stray more than 46° in angular distance from the sun, Venus must nearly always be within human sight in the middle of a clear day any time of year — if one but knows exactly where to look. Even though professional navigators traditionally neglect the diurnal Venus, who demands close calculation and usually some patient gazing before one may catch her eye, I sometimes used to call on her for help while flying the lonely Pacific during the Korean airlift — invariably to my advantage and delight. As it was often almost impossible to navigate accurately by the sun alone, when neither moon nor stars were in sight, Venus quite naturally became my second light. Her plotted altitude line thus protected many an unsuspecting high-priority passenger to whom such a clue from Venus at noon would have seemed no more real than a wink from a passing angel — which in sober fact may not be so far from what it was.

As to the question of the kind of world Venus really is underneath her dazzling raiment, it is hard to believe how much the scientists have been able to deduce from small clues. For example, Gerard Kuiper, using filters to exclude all but violet light, took hundreds of pictures that show six vague bands of otherwise invisible "climate" around Venus, comparable to the rainy doldrums, dry horse latitudes and windy jet streams of earth. The inclination of her axis of rotation, thus revealed as 32° from the ecliptic plane, suggests very diverse Venusian seasons. Meanwhile, regular cycles of 11-meter radio-wave intensity, evidently emanating from "storms" lurking on one side of the planet, indicated to radioastronomer John D. Kraus of Ohio State University a Venus day of 22 hours and 17 minutes.

Elsewhile, other observers were puzzled by the spectroscopic indication that water vapor is scarce in Venus' clouds (being detectable only in spectrograms made from space), because, they reasoned, a planet so earthlike should logically be expected to have had an origin and history close enough to Earth's to give it a comparable proportion of water along with most of the familiar terrestrial elements. Even the length of Venus' day hints at some sort of ocean tidal action to have braked her rotation toward the gentle terrestrial pace. If there are any watery seas on Venus, however, their vapor should show up strongly in her clouds instead of just the predominating carbon dioxide and faint nitrogen and H_2O lines found in her spectrograms.

Could Venus' natural juices have almost completely evaporated away, as almost surely happened to Mercury? Certainly not anywhere near completely, hinted the astrochemists. Yet the slight disparities in mass and position between Earth and Venus evidently have made a surprising chemical difference. For while Venus' diameter is only 227 miles less than the earth's, her one-sixth smaller mass with its correspondingly reduced gravity has undoubtedly allowed more of her atmosphere to escape — particularly her hydrogen, lightest of all gases and the prime ingredient of water.

On Earth, water vapor, if it tries to rise high, becomes cooled enough to condense into droplets which eventually fall back to the surface as rain. But Venus' atmosphere is almost surely too warm for rain because of her nearness to the sun, and her gravity has probably been barely able to hold on to the oxygen part of whatever evaporated H_2O she ever had. Moreover, as there is no evidence of free oxygen in her atmosphere now, what remains of this vital element has presumably long since consolidated its grip on the planet by combining with various other common elements such as carbon.

Such a hypothesis, at least, would explain the great abundance of carbon dioxide on Venus. And, interestingly enough it brings up the possibility that our lovely "evening star" may really be the heiress of more than all the fabulous wealth of fairytale and song. For if her oxygen has mostly gone into carbon dioxide, she must have carbon available in tremendous quantities with, very likely, a vast unoxidized residue now still remaining in some such natural form as oil or coal. Perhaps, as astronomer Fred Hoyle gaily suggests, the Venusian oceans are literally "oceans of oil" upon a planet "endowed beyond the dreams of the richest Texas oil-king."

Mars, the fourth member of the sun's family and first beyond the earth, is as different from Venus as Venus is different from Mercury. If Venus is Earth's twin sister, Mars is the little brother

of both and the most nearly proven abode of life among all the
heavenly hosts.

The most unusual thing about Mars from a human viewpoint
is his observability, which, oddly enough, is as much due to his
small size as to his propitious closeness to Earth at the very periods
he appears most "full" with sunlight. For, being smaller than
Earth to the degree that a plum is smaller than an orange and of
lighter substance, Mars has only a tenth the terrestrial mass and
therefore could not retain nearly as much atmospheric shroud
despite the astringent effect of a temperature that averages nearly
a hundred degrees (F.) cooler. Thus the Martian skies are
usually free enough of clouds so that we can see his rusty arid
plains and bricky deserts, which of course are why Mars looks
prevailingly red and why he was named after the bloody god of
war.

When telescopic seeing is most nearly perfect, astronomers can
pick out even minor details of the suggestive jasperlike landscape:
the dark brownish green of his Wedge of Casius, the bright green
of Mare Cimmerium, the strong bluish green in Syrtis Major and
other spots, the warm coffee color around his dazzling white south
polar cap, which is different from the pervading dragon's-blood
red of his vast Sahara-like lower latitudes. Some have described
his dominating colors as carmine, brown lilac, chocolate and slate
blue.

The colors change rapidly as the atmospheres of both Earth
and Mars shift and filter and refract the passage of light. And
large seasonal changes come in the slow Martian year (687 Earth
days) when first one pole, then the other, tilts toward the sun,
and Mars varies his solar distance by 20 percent, while greeny
growth (perhaps lichen) can be seen spreading toward the equator — a "wave of quickening" that astronomer Percival Lowell
once measured to move at 2.1 m.p.h. along the Martian valleys,
perhaps spurred by the spring flow in the "canals" bringing
snow water from the poles to the deserts.

The canal hypothesis is supported by the fact that the Martian polar regions have been measured to rise in summer temperature to just above 32° F., when the white changes to brown, then green. Although spectroscopy has not definitely confirmed the water vapor on Mars and atmospheric oxygen there is believed to amount to only a tenth of one percent of Earth's, astronomers now have small doubt that not only the snow but the clouds and the vegetation on Mars are real and fairly similar to their counterparts on earth.

Comparison between ultra-violet and infra-red photographs shows that Mars has a tenuous but deep atmosphere with clouds of a probable cirrus type prevailing over any others. These are bluish white, semitransparent, and drift from six to nineteen miles above the ground as measured by their shadows, forming belts roughly parallel to the equator. One giant W-shaped cirrus in 1955 "persisted for a month, evaporating every morning and reforming every afternoon." But occasional denser, yellowish, cumuluslike clouds are seen also, rarely more than two or three miles high and almost surely made of sand or dust. About every fifteen years (1911, 1926, 1941, 1958 . . .), these clouds form into what are probably giant dust storms, sometimes lasting several months and moving with eerie slowness over the Martian deserts, their top speed seldom clocked above four miles an hour.

Mars has also a thin stratum of violet haze between the high blue and low yellow clouds which, astronomers think, could be composed either of water droplets or ice crystals or, likely, both. Thus are revealed in a distant world the three main cloud types of Earth: cirrus, cumulus and stratus. Each is similar to some of our own clouds, yet different and literally unearthly. And they all float higher and slower than their earthly cousins, their loftier altitudes being due to the weaker gravity on Mars, which allows a more gradual pressure decrease with height and thus, strangely, means that above seventeen miles the atmospheric pressure is actually greater on Mars than at the same altitude above Earth.

On the surface, however, as revealed in the surprisingly detailed daily maps that have been made of Martian weather, conditions of both temperature and pressure are remarkably similar to those found about ten miles above the earth in our lower stratosphere. This fact is exciting to biologists and philosophers as well as astronomers because it means that, although the Martian atmosphere is thin enough for good observation, it is not too thin for life. Indeed, for the same reason that a ten-mile-high plateau on Earth (if there were one) would be bound to warm up to a comfortable temperature under direct vertical sun radiation on a windless day, temperatures up to 80° F. have been recorded on Mars' equator shortly after local noon, the Martian day being only 37 minutes longer than the earthly day.

Of course, one should expect any creatures on Mars to be at least as different from the animals of Earth as Earth's animals differ from one another, but there seems to be no reason why there should not be some which have evolved a Martian mode of life on the oxygen, hydrogen, carbon and other elements available there, especially if Mars should turn out to have been warmer and wetter in the critical early stages of his evolution. In fact, the recognized presence of vegetation on Mars, even if only lichen, requires something equivalent to animals to feed on it and create the carbon dioxide essential to all plant life.

Even on Venus, whose solid or liquid surface may be as hot as boiling water on Earth, there is thought to be a good chance of life in the turbulent middle altitudes of her lush clouds, which, according to Dr. Heinz Haber of the University of California, may include a teeming "biological airsol" of planktonlike microorganisms upon which larger flitting creatures feed — perhaps only to be preyed upon in turn by others still larger and better insulated from the hydrocarbonic surface below.

On cool Mars, of course, there appears to be little to encourage any sort of floating gaseous life, and the need for warmth may instead have driven evolution largely underground. Even though sunlight is admittedly vital in producing oxygen from plants, most animals can adapt themselves to continuous darkness. As for "breathing," lichen needs very little oxygen to produce a private atmosphere inside its own intercellular hollows "from which the cells of the parenchyma draw carbon dioxide and where the oxygen required for respiration can be stored." And enough oxygen to supply a man continuously is given off by the impact of daylight on a leafy area only the size of an average living-room floor.

Mars is particularly tantalizing because of his apparent wealth of fine detail just at the threshold of vision, but astronomers are eagerly watching current developments in telescopic electronics which may soon enable them to diagnose many more of his interesting complexities that now can only be guessed at.

Between Mars and the fifth planet, Jupiter, lies a vast expanse of sky strewn with nothing much but a few thousand asteroids or minor planets (to be discussed in detail next chapter), few of which exceed a dozen miles in diameter. This is an obvious gap in the order of the spheres that Pythagoras may have sensed intuitively but which Kepler felt so acutely that he once declared, "I have become bolder, and now I place a planet between these two," Mars and Jupiter.

A century and a half later, the continuing absence of Kepler's "planet" was made all the more conspicuous by Titius of Wittenberg, who worked out his famous rule of planetary distances that the German astronomer Johann Elert Bode was later to develop into the so-called Bode's Law, which gives precise mathematical expression to the musical intervals of the worlds.

Writing down a series of 4's, one for each planet, Titius and Bode added to the 4's the numbers 0 for Mercury, 3 for Venus, 6 for Earth, 12 for Mars, 24 for "the missing planet," 48 for Jupiter, and 96 for Saturn, doubling the number for each additional member. The resultant progression (with its decimal points moved one place) represented the approximate planetary distances from the sun in terms of the earth's distance. With the embarassing exception of Neptune, who eventually had to be replaced by the recently discovered Pluto, the scheme came remarkably close to the real distances:

	Bode's Law	Real (average) distance
Mercury	.4	.39
Venus	.7	.72
Earth	1	1
Mars	1.6	1.52
The gap	2.8	2.805
Jupiter	5.2	5.2
Saturn	10	9.54
Uranus	19.6	19.19
Neptune	38.8	30.07
Pluto	77.2	39.52

Whether this curious if limping harmony among our sister spheres could possibly have derived from chance alone is a question that draws by no means as clear a concert of opinions — more light on which will have to await Chapter 6, which touches on the remarkable raising of the sun's family, and Chapter 12, which describes the suggestively similar progression known as Balmer's Ladder in the spectrum.

Nearest and biggest of the four giant planets is Jupiter, who epitomizes in his extravagant behavior all the principal traits of this preponderantly outer and larger faction of the solar tribe. It is appropriate that he was named for the king of the gods, for he is not only a thousand times bigger than the earth and 317 times as heavy but contains seven tenths of the total mass of all the planets. Yet, since nothing of his actual size or mass could expectably have been known to the ancients and he is always exceeded in brilliance by Venus and sometimes by Mars, how they could have divined his greatness is something of a mystery. Was it his relative steadfastness that made the Babylonians call him Nibirru in association with their great god Marduk, whom the Greeks were to call Zeus? Or was it perhaps the subtle combination of his prominence and the dignified independence of his gyrations that elevated him to "Celestial Arbiter of the happiness of China" in the eleventh century B.C.?

Professors of astronomy like to call Jupiter "the regulator" because his overwhelming gravitational power has probably been a major influence in regulating the orbits of the other planets into approximately a single plane. At any rate, he looks the picture of the inveterate bully: bulging at the waistline, his muscles flabby but flexing mightily, and his dozen janissaries hovering to his beck and nod. Three of his great Galilean moons (of the four discovered by Galileo), in fact, are a good deal bigger than our own, and his family as a whole forms a kind of condensed edition of the solar system, his outer moons taking twice as long to circle him as the earth takes to go around the sun, his double escort of asteroids maintaining ever their same respectful distance for harmonic reasons we will examine in the next chapter, his fickle filiation of three-score comets shuttling feverishly to and fro. On the seemingly mystical subject of harmonics, I might mention the curious fact that the mean daily motion of Io added to twice that of Ganymede always turns out precisely equal to three times the motion of Europa — a relation $(I + 2G = 3E)$ that astronomers describe as "so exact and permanent that all three satellites can never exhibit similar phenomena at the same time."

Through the telescope, Jupiter himself appears a golden disk with many brown, yellow and reddish belts of latitude separated by grayish blue running about his middle. The impression that he is turning so fast he is distorted into the shape of a doorknob is confirmed by meaurement of his equatorial diameter, which exceeds his axis by 14 percent. Likewise his actual turning is soon noticed, for, big as he is, he makes a complete revolution every nine hours and fifty minutes, his equator coasting along at 30,000 miles an hour and constantly beset by howling storms that rile his atmosphere to a depth of several thousand miles.

If our own equator ever got going anywhere nearly so fast, the earth would surely rupture and newborn moons would burst forth roughshod from where Africa, India and South America now lie lazy in the sun. For someone has figured the ultimate rotational speed limit for each of our revolving planets, a speed reached when the centrifugal force at the equator becomes equal to gravity, and inhabitants, if any, start floating upward into the sky. In the case of Earth, the limiting day (or period of revolution) is 1 hour and 25 minutes — to approach which would be disastrous. Jupiter's limit is 2 hours, 58 minutes, Saturn's 4 hours, 9 minutes, the sun's 2 hours, 46 minutes. To attain a day only half as long again as this is considered to be tempting fate seriously. But the actual days of the planets as now observed are in no case shorter than two and a half times the calculated limits, so none of the solar family is expected to split a gut in our time — not even dizzy Saturn, which now comes the closest.

When you get to know Jupiter better, you discover that this bully boy's spinning is not uniform: his day is twisted, averaging some five minutes shorter at his equator than at his poles because his temperate and polar zones lag behind his tropics in their rate of turning. This is possible only because his visible surface is completely volatile, being just the upper deck of an atmosphere so huge the earth would be lost in it like a pea in a dish of whipped cream. And some of his latitudinal bands turn out to be super jet streams (many times swifter than those on Earth) outlined by the disparate westerly gales and cyclonic hurricanes perpetually fluting new channels all around his mighty girth.

Until this century, many astronomers thought Jupiter must be red hot from the pressure of his great mass and that his bands and rolling spots literally glowed from within. But as shadows cannot show on a red-hot poker, the photographed shadows of Jovian moons etched so sharply upon his clouds definitely proved him to be at least a good deal cooler than that. Then the difficult modern techniques of taking celestial temperatures were perfected enough to establish Jupiter's visible surface as ranging between 200° F. and 300° F. below zero.

The revelation of this bitter cold also threw new light on the mysterious pattern of absorption lines in Jupiter's spectral signature, the like of which had never been seen in any earthly analysis of chemical compounds. Careful work at length disclosed that "exactly the same absorption spectrum appeared when light passed through ammonia (NH_3) and methane (CH_4) gas for a considerable distance," identifying these two gases as the main components of the outer Jovian atmosphere. Then it was discovered that free radicals (elusive molecular fragments that normally exist for only a few thousandths of a second during chemical reactions) could be preserved by deep freezing and that the imine radical (NH), for example, congeals into a beautiful blue solid at $-193°$ F. while decomposed hydrazine (N_2H_4) freezes yellow at $-288°$ F., both colors perfectly matching blue and yellow bands on Jupiter.

As a result, according to Professor Francis Owen Rice, head of the Chemistry Department of Catholic University of America:

It seems almost certain that sunlight shining on Jupiter continuously generates free radicals in its outer atmosphere. On the basis of laboratory experience we can say that absorption of sunlight by the planet's methane and ammonia should liberate radicals such as CH_3, CH_2, NH_2, NH, NH_2NH and so on. Swept down rapidly to the colder depths of the planet's atmosphere by its great winds, the free radicals would be preserved there for, as we have seen, some of them at least are stable at low temperatures. This storing of sunlight in the form of high energy radicals deep in Jupiter's atmosphere would be analogous to the storage of sunlight in the form of coal in the earth (through the photosynthesis of ancient plants).

Not only might such a hoard provide a space ship visiting Jupiter with "an abundant supply of rocket fuel *par excellence* to refuel for the return journey to earth" but it introduces a whole new realm of chemistry which, although built of the same elements found on Earth, is full of more-or-less unearthly substances and potentialities, some of which may contain the keys to kinds of energy and life as yet undreamed by man.

♈   ♉   ♊   ♋   ♌   ♍

So far, only small beginnings have been made toward construct-ing a general theory of Jupiter's evolution, mostly on the basis of the known and deduced abundances of elements like hydrogen there. The fact that Jupiter is sufficiently far from the sun to be cold enough to condense the plentiful primordial hydrogen in immense quantities — particularly in the relatively sticky com-pounds of water (H_2O) and ammonia (NH_3) and the liquid methane (CH_4) — seems to be what gave him such capacity for growth. And once he had grown, his gravity must have enabled him to grab and hold still other gases like helium that would have escaped a smaller planet. In this way Jupiter's bulk must have waxed rapidly bigger and bigger, attaining majority in about a hundred million years, leaving only the decreasing quantities of gases beyond his reach for the remoter giants of Saturn, Uranus and Neptune.

The fact that Jupiter has an average density about the same as cheese, only a third heavier than water, strongly supports this concept of his preponderantly hydrogenic composition — espe-cially since the pressure at his center (thirty million times that of earthly air) must give him a heavy core. The consensus of science now postulates a small Jovian core of highly compressed and hot metallic rock surrounded by a layer some 20,000 miles thick of warm superdense "ice" and cool solid ammonia surmounted by a comparable ocean of very cold liquid methane, the mountainous waves of which are driven by the perpetual storms of his raging atmosphere of helium topped by fumes of ammonia and methane. As if such a cosmic ferment of uric-flavored marsh gas were not enough, Jupiter must also include many minor compounds such as cuprene (created by ultra-violet light striking methane) which, whirling about in his ammonic clouds, could account for some of the reddish streaks we see. Or sodium blended with ammonia that might well tint his great bands of grayish blue.

The turbulent interactions continuously embroiling the Jovian atmosphere must, of course, generate superthunderstorms and catastrophic typhoon-blizzards of a violence scarcely conceivable to Earthians. Radio telescopes have furnished strong direct evidence of these storms by reacting more loudly to Jupiter's voice than to anything else in all the heavens. In the words of Harvard radio-astronomer Gerald Hawkins, "Jupiter is the performer that really dominates the air. When heard over a high-fidelity system, his roars and rumbles almost convince one that the Romans were right in their ideas about the gods."

One may speculate also that the freezing ammonia clouds in some of his blizzards produce sticky greenish snowflakes flitting errantly downward for so many hundreds of miles that their steady accretion by collision with other flakes must soon make them as big as mattresses and perhaps eventually as huge and terrible as bombers swooping wantonly through the black depths only to splash at last into the nightmarish methane ocean.

Although a good deal of guesswork is needed to rationalize any sort of vivid picture of these moiling, effervescent regions under the great shroud, we can, by Jove, actually see the rampaging winds of his outer surface through modern telescopes. We can pick out his trade winds with their frenzied hourly shiftings of form and color as the bloated giant whirls dizzily on his way, the snakelike polar fronts, even the jovial horse latitudes and, significantly, one or two mysterious spots or tropical whorls that linger in view with a curious persistence over long periods of time.

There is the Great Red Spot, for instance, first described in 1664 by Robert Hooke and still plain to see — a brick-red oval 30,000 miles long near Jupiter's equator, which sometimes fades to orange, then to brown, now moves north a little, now south, occasionally lurches almost 90° east or west of its mean abode yet somehow always remembers in the end to return to its original stamping ground. A lesser spot, known as the South Tropical Disturbance, has behaved with even greater license, circling wantonly around the entire 270,000 miles of equator about every two years since the turn of the century. But sometimes these two spots have seemed to chase each other, dodging and jockeying along side by side, dancing a little, then reluctantly separating so the South Tropical Disturbance could complete another biennial tour. In 1949, however, after fifty romping years, the latter faded from view altogether, perhaps submerged or dispersed by some invisible influence and, to my knowledge, has not been seen since.

It has been postulated that these tremendous spots (each bigger than Earth) might really be clouds of volcanic dust belching upward from Jupiter's rocky core or perhaps the manifestation of some unearthly type of storm. But why should a "volcanic" cloud circumnavigate Jupiter biennially? Or is there an imaginable mechanism by which one single storm might keep its identity for three centuries?

A California meteorologist, Dr. Yale Mintz, may have uncovered the vital clue. He kept records of Jupiter's spots and the sun's radiation for several years and a few years ago came up with what looks like a significant correlation: nearly every time the sun lets loose an extra burst of ultra-violet light, Jupiter breaks out in new spots.

Might this not be the photosynthetic triggering of cuprene from a ripe methane cloud? Or the spawning of a fresh generation of free radicals within some pregnant vortex of ammonia? I know of one astronomer who thinks the Great Red Spot is most likely a floating island of solid helium. Whatever it is, something that may be related to it has been observed on Earth. Tropical high-altitude storms, hardly known outside the weather bureaus, have been found to form just after the same ultra-violet sunbursts, and these storms (often 1,200 miles in diameter, floating 30,000 feet up) would be but tiny white spots if seen through a Jovian telescope.

So it is probable that at least some of Jupiter's spots are great storms too. And being in very different thermochemical surroundings, they should be expected to behave differently than on Earth. Perhaps some unknown kind of Jovian "volcanic" jetsam also influences some of them and loosely ties them to one area in the manner that lenticular clouds in our own sky are tied to particular contours of hills. But, of course, far stranger things than we know on Earth must happen all over the sky and almost continually on a planet as big and boisterous as Jupiter. In September 1955 it was discovered that "one of a pair of small white spots located near the huge red spot" is the main source of the unequaled Jovian radio outcry. What could be going on there or what new revelation will show up tomorrow is almost too uncertain even for guessing.

The sixth planet from the sun is Saturn, almost as big as Jupiter but even more giddy and perhaps twice as gaseous. Weighing only seven tenths as much as water, she is literally more buoyant than a wooden croquet ball and would float high on any watery ocean large enough to support her.

To the ancient Greeks Saturn, oddly enough, personified Cronos or Father Time, lord of a golden age of innocence and plenty. But, from our modern telescopic perspective, the planet seems definitely feminine, like Saturnia (an ancient name for Italy), her main distinction being the broad-brimmed hoop of skirt engirdling her buxom waist.

I will never forget my first glimpse of Saturn through a large observatory telescope — an experience emotionally comparable to one's first solo flight — when she made me think of a fat Carmelite nun in white habit and wide-winged coif, her halo of spectral purity enclosing that magic round form that just floated serenely upon "nothing" — so delicate and so potent in her unassailable authority as a world far bigger than our own.

What is dynamically and chemically true of Jupiter should be generally true of Saturn also, her main distinctions being her unique ring system, her mass less than a third of his, and her temperature about 40° F. colder. Certainly her creamy vesture of methane and ammonic clouds in churning latitudinal bands is a near duplication of his tawny stripes, even to occasional bright spots beside her equator — though her frigid saturnalia appears both paler and more stable than his, probably because more of her whirling gases (particularly ammonia) have condensed into clouds and more of her fuming mists have frozen into snow.

One of the great mysteries connected with Saturn is the still unanswered question of how the ancient Maoris of New Zealand knew about her rings — for there is evidence that they did have a Saturn ring legend long before the days of Galileo. Could they have had concave parabolic mirrors in some long-forgotten civilization? Is it conceivable that they descended from a great "lost continent of Mu" in the Pacific Ocean that had advanced to the discovery of optical lenses before vanishing practically without a trace?

Far from reducing the number of Saturine mysteries, the large modern telescopes are raising new controversies as fast as they reveal new data. At first it was taken for granted that Saturn's rings must be made of the same stuff as their tumid mother, but gradually the realization came with better magnification that there was something very ethereal about them. Not only can one look clean through the rings in places but certain of their edges just dissolve gradually into the sky. The inmost ring is as of translucent crepe, very hard to see except by its faint shadow upon the planet, the colors of which show through it as pale yellow at the equator, turning more orange and reddish at higher latitudes and finally slightly green at the poles.

The rings are geometrically so perfect as to seem unnatural. They are absolutely smooth, continuous, and untarnished, and they lie in the exact plane of Saturn's equator. When tilted to their maximum of 28° in relation to the earth, they reflect nearly twice as much sunlight as does the planet proper, but virtually disappear for a day or two when edge on. It is believed that they must be less than ten miles thick and, some astronomers think, only a few inches. In any case little doubt remains that they are the flattest-known phenomenon in nature in relation to their thinness, which proportionately far exceeds the paper of this page.

You might think that the thin ice covering a great lake would be flatter and thinner than Saturn's rings. But no: such ice, however thin, must bulge convexly upwards like all the earth's liquid surface. The rings of Saturn, on the other hand, are absolutely flat for 500,000 miles around with a thickness at most only 1/17,000 of their outside diameter.

The material of the rings puzzled astronomers of the seventeenth and eighteenth centuries, but since then overwhelming evidence has demonstrated that they must be made of coarse dust, including a certain amount of ice in the form of crystals, perhaps formed around the dust. Obviously if they were single solid pieces like wheels, their outside edges would have to move faster than their inner edges as they turn about Saturn. But the spectroscope proves that their inside parts move faster, and exactly at the speeds required by Newton's law of gravitation and Kepler's laws of motion for numerous separate bodies in circular orbits. The spectroscope can readily measure the approach or recession of any light's source by separating the light into colors according to wave frequency or pitch, then measuring this frequency. In the same way, the changing pitch of a loco-

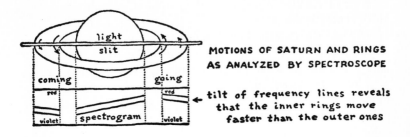

MOTIONS OF SATURN AND RINGS AS ANALYZED BY SPECTROSCOPE

← tilt of frequency lines reveals that the inner rings move faster than the outer ones

motive whistle (measured by your sense of hearing) tells you whether the train is coming or going. This is the well-known doppler principle mentioned earlier as a coming tool in space navigation.

The granular nature of Saturn's rings is revealed also by their great reflective power, powder reflecting more light than the same material in larger pieces, and from their average density, which has been calculated at less than $\frac{1}{800}$ of the very low density of Saturn proper. There may be occasional rocks in the outer ring, but it is believed that few of the particles are larger than small gravel or hail or sand, grading down to frosty dust at the inside edge. On the other hand, the rings could not very well be made of anything as tenuous as smoke, nor contain particles even as fine as white flour, else molecular motion or the pressure of sun ions would long since have dispersed or pushed them off into space.

In view of the modern theories of moon evolution, it is not hard to understand that Saturn's rings may well be the remains of a satellite that drew too close and cracked apart, to be slowly ground up in the Saturnine mills. The rings themselves, as seen from the planet, would now appear like cosmic grist wheels filling most of the sky and actually turning in both directions at once: the inner parts eastward (faster than the planet), the slower outer ones westward. And this curious performance is a clue to the differences in the rings, accounting for the fact that there are not just one or two rings but at least three, the divisions coming at the nodes of resonance.

To grasp the entire mechanism you need to visualize a modern superhighway, several lanes wide, running around the shores of a small circular island with thousands of cars driving along all the lanes in the same direction — the ones on the inside of the curve going the fastest. The laws of this speedway, of course, are Kepler's Laws of Planetary Motion, requiring that the inmost lane overcome its strongest gravity by greatest centrifugal force (produced by speed) while each successive lane outward goes more slowly, the whole flow of traffic tapering its velocities in progressive stages to the gentle outermost lane.

Each ring of Saturn, indeed, has been spectroscopically measured to have definite speed limits: a minimum speed as well as a maximum. If any particle in any ring could fail to respect either of these limits, it would automatically and literally be expelled from the ring, pressed either outwards or inwards according to whether centrifugal force or gravity had the greater influence. And as if it were not remarkable enough for each revolving ring thus to have its separate range of speeds, there are the gap speeds which are arbitrarily forbidden to any of them by resonance, these taboo velocities being interspersed in the gaps between the graduated speed zones much as if cars were prevented from crossing from the 20–30 m.p.h. lane of the highway to the 40–50 m.p.h. lane by invisible, infallible cops who pounced on anyone traveling at a speed between 30 and 40 m.p.h. and eliminated him.

The separations between the rings thus created by traffic-speed enforcement are called Kirkwood's gaps, after Daniel Kirkwood, who in the 1860's defined the principle of orbital resonance, one of the major influences in the music of the spheres. In this application of Kirkwood's principle, it soon became clear that particles probably once occupied the ring gaps and would still be there if it were not for the almost invisible police action of the inner Saturnian moons, which, from scores of thousands of miles away, wield their magical influence — not with threats like traditional cops but with subtle gravity exerted in compound waves of vibration that are just as impossible to resist as the melodies of the Pied Piper.

The key to these potent harmonies of Saturn, then, is the node, which astronomically is a line of conjunction between force fields as musically it is a zone of rest in a vibrating body. It is also the very same influence, described in Chapter 3, that plucked the umbilical chord of our own moon when she first swung free of her mother earth, and that imposes the strict equation $(I + 2G = 3E)$ among Jupiter's Galilean moons (page 87). It is a syzygy of rhythms among the worlds, a sympathy of vibration like that familiar push used to help a friend swinging in a swing. If the moving swing has a natural period of two seconds and you give a push regularly every two seconds, your friend will swing farther and go higher. Most other push intervals would not help the swinging because they would form discords unsympathetic to the swing's slow "vibration" rate, but simple multiples of two seconds would help, such as 4, 6 or 8 seconds. And a few fractions too, like 1, ½, or maybe even ⅔, ⅖ second, and so on, to a slight extent.

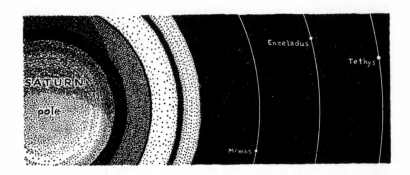

In the same manner, Kirkwood's gaps were pushed out largely by Saturn's three inmost moons, fast Mimas, mysterious Enceladus, and tough Tethys, a trio of cosmopolitan troubadours who tuned in on all ring particles to which they were harmonically related. Their main chorus was directed upon what is now the largest gap, called Cassini's division, which separates the two bright rings by some 2,500 miles. This is where the ring particles once moved in a circuit period (month) of slightly more than eleven hours — which happens to be just one half of Mimas' period, one third that of Enceladus, and one fourth that of Tethys. As Mimas and Tethys thus combined their pull every fourth time that the eleven-hour particles revolved around Saturn, Mimas and Enceladus every sixth time, and all three moons in unison every twelfth time, gradually the gap was cleared to its present dimensions and, by more modest harmonies in the lesser gaps, the rings were made plural and musically molded to exactly what we see there today.

The farther out we go from the sun the weaker must be the patriarchal leash of gravity. And in the case of the seventh planet the solar lassitude may have contributed to the curious fact that Uranus rotates on his axis almost at right angles to all the other planets, giving him extreme seasons of continuous light and darkness lasting up to forty years. This phenomenon may be a relic also of a close shave with some large passing body in the remote past, for it includes all five of the Uranian moons, which circle like choir boys right over his equator.

Uranus (named after Urania, the muse of astronomy) is actually visible to the naked eye but, being of the sixth magnitude, is so faint he was not "discovered" until 1781 when William Herschel, appropriately a professional musician as well as an amateur astronomer of Bath, England, noticed a "comet" among the stars of Gemini. A check of the Royal Observatory records, however, quickly revealed that the same object had been seen and recorded more than twenty times in the preceding century, each time as a star, and its slow plodding pace across the heavens, now proved through its successive positions, soon established it as a planet circling twice as far from the sun as the remotest previously known planet, Saturn.

When astronomers later tried to calculate Uranus' exact orbit, making precise allowance for the disturbing effects of Saturn and Jupiter, they found that the observed positions of Uranus never came out quite as Newton's equation of gravity said they should, the accumulative error by 1843 amounting to an intolerable two minutes of arc.

What could be the matter? Was there still another planet up there somewhere pulling Uranus off course? A student of astronomy at Cambridge University named John Couch Adams believed this so strongly that he actually computed the position of the hypothetical world in 1845 by "inverse perturbations" deduced from the facts then known about Uranus. Somehow this unprecedented intellectual accomplishment failed to stir the British Astronomer Royal to look for a new planet, and the following year Urbain Leverrier of the Paris Observatory, who knew nothing of Adams' work, virtually duplicated it, with the successful result that the eighth planet, Neptune, was actually spotted by telescope in Berlin on the night of September 23, 1846.

This classic episode in astronomical history was a doubly triumphant demonstration of the cosmic validity of the law of gravitation. And it was repeated again in the present century when small residue perturbations in the orbits of both Uranus and Neptune required the presence of a ninth planet, Pluto, which was finally revealed to Clyde Tombaugh on March 13, 1930, after a quarter-century's search inaugurated by Percival Lowell, whose initials are immortalized in the first two letters of its name, as is Tombaugh's name in the last two.

THE THREE OUTER PLANETS

Both Uranus and Neptune are naturally in the class of giant planets, having diameters about four times Earth's. Their chemistries and densities closely resemble those of Jupiter except that, being colder, their ammonia is more condensed, leaving them the residue of gaseous methane and free radicals that gives Neptune his appropriate sea-green pallor.

Pluto, on the other hand, being probably smaller than Mars and an ignominious speck even through the 200-inch telescope, shows no sign of having received any appreciable portion of the primordial hydrogen spilling from the sun, and some astronomers suspect he may be not a born planet at all but a moon that "got away" from Neptune. Not only is his orbit an ellipse more elongated than any other planet's but it passes inside (and almost intersects) the nearly circular pathway of Neptune. Gerard Kuiper thinks Pluto probably won his promotion from an orbit around Neptune as a result of the giant planet's loss of gravitational mass through evaporation during his early stages of solidifying. This is suggested further by Pluto's lazy rotational period of six days: suspiciously long for a planet but just about right for a moon of Neptune that (as moons are wont to do) revolved as fast as it rotated by keeping the same face always turned toward its primary.

Whether the solar system harbors any planets beyond Pluto is an open question, but it seems unlikely that there are any major ones that far out in view of the trend toward smallness among the known hub and rim planets.

Beyond the sun's influence altogether, there seem likely to be countless myriads of planets in all directions, although their presence at such a range can only be deduced (not seen) by known methods of science. The only specific nonsolar planet so far generally accepted is at 61 Cygni, a double-star neighbor of the sun, where a supergiant planet "fifteen times as big as Jupiter" has been detected. But already it must be apparent that, even if only one star out of every thousand has planets of any kind circling around it, the Milky Way alone would contain better than a hundred million planetary systems. That should provide possibilities enough to satisfy the most pessimistic that there is virtually certain to be life comparable to ours in many parts of the sky — and, according to the statistical law of probability, a fair percentage of the life will turn out to be more advanced than anything yet developed on Earth. Indeed, it was for the very purpose of getting in touch with this outside intelligence that the new National Radio Astronomy Observatory at Green Bank, West Virginia, began in 1960 its Project Ozma to listen seriously and methodically for artificial radio signals, for some sort of improbable sequence of impulses — in short, for a significantly patternful message from the spheres.

5. Gadflies of the Void

IF YOU, DOWN THERE, should suppose that the only solid bodies that pass between the earth and the sun are Venus, Mercury and our moon, you would not be entirely correct. For there are lots of minor worlds, not massive enough to be called planets yet not moons either, that swing inside the earth's orbit, also inside Venus' ethereal bower and sometimes even inside the cramped precincts of Mercury.

The heaviest of these bodies are the asteroids or, more logically, planetoids (minor planets), varying in size from a medium moon to a soaring Rock of Gibraltar. Smaller ones are meteorites. And bigger, lighter ones, made of practically nothing but a frozen nucleus that evaporates into glowing gas when near the sun, are comets.

Although Kepler and many other astronomers had hunted during the seventeenth and eighteenth centuries for the "missing planet" between Mars and Jupiter in their efforts to tie together the disjointed music of the spheres, it was not until the first night of the nineteenth century (January 1, 1801) that Giuseppe

Piazzi of Palermo stumbled upon a seventh-magnitude "star" that had changed its position westward since the night before. After watching it for several months, during which time it stopped moving west and turned east, he wrote Bode that he had discovered a new "planet" — perhaps the missing one that would make Bode's Law complete. Before the letter was delivered, however, and before he had determined the planet's orbit, Piazzi fell sick and his discovery escaped behind the sun.

It was only the work of a brilliant young German mathematician named Karl Friedrich Gauss (of whom we will hear more) that enabled Piazzi to find the "planet" again when it re-entered the night sky at the end of the year. And its orbit was thus revealed to occupy just the region between Mars and Jupiter that Kepler had predicted must contain a planet — and Bode was overjoyed at the apparent fulfillment of his law.

When the new "planet" turned out to be only 480 miles in diameter, however, Piazzi, naturally disappointed, named it after a female deity: Ceres of the harvest. Then when another little body was discovered a year later and two more in the next five years, all were named in similar vein: Pallas, Juno and Vesta. Although no more turned up for a generation, there was a burst of discoveries in 1847, and the rate has been increasing ever since. Following the first three hundred asteroids, all named after mythological characters (mostly female), each one has been given at least a number, and the total now known is approaching 30,000 at the rate of several new ones every night, the undiscovered ones still outnumbering the discovered by an estimated ten to one. Without modern photography it obviously would not be possible to keep track of such a swarm. And, even so, much of the work is done by the Recheninstitut in Berlin, which has been operating for more than sixty years as a special clearinghouse for asteroids.

The weirdness of these elfish orbs can be suggested by the fact that little Ceres is by far the biggest one known. Her nearest rival, Pallas, is a mere 300 miles thick. Then comes Vesta, who, although the only asteroid bright enough to be seen with the naked eye (if you know exactly when and where to look), is but 240 miles in diameter, and Juno half that. Almost all the others are less than 50 miles thick, the estimates having to be based on the amount of light reflected. And the density of asteroids must be correspondingly small to avoid observable perturbations in the orbit of Mars, the total weight of all their thousands (known and unknown) being estimated at only one percent of the earth's.

Of course, one must not visualize these demiworlds as being little round replicas of Earth or Venus or Jupiter, for they are much too small to be able to hold on to an atmosphere, and almost all are very irregular in shape. This is surmised from the even rhythm of their variations in brightness as they rotate and has been generally accepted as evidence that they are not aggregations of tiny particles or condensed droplets, which would almost certainly have gradually built up smooth spheres, but rather are jagged chunks of a once-large planet that somehow broke into many pieces, perhaps because of the tidal forces of Jupiter.

This hypothesis is supported also by the asteroids' orbits, which, with a few exceptions, converge closely enough to suggest a common point of origin between Mars and Jupiter. And it is hardly contradicted by the fact that a few out of so many susceptible busybodies should show signs of having at some time fallen under the gravitational influence either of neighboring Mars or potent Jupiter, both of whom, it seems more than likely, have thus actually tamed wild asteroids into docile moons.

Certainly the bias of Jove is evidenced by the strong tendency of these nomads to let their nearest and farthest points from the sun come at similar locations. And they show definite Kirkwood gaps on a much larger scale than the rings of Saturn, their teeming orbits conspicuously avoiding those solar distances at which their periods of revolution would be a half, a third, two fifths, etc., of Jupiter's own year — converts from such fractions presumably being the source of at least a few of the smaller Jovian satellites.

But the music of these great and tenuous asteroidal rings, which reach invisibly all the way around the sun and the four inner planets, is revealed not only negatively through nodal gaps but also positively in definite concentration points where the celestial gnomes are most numerous. Two of these places were predicted by the mathematician Joseph-Louis Lagrange, even before the discovery of asteroids, in his famous conclusion regarding the difficult "three-body problem" that "the vertices of an equilateral triangle form a stable configuration." Indeed, he implemented this theoretical solution, for which no celestial example was then known, by imaginatively postulating "a small body moving around the sun in such a way that its distances from Jupiter and the sun would remain equal to the radius of Jupiter's orbit." And of this intellectual figment at the third corner of the equilateral Jovian triangle, he explained that, even if it be disturbed, it would just oscillate around the vertex which is its harmonic home.

How thrilled would Lagrange have been if he could have witnessed the discovery of Achilles in 1904 and the proof of his beautiful concept in the dozen other asteroids now known to occupy just the nodes he specified, literally forming vertices at the required radial distances, seven of them before and five of them behind Jupiter — acting in this case not as moons but as little brothers of the planetary king. With each of their members bearing the name of a Homeric hero, these two delegations are appropriately known as the Trojans. And they revolve grandiosely around the great sun every twelve years while respectfully circulating at the same time about those mystic nodes just 484 million miles before and after Jupiter where their deputized authority can hardly be disputed even by the gravitational blandishments of Saturn, who passes slightly closer to them than Jupiter once each twenty years.

It is considered likely that in the early days of the solar system there were hundreds of times more asteroids than now remain and that, as they wheeled about the vast interplanetary skies like migrating birds, their numbers were steadily diminished by the slow grinding action of tides and collisions and near collisions over billions of years, the resulting randomized orbits bringing a certain percentage of them each millennium into the atmospheres of planets and the sun to be bogged by friction and eventually merged into the bulk of the major worlds.

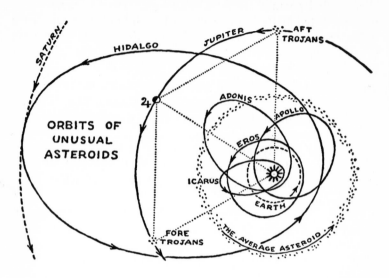

Most of the relatively few survivors of this relentless process are naturally those with the most strait-laced and conservative orbits, leaving only the handful of erratic ones currently champing at their aphelions just beyond Jupiter's gravitational lasso (like wild Hidalgo) or pushing their perihelions within Mercury's scanty beat (like swooping Icarus) or perhaps tempting fate in wanton swipes at Earth (like tiny Hermes, who brushed by us at 300,000 miles in 1937, almost as close as the moon). Of all the asteroids, however, Eros is probably the most interesting and useful. He is roughly shaped like a brick some 21 miles long, 10 wide and 5 thick, which rotates about its shortest axis. Astronomers particularly appreciate him as a sort of celestial benchmark because he regularly swings close enough to Earth

to provide the largest usable parallax for accurately measuring the sun's distance. And being bigger than either of Mars' moons yet practically free of gravity, Eros is an obvious candidate for an early, easy destination for the pioneering space ships. In fact he could well become the first outside world actually to feel the strange tread of man, perhaps as soon as 1975, when he is due for his next rendezvous with the earth!

If you wonder what it would be like literally to touch an asteroid, you might consider a not-unrelated phenomenon that happened right on the earth on February 2, 1922, when a Negro sharecropper named Ed Bush, near Baldwyn, Mississippi, heard a strange humming in the sky which he thought must be an airplane. Looking up, he was surprised to see only blue emptiness. But the humming rapidly increased into a rush of air that ended suddenly when a dark stone thudded upon the ground about ten feet away, burying itself three or four inches into soft clay.

Running to tell the plantation owner, Judge Allen Cox, Ed brought him back in a few minutes to see his "stone from the sky." The judge picked it up. It weighed about a pound and, as the judge reported it afterwards, "was still hot. Not hot enough to burn, but very decidedly warm, and it gave off a smell like brimstone or a flint when it has been struck with steel."

Such are the rare cases of meteorites seen to land on earth. Meteorites, so far as is known, are just small editions of the asteroids and the only definitely unearthly things that humans can pick up and handle and analyze in a laboratory. Being billions of times more numerous than asteroids and, to a much greater extent, at the mercy of any gravitational fields they enter, they naturally are a good deal more apt to be captured by Earth. But since meteorites naturally increase in numbers as they scale down in size, the great majority of them are mere pebbles rather than stones or boulders. And of course as the scale continues farther downward they soon become grains so tiny that the friction of striking the atmosphere burns them up completely. These brief apparitions are traditionally called meteors and are the common "shooting stars" familiar to anyone who goes outdoors at night. They evidently got their name from the Greek *meteoros*, "above the air," probably without serious thought that such "golden apples" dropping from the tree of heaven in Atlas' garden of the Hesperides might sometime come all the way down to Earth and be touched by mortal men.

The modern word meteorite, as now used in science, applies to the material body as distinct from the luminous appearance of these objects, that is, to any celestial unit smaller than an asteroid, which would mean, roughly, less than a few hundred feet in diameter. But there seems to be no defined line between asteroids and meteorites for the understandable reason that bodies of such bordering magnitudes are historically so rare the question has never come up.

The earliest meteorite in history was recorded in China in 644 B.C., and probably the earliest in the West was the famous "stony star" that fell in Aegospotami, Thrace, in 466 B.C. Such objects were located so rarely that they were naturally considered divine — the apports of gods — even up to the nineteenth century. Indeed, the Ephesians are described in the Bible as worshipping their great goddess Diana in the person of her "image which fell down from Jupiter" (Acts xix.35). The famous black stone in the Kaaba at Mecca, venerated by the Moslems, is almost certainly a meteorite. And in Chihuahua, Mexico, a meteoric iron weighing nearly two tons was found, wrapped in mummy cloth, in a Montezuma grave.

By the nineteenth century, however, science had come to distrust miracles on principle, and when "a shower of stones fell out of a clear sky onto a quiet village in Gascony," the French Academy replied to the detailed report signed by three hundred witnesses with "regret that in our enlightened age there can still be people so superstitious as to believe stones fall from the sky." Even President Thomas Jefferson, a broad-minded naturalist, on receiving a request in 1807 from two professors in Connecticut for permission to excavate a freshly fallen stone, declined with the comment, "It is more likely that two Yankee professors are lying than that a stone fell from the sky."

Yet now, a century and a half later, we have dozens of authenticated observations of meteorites landing on Earth and some 1,400 known meteorites in the world's museums and exhibits ranging from greenish-black pebbles called tektites to the 60-ton block of iron which still lies where it fell in Hoba West, Grootfontein, South Africa. New ones are being discovered at the rate of about twenty-five a year out of the few chunks that actually reach solid ground — most of which, of course, must be lost in forests, deserts, glaciers, lakes and oceans.

All of those smaller than very coarse sand when they hit the atmosphere are inevitably and invisibly roasted away in a fraction of a second by the sudden heat of impact. This includes probably more than 99.999 percent of the dozen-odd tons of space debris that daily are believed to collide with Earth — mainly in the form of an estimated 750 quadrillion microscopic and nearly microscopic particles of dust spread throughout the solar system to the unimaginable thinness of less than a hundred pounds in each volume of space the size of Earth. Even this tenuity, however, is some thousands of times denser than most interstellar dust beyond the solar system, and it is by no means evenly distributed.

Thus, although meteors coarse enough to flare into terrestrial visibility are traveling through space with an average separation of about 250 miles, this interval may pack down to 25 miles or less during "meteor showers." The normal bright meteor you see in the sky, according to Fred Whipple, the authority in this field, is actually the vaporization of an object smaller than a pea, and it hits the upper air at between 7 and 50 miles a second. It may start to glow as high as 100 miles from the ground and usually is at peak intensity when about 60 miles up, quickly oxidizing into fine ash and disappearing by the time it is within 30 or 40 miles of Earth — except in rare cases.

Of course, one could not see a light the size of a pea 100 miles away. The meteor is visible only because of its brilliant flare-up to an intense white blaze a foot or more in diameter, produced by the terrific friction, and the fact of its speed making that sudden dramatic streak scores of miles long, which may linger as a hollow luminous cylinder for several seconds before the ionization has dissipated.

The speed of entry into the atmosphere has to be at least 7 miles a second, which the earth's gravitation alone would impart. Unless the meteorite is overtaking us, some of the earth's orbital velocity of 18.5 miles a second must also be added — not to mention the earth's rotational speed. And then there is the speed of the meteorite in relation to the sun, which can be as high as 26 miles a second at our solar distance without forcing it out of the system altogether. Therefore, if the meteorite is moving around the sun counter-earthwise (which relatively few are) and everything adds up to the maximum, it could strike the terrestrial air at close to 50 miles a second.

Any higher speed would indicate the body had come from outside the solar system, but there is no accepted evidence that this has occurred, and the highest measured meteor velocity (by triangulation) so far is 46 miles a second, with the average coming to about 25 m.p.s. The redder, slower, more widely separated ones appear mostly before midnight and the faster, hotter, bluer ones arrive in the morning. The reason for this disparity, of course, is that during the P.M. hours you are riding the rear half of the earth where only the meteors that overtake it can appear, while in the A.M. hours you advance around the forward terrestrial face where the addition of head-on collisions approximately doubles the numbers and velocities.

Notwithstanding the fact that meteorites produce a white heat as they stab into the atmospheric wall, the heat is almost entirely swept off their sizzling surfaces by the ferocious impact of the air as it jerks them to a virtual halt. In consequence, stones large enough to reach the ground are apt to land at subsonic speeds, as Ed Bush noticed in Mississippi, when the coolth of their interiors will absorb so much of their residue surface heat that they can be handled immediately without discomfort. The bigger they are, in fact, the cooler they will be as soon as the heat has had time to equalize, for the large ones naturally retain much more of the interplanetary cold. Indeed, it is recorded that one of the biggest pieces of the great meteorite that fell in Dhurmsala, India, in 1860, was "found in moist earth half an hour after the fall, coated with ice." Another sky stone landed so gently one winter near Hassle in Sweden that it bounced off the ice of a lake without breaking it, then came to rest without appreciably melting it.

Considering that each square mile of earthly surface receives an estimated average of only one meteorite every thousand years, it is not surprising that people almost never get hit by them. Nor need one wonder that there is no record of anyone's having been killed by a meteorite in all history, although such a distinguished fate is steadily getting more and more likely and is bound to happen eventually, as we shall presently see. As a matter of fact, there have already been a number of significantly close shaves, mind you — like the time a large stone hit the earth between two carters on a road at Charsonville, France, the impact heaving the ground up six feet high beside them; a few cases of houses damaged; and an unverified report of a Japanese girl struck and wounded half a century ago.

The classic case of meteorite injury, however, and the first fully authenticated instance on record of any human being hit by something out of another world, is the recent episode of Mrs. Ann Elizabeth Hodges of Sylacauga, Alabama. A plump housewife of thirty-two, she was taking a noontide nap covered with two quilts on a sofa in her one-story frame house early in December 1954 when suddenly a "brilliant fireball" streaked downward from the western sky, making a trail of smoke that was seen by hundreds of people as far away as Mississippi and Georgia. Over Alabama it exploded (probably from the pressure and heat) and a boom "like thunder" drew heads out of windows for fifty miles around as the separate pieces and molten spherules fell over the wood-patched farmland.

Mrs. Hodges did not hear the burst in the sky but was awakened shortly afterward with an unaccountable shock. As she recalled it later, "Mama came running in" from the next room "and asked me if the house was falling down. I said I didn't know. I thought it was the chimney. I got up and started out of the house. Then my hip began hurting."

Just after that, the two women noticed the jagged hole in the ceiling and found a black, nine-pound stone on the floor. They were quite excited, but it was nothing to the reaction of the world outside. Within a couple of minutes "neighbors came flooding into the house, followed by cops and more neighbors." A doctor took Mrs. Hodges to his office to x-ray her space wounds but found only bruises on her hip and hand. Maxwell Air Base in Montgomery, fifty miles to the south, sent forty airplanes out looking for the wreckage of "a burning airliner." A couple of hours later, an Air Force helicopter landed in the Sylacauga schoolyard, and its crew took charge of the "angular rhombus" meteorite.

When Hulitt Hodges came home tired and hungry from his job as a tree surgeon, his wife greeted him as gently as she could. "We had a little excitement around here," she began. "A meteor fell through the roof." But Hulitt Hodges quickly reddened into a fury of frustration. Not only did he have a bruised wife, a hole in his roof and hundreds of people tramping open-mouthed through his living room, but the stone that caused it all, "his" meteorite, had been "stolen" without his even seeing it.

The ensuing fuss and commotion were not much eased by the mounting stream of telegrams, long-distance phone calls, photographers, reporters, buyer's agents and a lawyer who convinced Hodges that the elusive stone from space was worth "possibly five thousand dollars." As Mrs. Hodges retired late in the evening to a hospital with an attack of nerves, she had just enough strength to answer a reporter's final question: how does it feel to be the first person in the world hit by a shooting star?

Said Ann Hodges, "I feel bruised."

If the chances of some human somewhere getting hit in a hundred years are "only three out of ten," as figured by meteorite expert Lincoln La Paz of the University of New Mexico, obviously such a score could apply only to people below the meteoric rampart of the ionosphere. Out where I am in airless space, on the other hand, it is strikingly different. Here we must face all the sub-pea-size pebbles and grains and grit that would burn up before reaching Earth. Even though they are much smaller than some of the big ones that last all the way to the ground, these little space nuts are a billion times more numerous and moving a hundred times faster than any earthly bullets. Certainly they are a ponderable hazard that must be reckoned in the price of interplanetary freedom.

So we are grateful to Dr. Whipple for inventing the "meteor bumper," already standard equipment on nearly all manned space ships projected or under construction. It is a guard made of thin metal sheeting placed an inch or so outside the ship's hull to shatter "99 out of 100 small meteors."

At first thought, one would not suppose any object moving dozens of miles per second could be stopped in an inch. But Whipple explains that all but the biggest of these kernels will explode so completely and instantaneously in the intense heat of impact that no molecular structure describable as solid will survive the bumper, only a harmless powdery splash reaching the ship itself in the borderline cases. It is simple enough, of course, for a physicist to calculate how much kinetic heat each size and speed of meteorite will produce and therefore to what depth it can volatilize the metal of bumper or hull.

Even the exceptional bodies that are massive enough to penetrate the main skin of the space ship need not necessarily do serious damage if they don't happen to strike a transistor or a human head, for self-sealing devices will automatically plug a leak and pressure-sensitive alarms can warn of emergencies. A case in point is the report from space rocket Pioneer V that in its first 1,040,000 miles of travel around the sun it had "87 slight impacts from micrometeorites and 5 heavier ones . . . but nothing really damaging." However, if Whipple is anywhere near right in his prognosis that even a bumper-equipped space station 250 feet in diameter will actually be punctured by meteorites about twice a month, the long-range hazard of those gadflies must be taken very seriously. The white heat produced by their velocity can be so explosive, despite their small caliber, that to be hit by one may feel more like a thunderbolt than a bullet. And there is no doubt, at least, that the problem must be lived with and settled in its fashion just as men have had to go on living for months in a leaky submarine or under fire on a military front.

Of course this problem may never be completely "solved" in the sense that the problem of a cold room is solved by a stove. For it brings into play a larger realm of nature and a mega-world of speeds and relationships to which no known form of life (with the possible exception of dry spores) has so far adapted itself or perhaps ever seriously tried. An inkling of what is involved can be had by considering the recent frightening case of the squadron of jet fighters that flew almost head on through the middle of another formation of jets without any of the pilots noticing it! Yet a speed differential of mach 2 (twice the speed of sound) is almost like standing still compared to the differences inherent in a meeting of space vehicles. Here the permissible margin of navigational error shrinks almost to zero. To be as much as one second late in a rendezvous with a space station, unless you have closely matched its speed beforehand, almost inevitably puts the station out of sight, a situation not solved by its continued recession at whatever disparity in miles per second still separates your speeds.

Even when improved radio devices for "homing in" and automatic speed-blenders designed to avoid such errors have become standard space equipment, the increase in speed differentials as astronautical evolution unfolds is bound to cause serious meeting mishaps, including collisions. And a space collision obviously will seldom be the gentle sideswipe of the earthly highway which you can "see coming" but will more likely strike completely without warning — producing a lightninglike disintegration from explosive friction and heat, with death mercifully instantaneous to all. Each succeeding crash, of course, must compound the overall danger by adding new derelicts to the entropy of the universe.

The basic problem of developing safeguards against any kinds of collision in space turns out to be a surprisingly profound one — as if so by divine intent — for thus far none of the experts has been able to get around what is called the "paradox of proximity," a strange and immutable mathematical law which evidently makes the unavoidability of collision increase directly in proportion to the combined speed of approach of any two objects. Although slow-moving ships at sea can normally recognize a collision situation in time to avoid it, even they sometimes misjudge and hit head on. Cars and airplanes have more trouble, despite better-defined traffic lanes and stricter "rules of the road." But high-speed rockets and space ships that do not keep exactly to the lanes and speed bands assigned them will be definitely at God's mercy so far as collisions are concerned, neither telescopes nor radar being able to warn them in time. Dodging a meteorite intentionally (unless you are lucky enough to be within much less than a mile a second of matching it in velocity) is considered absolutely impossible by known means.

The reason is that the bearing between any two "straight-moving" collision-bound bodies or vehicles remains constant, while the bearing between two vehicles that will pass each other closely remains so nearly constant until so late that by the time any bearing change is definitely recognizable it is too late to act unless the approach speed is slow, the degree of required slowness depending on your perceptiveness of bearing change, rapidity of decision and maneuverability of your own vehicle. To sidestep danger by "evasive action" ahead of time "just to be on the

fe side" is clearly out of the question, because any such random
maneuver is as likely to bring you toward a collsion as away from
one, especially with the intentions (if any) of the other vehicle
unknown.

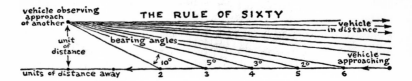

For example, the bearing of an approaching object headed to
miss you by a full mile will change only one degree in closing
from 12 to 10 miles' range, which (with current flight instruments)
is hardly enough of a change on which to base reliable judgment. Accelerating relatively slowly, the bearing will change but
2° in closing from 6 to 5 miles, 3° from 5 to 4, 5° from 4 to 3,
and 10° from 3 to 2. As the product of the three figures in each
of these last four cases equals 60, the strange mathematical law
has been called the "Rule of Sixty in Motion." This holds
true down to two miles or twice the passing distance in whatever units it is measured. But it is obvious that as the time
available for perception, decision and evasion diminishes while
the rate of bearing change increases, the surer you are of which
way to dodge, the less time you have for dodging. And if
there is no telling whether an object is going to hit you or miss
you by a mile until it is only a few seconds away, even an
atheist would have to admit that prayer is at least as safe a bet
as the most eagle-eyed vigilance. And this goes for avoidance of
anything in the material cosmos from the smallest stone to the
largest star.

If, then, we are intrinsically too clumsy to dodge meteorites,
may we not at least look the rascals in the eye and take a
reading on our fate? What have these rare captives to say for
themselves? Can we curry a clue from our battle-scarred prisoners
of war?

Although meteorites, like hailstones, often show fluted surfaces and sometimes a cone or other symmetrical shape suggesting a stable attitude in flight through the air, this superficial feature bears little relation to their basic structure. Chemically they are usually classified in three main divisions: irons, stones and stony-irons which are sponge-shaped alloys with rocky matter in the holes.

All of the largest-known meteorites (the Hoba West, the three brought by Peary from Cape York in Greenland, the 16-ton Willamette of Oregon, the 27-ton Bacubirito and other great ones in Mexico and elsewhere) are irons, apparently because only such dense metal is tough enough in large mass to sustain the shock and heat of earthly arrival. The typical meteoric alloy of 91 percent iron, 8 percent nickel, 1 percent cobalt and minor materials gives a strong hint of the deep interior of the earth if one can accept the theory that these are truly the shattered bones of a sister planet.

The stony meteorites are much more numerous but smaller and harder to find or recognize. The biggest stone ever known to have landed intact (in Arkansas) weighs 750 pounds. Another, of which more than three thousand exploded fragments have been recovered (in Kansas), has an aggregate weight of 1,325 pounds. Their almost unclassifiable varieties can be roughly divided into chondrites and achondrites, the former consisting of hard, rounded, hail-like chondrules weakly cemented into conglomerate masses of olivine, bronzite, feldspar, etc., while the latter are even more varied and crumbly mixtures dominated by silicates, sulfides and limestones.

Dr. Harold C. Urey, astrochemist, says, "The structure of the chondrites suggests that they were formed during very large-scale storms as might be expected" in the "turbulent . . . convection cells" of a "protoplanet" about 100,000 miles in diameter. His detailed reasoning as to the "characteristic structure of the chondrules," which "must have accumulated into larger bodies together with cementing material," been "broken by collisions, assembled into large and small objects, and the process repeated," fits in rather nicely with evidence that the crystalline patterns of

iron meteorites and occasional traces of diamonds found in some
of them could have been formed only under the conditions of
enormous pressure and heat that would exist in the interior
of a good-sized planet. The average age of meteoritic metal
of between four and five billion years, as determined by radioactivity, is also consistent with the generally accepted age of the
solar system.

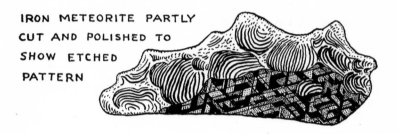

IRON METEORITE PARTLY
CUT AND POLISHED TO
SHOW ETCHED
PATTERN

"On detailed microscopic examination," according to physicist
S. Fred Singer, "metallurgists can even see in the meteorites evidences of the sudden release of pressure, presumably due to an
explosive collision, which disintegrated the planet. The signs
are certain distortions in the crystal structure and sudden transformations of phase in the content of the iron-nickel alloy."

Even the mysterious class of glassy meteorities known as tektites, which no man has ever reported seeing fall from the sky,
have recently been reconciled to the shattered-planet hypothesis.
Made of semitransparent greenish-black silicate "fairly similar
to obsidian," these curious flight-folded blobs have been found
by the millions over various parts of the earth from Bohemia to
Australia. They may well be the "ancient black stones" that
mystified Antoine de Saint-Exupéry while wandering upon his
inaccessible virgin plateau of minute sea shells in the Sahara.
In any case, physicist Ralph Stair of the National Bureau of
Standards thinks they originated upon the missing planet's low-
density surface, which had "separated like cream when the heavier
metal and rock sank toward the center"; when the planet disin-

tegrated, the tektite material was flung recklessly into the sky so that, eons later, a tiny percentage of its glassy pieces could ram our atmosphere to melt and splatter upon our land and sea and ice.

The major debris from this postulated planet-crash — or whatever kind of dissolution it was — is still strewn capriciously all the way around the sun and, together with other jetsam (evidently from comets), forms a vast wreath of meteoric streams, some of which regularly encounter the earth on her yearly rounds. So we have the Perseid meteor showers every August 11, the fiery streaks seeming to radiate out of the constellation of Perseus, the Orionids out of Orion about October 22, the Taurids from Taurus on November 9, the Leonids November 15, the Andromedes around November 20, the Geminids December 11, and so on — the intensity of each shower varying from year to year according to the density of the stream where the earth rolls through it. More than six hundred such streams have been identified, some (like the Perseids) moving almost perpendicular to the earth's orbit, some (like the Andromedes) barely overtaking us in a nearly parallel course, and some (like the Leonids) moving in a contrary direction to hit the earth head on at a combined approach speed of 44 miles a second.

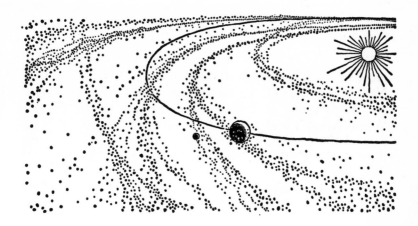

Although the vast majority of these currents are much too far away to encounter the earth at all, it is not hard to see that their average plane makes an angle of only 3° with the earth's orbit and that they form a sort of brim around the sun — not as definite or thin or smoothly circular as the rings of Saturn but more lens-shaped, thicker than the solar diameter in places, unevenly elliptical and rippling as in a breeze. This ecliptic halo is just visible, even with the naked eye, above the hidden sun on a clear moonless night, especially in low latitudes shortly after twilight in late winter or before dawn in the fall. Known as the zodiacal light (or *Gegenschein* where opposite the sun), it is a delicate wedge-shaped solar glow (about 15° wide at the horizon and tapering upward some 30°) reflected off the quadrillions of tiny grains flowing like bullets of dust about the sun, and which, according to one calculation, would be numerous enough to account for the light even if none of the motes were larger than ⅟₂₅ of an inch in diameter or less than five miles apart.

That there is more than dust or small particles involved in these streams, however, is evident from the fact that so many of their orbits have been found to match the orbits of comets. First

METEORITES STREWN CHARACTERISTICALLY AROUND A COMET'S ORBIT

proof of a cometary-meteoric bond came in 1865 when H. A. Newton and later G. V. Schiaparelli tracked down the course of Tuttle's comet of 1862 to the exact trail of the Perseids. When Temple's comet in 1866 turned out to be following the path of the Leonids, Encke's that of the Taurids, Halley's the Aquarids, Biela's the Andromedes, etc., the last lingering doubts disappeared.

Then in 1885, near the end of the annual Andromede shower, on the evening of November 27, during which three trained ob-

servers estimated they saw "forty thousand meteors in four hours,"
an average of nearly three per second, an eight-pound chunk
of meteoric iron landed near Mazapil, Mexico, at 9 P.M. This

astronomers have confidently accepted as "a piece of Biela's
comet," probably the first cometary fragment ever examined by
man. Scientists have since learned about such huge meteoric
evidences as the ¾-mile-wide, 500-feet-deep Barringer Crater (some
times called Canyon Diablo) near Winslow, Arizona, and recently
the two-mile-wide Chubb Crater in northern Quebec. Moreover,
these vast holes in the earth's surface have so far failed to provide
proof that they were made by any such large solid masses as
asteroids, which would seem to be required for them, and, despite
extensive drilling and the use of modern detection instruments,
nothing unterrestrial of comparable magnitude has been discovered
in or near them. The largest meteorite found within six miles
of the Arizona crater weighed only half a ton, and the total of
hundreds gathered from the 113-square-mile circle inside that
radius amounted to but twenty tons.

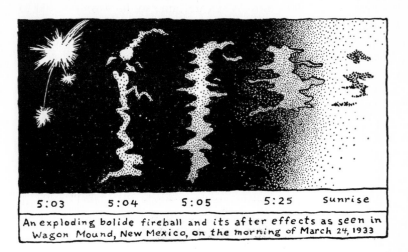

An exploding bolide fireball and its after effects as seen in
Wagon Mound, New Mexico, on the morning of March 24, 1933

On the other hand, something really sensational happened on the morning of June 30, 1908, in central Siberia. Over the vast birch and evergreen forest between the Yenisei and Lena rivers a few hundred miles north of Lake Baikal and the Trans-Siberian Railroad, a tremendous "fiery body" suddenly appeared so high that it was seen 1,000 miles away as it moved swiftly across the sky. The roar was described as "deafening" at 500 miles, and the pressure wave made a sharp peak on the barograph at Kirensk, 300 miles southeast. A Russian in Kansk, 400 miles southwest, reported, "It happened in full daylight. A blue ball half the size of the moon came down — moving fast. It left a bluish wake, stretching for almost its whole course but fading at the end."

Another Russian in a boat on the Angara River, at half the distance saw "a bluish light flash in the north, while from the south came a fiery thing twice as big as the sun, and leaving a wide streak of light behind it."

A peasant sitting on the front steps of his little house in Vanovara, a mere 50 miles south, felt a wave of such heat after the object fell that he thought his clothes would burn. Then as he tried to shield his face with his arms, a sudden invisible blast knocked him off the steps so hard he lost consciousness. This was presumably the shock wave of impact arriving about four minutes after the crash. When he came to, he was dismayed to see that his house had collapsed.

Meanwhile, 350 miles farther south, a train made an emergency stop because of "earth tremors." And next day a herd of fifteen hundred reindeer was found dead north of Vanovara in a region where all the trees were leaning away from the blast center.

Because of the inaccessibility of this swampy region and the later confusion of war and revolution, it was 1928 before an expedition was sent out under Professor L. A. Kulik of the Russian Academy of Sciences to make an on-the-spot investigation. Professor Kulik at length reported that he found an area about fifty miles in diameter "completely devastated" with all the original trees dead and uprooted outward with increasing severity, from one point "as if by a giant blowtorch." Within a mile of this center he counted about two hundred separate craters ranging up to 150 feet in diameter. Although he did not succeed in digging out any meteoric fragments because of the water that flowed into every hole, he estimated that the total weight of the pieces might be "around forty thousand tons."

Astronomers had already realized the phenomenon must have been connected with the annual Pons-Winneckeid meteor shower of June 29 and they easily verified the further significant fact that the Pons-Winnecke comet on its six-year orbit was only three million miles (a thirtieth of the solar distance) from the earth at the time of the crash. That, I think, is the second closest that the earth has come to the nucleus of any comet in modern history. In any case, it makes it almost certain that the 1908 fireball was an offshoot of the Pons-Winnecke comet. Which in turn provides a strong clue as to what comets are made of.

Until modern times, no one knew how far away comets were or what they signified, and the dramatic tails of these rare and unpredictable visitations understandably were feared as omens of tragedy and associated with occultism and the beards of prophets. The very word "comet" came from the Greek *kometes*, "the long-haired one," and its appearance symbolized the mystery of flowing locks which, half-revealing, half-concealing, fascinated more than they enlightened. Had not a bushy-tailed comet foretold the death of Caesar? And another that of Vespasian even while he denied it, saying it couldn't mean him since it was hairy and he was bald?

It seems to have appeared fairly plausible in those days that comets were really disembodied spirits of some unusual kind. Certainly they had a sort of mental quality not unlike thoughts moving among the stars. Whence came they? And whither did they go? No man could say. But if one had an open mind, one could learn from them to mark well each fleeting thought, to inscribe it deep in memory so it might eventually be turned to account. For once a thought is beyond one's ken, how can one foreknow its return? Like a comet its orbit is unknown, perhaps hyperbolic. Perhaps it is harnessed to some foreign star. Or perhaps it just travels straight and free and — who knows — may be utterly powerless ever to regain this world of sense.

Despite many such broad and a few quite reasonable ideas on comets taught by early Greek philosophers, Aristotle, the famous chronicler of old wives' tales on meteorology, maintained comets were actually nothing but "exhalations from the earth to the upper atmosphere." And his view prevailed throughout most of the world for fifteen centuries. Even Ptolemy's great *Almagest* did not classify comets as heavenly bodies. And when a bright one appeared in 1456, the Church, unable to understand it, could only pray indiscriminately, "Protect us, O Lord, from Satan, the Turks, and the Comet."

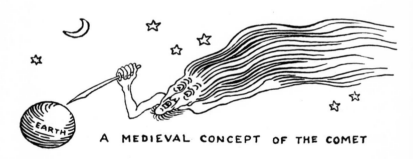

A MEDIEVAL CONCEPT OF THE COMET

A typical description of the great comet of 1528 by an awed observer said it looked "so horrible and produced such great terror in the common people that some died of fear and others fell sick. It appeared to be of excessive length and was the color of blood. At its summit rose the figure of a bent arm, holding in its hand a great scimitar as if about to strike. Three stars quivered near the tip of the blade. On both sides of the rays of this comet there appeared a great number of axes, knives and blood-drenched swords, among which were many hideous slowly-shifting faces with beards and bristling hair."

It was methodical Tycho Brahe at Uraniborg who first penetrated the mystery of comets with some solid fact. Comparing his
own precise observations of a comet in 1577 with observations
made at Prague, he calculated the comet's parallax accurately
enough to prove it was "at least six times as far away as the
moon," and at some points so much farther away than at other
points that it must have passed right through the "spheres" of
the planetary orbits, casting serious doubt upon their presumed
rigidity.

Yet although this evidence may at last have convinced people
that comets had nothing to do with lightning or weather, it did
not diminish "the wholesome moral effect" the comet of 1662
had in Boston in warning the populace to abstain from "volup-
tuousness and abuse of the good creatures of God by licentious-
ness in drinking and fashions in apparel" — an accomplishment
that might well require an atomic missile today. Indeed, it was
only after Edmund Halley, the second Astronomer Royal of
England, noticed a striking similarity in the recorded paths of the
comets of 1456, 1531, 1607 and 1682, that the comet figure
noticeably started its decline from Olympus. For Halley was
the first to establish that comets, like planets, were amenable to
Newton's new law of gravitation, and he became so convinced
that the comets of 1456, 1531, 1607 and 1682 were really
the same one swooping around and around the sun that he
confidently predicted *the* comet's return about the end of 1758 or
early in 1759. In doing so, he correctly attributed the
disparity between its last two periods to the gravitational influence of Jupiter, who, passing close to the comet during its
earlier round, had delayed it more than a year.

Halley himself could not live long enough to see his comet
return, but his prediction is a classic in astronomy, and observers all over Europe reached an unprecedented pitch of excitement in 1758, the first year in history when a comet was
definitely expected. And sure enough, an amateur named

Palitzsch spotted the faithful visitor on Christmas night, and within a month hundreds of astronomers were jealously measuring it as it drew near, reaching perihelion on March 12, 1759.

This dramatic triumph of human science naturally stimulated a flurry of comet hunters in the succeeding years, among whom none was more ardent than Charles Messier, the assistant director of the Paris Observatory, who tirelessly combed everything in the visible heavens with his telescopes, particularly the promising western sky after nightfall and the east before dawn, inadvertently stumbling upon and recording a number of mysterious "'fuzzy stars" that looked tantalizingly like tailless comets except that they would not move. Of course, there was no one to tell Messier that most of these nebulous annoyances would ultimately prove to be very remote "island universes," each big enough to contain far more stars and comets than all he had ever heard of. Instead, his single-minded passion carried him to such lengths of comet concentration that his compatriot La Harpe needed but one anecdote to engrave his personality forever into the annals of astronomy. "Messier is a very worthy man," wrote La Harpe, "and has the simplicity of a baby. Some years ago he lost his wife, and his final attentions to her prevented him from discovering a comet he was on the search for, and which Montaigne of Limoges got away from him. He was in despair. When a friend condoled with him on his loss he replied, with his head full of the comet, 'Oh dear! to think that when I had discovered twelve, this Montaigne should have got my thirteenth,' and his eyes filled with tears until, remembering what it was he ought to be weeping for, he moaned, 'Oh, my poor wife!' but went on crying for his comet."

In the last two centuries astronomers, tracking back through the earlier circuits of Halley's celestial roundsman, have identified it as early as 240 B.C. and discovered it is none other than the famous comet of A.D. 66 that announced the fall of Jerusalem, provoking Josephus to inquire: "What shall we say to the comet that hung over Jerusalem for one whole year together, in the figure of the sword?" It is also woven into the Bayeux tapestry as the bearded star of 1066 that foretold the Norman Conquest. On its twenty-eighth recorded visit in 1835 it came just in time to officiate over the birth of Mark Twain who, seeing "my comet" back again on April 20, 1910, in his seventy-fifth year, rightfully concluded that he had rounded out his own allotted orbit and, next evening at 6:30, passed away — followed in due course by the comet.

But if Halley's is the best-known comet, its significance pales before the growing multitude of others, some half-dozen of which turn up annually, a good two thirds of them apparently never having been seen on Earth before. Although it is not easy to keep track of comets, whose heads, tails and even orbits are notoriously variable, about four hundred were recorded by naked eye before Galileo's day, and now the orbits of more than a thousand have been carefully plotted and sorted. These are of an amazing variety, ranging from the conservative Schwassmann-Wachmann comet discovered in 1927 swinging around its orbit that is more nearly circular than Mercury's and lies wholly between the paths of Jupiter and Saturn, to such wild ones as the great dagger-shaped apparition of 1843, which missed hitting the sun by a narrower margin than any yet known.

As described by Charles G. Abbot of the Smithsonian Observatory, the latter

blazed out suddenly in full daylight on February 28, 1843. It was seen simultaneously in Mexico, the United States and southern Europe. On the steamer *Owen Glendower*, off the Cape of Good Hope, the passengers were surprised to see a short, dagger-like object following the sun toward the western horizon. The head of the comet was then situated only 1°23′, or little more than twice the sun's diameter, from the center of the sun itself, and observers in Italy were able to trace the tail four or five degrees at midday. On March 3 the tail measured 25° and on March 11 a second tail, twice as long as the first, shot out in a single day. The Russian, Boguslawski, estimated the length of tail at 581 million miles on March 21, or longer than the radius of Jupiter's orbit. When the comet went closest to the sun, its center was but 78,000 miles outside the sun's surface (a third of the distance between earth and moon). The comet went right around the sun through 180° of its path in 2 hours 11 minutes at the rate of 366 miles a second.

The general conclusion of the study of cometary orbits to date is that probably all of them are elliptical, indicating that comets circulate entirely within the solar system and are not, in any known case, strangers passing through from outside. Even though a few of their orbits have been plotted as parabolic or slightly hyperbolic where near the sun, this is likely due to the perturbations of Jupiter and other local warpings of a closed over-all course. For comets are very susceptible to gravitational influences.

The latter observation, long since confirmed, is naturally a strong indication that, despite their spectacular appearance, comets are surprisingly light in mass. The gaudy one that swooped among Jupiter's moons in 1889 without distracting a single little satellite from its accustomed beat is a good illustration of this lightness, for only the blustering comet itself was lured off its route. And three years earlier Brooks' comet in 1886 had been literally "thrown for a loop" by Jupiter when its swipe at the jovial giant summarily reduced its own period from 29 to 7 years.

About seventy comets, it turns out, actually have orbits so closely tied to Jupiter's that they are spoken of as members of his family. These all go around the sun in the same direction as the planets, their aphelions close to the Jovian circuit and their periods averaging a little more than half his year. And theory suggests that all these filial bodies originally enjoyed much larger orbits and longer years until as chance perturbations brought their perihelions closer to Jupiter, one by one he captured those that moved most nearly parallel to himself, progressively bending their paths toward the sun and shortening their years. Encke's comet, for instance, the first of the family to be recognized, in 1819, now has the tightest-known cometary orbit of three and a third years and therefore is a good bet to be the oldest current member.

But Jupiter is not the only planet to have captured a covey of comets. Similar if smaller families are attributable to Saturn, Uranus and Neptune, who, one can surmise, will pass some of these thralls slowly inward from household to household like wayward orphans until they finally waste away. Halley's comet, for example, probably a relative newcomer to planetary circles, is now considered a member of Neptune's clan and, having a retrograde orbit, should offer stubborn resistance to capture by Uranus or any other forward-revolving body. Almost half the outer comets, however, drifting apparently at random, have been found to be flowing in the general direction of the planetary tide and are ultimate candidates for the Jovian mill, the rest revolving, if not withershins, at least at some wide angle off the ecliptic plane. Their average orbital period has been estimated by A. C. D. Crommelin, the British authority, as a leisurely 40,000 years.

Biela's comet
breaking in two
1846

A different and closer kind of cometary grouping is that exemplified by Biela's comet, a member of Jupiter's family with a six-and-a-half-year orbit. Upon its third observed return, in 1846, a strange protuberance appeared on its glowing head. Then, in plain view of the astronomers, the comet broke into two parts which moved off into the distance, steadily increasing the gap between them. In 1852 the pieces reappeared, swinging back around the sun one and a half million miles apart.

But something even more drastic happened to the great September comet of 1882. Plainly visible in full daylight, it swooped through the sun's corona only 300,000 miles from the white-hot surface at better than a million miles an hour, its head being violently disrupted by the huge tides raised by the closeness of the sun. And the disruption almost immediately became a split, whereupon each nuclear half split again like generating amoebae, resulting in four sections which spread out in the direction of the departing motion. Although this comet had not been a member of any known planetary family, astronomers soon calculated from the four new slightly diverging orbits that the separate quarters will "return as four comets" of a new group between the twenty-fifth and twenty-eighth centuries.

A later reverse calculation into the past was no less fruitful in showing that the five great comets of 1668, 1843, 1880, 1882 and 1887, all of which narrowly missed the sun on strikingly similar orbits, were almost certainly once parts of a single great comet which, in a previous gyration, also burst asunder from the strain of a close shave with the sun.

Thus we have a trend in comets, an apparent tendency to evolve not only by being drawn toward the sun like moths to a flame, but by successive solar tidal disintegrations. Whether many of the constituent cometary parts ever recombine in the lazy outer reaches beyond Pluto is unknown, but at least the solid meteoric components seem to sieve out and gravitate toward the sun. Ever since the separating halves of Biela's comet were last seen in 1852, no gaseous glow has reappeared, but rather a new swarm of meteors has turned up on Biela's old orbit, and these have continued to encounter the earth every November as the aforementioned Andromedes, just as the disappearance of Temple's comet produced the Leonids, and so on. And all these sundry vagabonds of the void seem to keep spiraling "downward" like hail toward the sun at a very slow but calculable rate which Harold Urey says should pull in every grain and stone up to six inches in diameter from as far out as the asteroidal zone within three billion years.

What mainly distinguishes the comets from meteoric and larger solid bodies of course is their extremely low density, an unmistakable sign of their gassy nature. For if the denser debris of the sky derives largely from the grinding of the iron inner planets, the giddy comets are just as surely mere scraps of flatulent superfluity somehow unassimilated by the turgid outer planets.

The spectra of comets, indeed, shows them to consist largely of compounds of the common gases hydrogen, nitrogen and oxygen, with carbon and bits of such metals as sodium, iron, nickel and chromium — the preponderant stuff of the outer giants. Ever since the great comet of 1882 passed between sun and Earth, turning completely invisible to the biggest telescopes as viewed against the solar disk, we have known that a comet may contain no solid nucleus of observable size, no opaque lumps much beyond meteoric dimensions.

The leading comet model is Whipple's carefully reasoned swarm of methane, ammonia and water molecules that freeze in outer space and, mixed with metallic dusts, tend to stick together as snow crystals, flakes and ultimately (after hundreds of millions of years) huge "gritty snowballs" as big as asteroids. There are "probably some twenty billion" of these curious conglomerations, according to astrophysicist George Gamow, "moving mostly far beyond the orbit of Pluto within a sphere about three light years in diameter." Gamow estimates their average weight as around ten billion tons, which is astronomically quite insignificant and would bring the total mass of all the comets to less than a thirtieth part of the earth.

Obviously there is much less than one chance in a million that any given member of this immense reservoir of meandering snowballs will get seduced into the planetary regions in our lifetime, and those seen looping around the sun are as rare as albino butterflies at a masthead lantern. They also must have undergone a dramatic chemical change as they approached this inner region. For when the solar heat melts a comet's outer surfaces, the body sizzles like pork in a flame. It starts to fuss and fume and its grit to fritter away into the expanding clouds of glowing gas. Layer after layer of the frozen methane and ammonia and finally plain water ice is aroused from hibernation and the crystallized nucleus softens and evaporates into the growing luminescent coma that may pulse or flare, according to the little-understood combinations of its elements, sometimes briefly exceeding the sun in volume and, as it draws within the asteroidal zone, usually shooting out a spectacular tail.

In 1909, to cite a not-untypical case, Halley's comet had a coma measured as 14,000 miles in diameter when it got to within three times the earth's distance from the sun, and its tail was scarcely a bud. By the time it was only twice as far away as the earth, the coma had swelled to 220,000 miles across, and the tail was reaching out for scores of millions of miles. At perihelion (inside Venus' orbit) the coma had shrunk to 120,000 miles again, while the tail exceeded 100 million miles; then in passing the earth's orbit on departure the coma surprisingly puffed way up to 320,-000 miles!

Some of this variability may be accounted for by such free radicals (page 89) as imine (NH), hydroxyl (OH), methylene (CH_2), which are stable at very low temperatures as must exist in a comet much beyond Pluto but which become explosively reactive as soon as they are heated a few tens of degrees above absolute zero. According to a recent suggestion by Bertram Donn and Urey, the explosion of thawing radicals may be damped for a while in a sun-bound comet by their dilution in an overwhelming mass of stable molecules. But as the rising heat evaporates the stable material, the radicals will become more and more concentrated until some outside trigger of energy like a solar ion or a cosmic ray sets off a "chain-reacting explosion" which must "continue until it runs into a large concentration of stable molecules or of meteoric material in the ice." Then the comet can subside again.

The initial mystery of the tail is only slightly more easily solved. As one astonished observer of the comet of 1843 pointed out, when the head completed a semicircle around the sun in two hours and eleven minutes, the 580,000,000-mile tail also swept around, always streaming away from the sun, its tip "traveling" more than 1,800,000,000 miles in 131 minutes at about 230,000 miles a second — which would be exceeding the speed of light! The answer, first intimated in the seventeenth century by Hooke but not generally understood even in the nineteenth, is that a comet's tail does not remain the same tail any more than a stream of water from a hose remains the same water. The modern evidence is that it is composed of flowing components of very thin gas and probably particles of fine dust (less than 1/100,000th of an inch in diameter) that are continuously shot away from the comet's head by the added impact of sunlight and solar ions upon the coma's vacillating chemical pressures.

Although these submicroscopic particles are naturally attracted by the sun, it has been found that "upon a molecule of gas which absorbs its radiation, the solar pressure may exceed the solar attraction as much as 150 times." Also, "a 100-foot balloon in space" can be "pushed out of its orbit by solar radiation at rates up to 3.7 miles per day." A comet thus wastes away in the manner of a burning candle, its luminous "smoke" dispersing never to return, its nuclear "wick" (probably containing many such meteoric lumps as landed in Siberia in 1908) giving its gassy head a stable center of gravity.

Although some comets do not show any tail at all, at least nine out of ten begin to sprout one when they reach the region of the inner planets, and the tail is likely to be well developed by the time they swing inside the earth's orbit. It may be bushy or bobbed or fan-shaped and often forms some sort of hollow cone or flamelike envelope which is certain to be constantly changing, occasionally even flickering — perhaps partly under the influence of

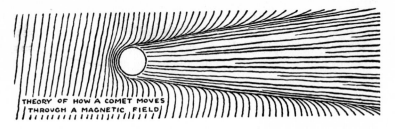

THEORY OF HOW A COMET MOVES THROUGH A MAGNETIC FIELD

passing magnetic gradients. Sometimes a second or third tail will appear near perihelion. Borelli's comet in 1903 sported nine at its climax, and Morehouse's in 1908 dropped one tail only to grow a complete new one two days later.

In any case, all the evidence shows that comet tails, directly or indirectly, are fleeting gifts of the sun which, like roses or maidens, bloom today but should not be expected to look the same tomorrow. You can actually see the streams of luminous ions jetting forth from the fluorescent gas of the coma like strange slow flames, their divergent initial courses ultimately curving downstream together in blended obedience to the powerful pressure of the sun — downstream being characteristically away from the sun regardless of which way the comet is moving, so that a receding comet lets its tail blow ahead of it like a freight train's smoke before a following gale.

Even when the separate spouts of a single comet make it look like a fish with graceful curving fins and translucent tail, the spectroscope reveals that the various caudal streams are really composed of different elements being discharged at different velocities like jets of several strengths coming from the same hose nozzle. It may in fact be the sparseness of comet gases that makes this multidischarge possible while at the same time the tails defy human imagination for sheer emptiness. At least one estimate has it that 2,000 cubic miles of comet tail contain less matter than a cubic inch of ordinary air. Which, if true, should enable almost any schoolboy to heft a real comet tail, if only he could manage a grip on one.

Following through with the concept that the comet tail serves as the smoke from a candle, we find that once a comet falls into the gay debauchery of swooping around the sun with a flashy tail, its days are numbered. Even though its frozen inner nucleus may still be fairly well insulated from the solar heat by many coats of dust (as theorized by Whipple), the mad indulgence can permit it only a few dozen or, at most, a few hundred passes at the sun before it is completely disintegrated into its meteoric components like Biela's and other obviously dying comets. Of course it may kick and spit and flare up a few times, as did Schwassmann-Wachmann's perennial comet that brightened a hundredfold in four days of 1934. Few of them, however, can hope to escape so successfully as did Lexell's will-o'-the-wisp in 1770 after making the closest observed approach to the earth of any comet in history — one and a half million miles — only to fail to show up on its next scheduled return in 1776, having declared its own independence in the appropriate "spirit of '76" after a sharp orbital clash against the tyranny of Jupiter.

ACCRETION AXIS OF SUN — WHERE POOL OF COMETS IS REPLENISHED

The depletion of comets, of course, takes into consideration only the outflow of the comet reservoir. R. A. Lyttleton of Cambridge University feels sure the reservoir must also have some sort of an inflow — an accretion of source material that, he postulates, is likely to be the galactic clouds of dust and gas that are strewn more or less invisibly among the stars. The sun presumably plows through this raw material off and on and, according to Lyttleton's calculations, must pick up a certain amount of it by gravitational attraction, particularly along an "accretion axis" in the solar wake where centers of density in the irregular inward flow of captured cloud molecules gradually thicken and knot into comets.

Whatever their actual evolution, these celestial fireflies are not only the most spectacular of visitors in the sky but perhaps they may yet justify, to a greater extent than we now realize, some of the ancient apprehensions as to their ultimate danger for the earth. Indeed, if the Pons-Winnecke comet spat out the Siberian fireball in 1908 from three million miles away, just think what Biela's comet *might* have produced when it brushed within a 20,000-mile whisker of the earth's orbit a bare month ahead of us in 1832. If it had chanced to come a few weeks later, could not a hundred Barringer and Chubb craters have resulted, perhaps wiping out whole towns or cities with the impacts of the comet's still-frozen nuclei, later melting away to a mere trace of metal as in Arizona? The greater grow the cities of earth and the denser her population, the surer must occasional disaster come from this source. How would a trigger-itchy dictator with atomic arsenal react even today to an unidentified object descending from the general azimuth of his potential enemy and exploding upon his capital with catastrophic violence?

Certainly man in his material lowliness can neither predict nor prevent such an empyrean provocation nor stem the will of God. Nor can he descry what unsuspected breeds of cosmic gadflies may yet arrive at any moment out of the black reaches of space with motive unknown to sting the tender, and ever-tenderer, flesh of Earth.

6. introduction to the sun

COME UP HERE WITH ME if you would meet the ancient father of our world. "Come," as Empedocles said in Agrigentum in 450 B.C., "and I shall tell thee first of all the beginning of the sun, and the sources from which have sprung all the things we now behold — the earth and the billowy sea, the damp vapor and the titan air that binds his circle fast round all things."

There may be some people living down on Earth, even in habitually sunny lands, who manage to take our nearest star, the sun, for granted. But to most humans I think El Sol is so closely tied to their moods and emotions, if not their health, that he is in large degree the very spunk and soul of the world — literally the light of life on Earth.

Even to say that our home globe is a floating speck of ash that reflects a minim of solar glory is almost a cosmological exaggeration, so great is his bulk and brilliance compared to the earth's: his volume one and a third million times larger, his brightness that of a perpetual hydrogen-bomb burst 865,000 miles in diameter that radiates some hundred thousand *tons* of light per second.

SACRIFICING TO RA, THE SUN GOD IN ANCIENT EGYPT

Yes, light has weight and can be measured in tons, as we shall presently see. And the ancient intuitive understanding of this now proven fact may be a contributing factor in the almost universal early deification of the sun as a god: great Ra of the Egyptians, bright Mithras of the Persians, beautiful Apollo of the Greeks, and other blazing deities from China to Parthia to Stonehenge to the Inca "children of the sun" in Peru. Indeed, with great justification have these man-projected solar personalities held sway over our pristine superstitions for unnumbered eons, even as the living sun has lorded it over the phoenix earth — our pulsing world that was born of brimstone, suckled in the whirling maelstrom of planetary motion, raised from fire to ashes to smoke to gas to liquid to solid to fusion to fission to fire . . .

Yet the sun is benign as well as overwhelming. Ever since he incubated the molecules of organic birth, the sun has had a wonderful and direct effect on life, showing a quality that is mysterious and indefinable but nonetheless real. Even before he taught seaweed to be a tree he was godfather to all the creatures of the deep, and later to the buzzing insects, the beasts, the birds. I hear that the cages where falcons are quartered traditionally face to the east because "the morning sun is very beneficial" to them, especially to the small and beautiful kestrel, embodiment of Osiris or Aurora, whose burnished plumage flashes rubies of light caught from the sun. And it is said the Arctic tern loves the daylight so much he will fly with the summer from pole to pole so that the sun almost never sets from his sight.

Perhaps it is for the same reason that when a man feels weary or depressed or in pain, just stepping into clear sunshine does something to him. I have felt it often. Sunshine is manifestly more than heat and light and invisible rays — even as the whole can be greater than the sum of its parts. It is something subtler, nearer to the spiritual, something close to the quick of life itself. It seems to me that the sun has in some degree the quality of a patriarchal blessing — a bestowal of that special feeling of security that comes through the love of dear parents still living in the old family homestead where one was born and raised. For the sun is verily the birthstead of the whole earth, and the warmth of human blood is as surely our heritage from him as the salty savor of

THE SUN'S-EYE VIEW OF WESTERN EUROPE – SEASON BY SEASON

our sweat and tears was given us by the briny ocean where our flippered ancestors swam and loved and died some three hundred million years ago. The terrestrial seasons *are* his very gaze — summer made by his straight-down stare, winter decreed where he looks askance, spring and autumn at angles between. Even the growing perspectives of our minds may come more from his influence than we know, as all days are parts of the same day in the eyes of the great one who shines continuously on the other side of the darkest night. Indeed where the sun looks it is ever day and "time" itself stands still and clocks strike only noon, noon, noon as the twilight vanishes before his face.

Knowing the glory of this parental star of our world, through modern science as well as personal adventure, it is easy to understand the degree to which the sun still impresses primitive peoples. Could any college-trained orator be more eloquent than the South Sea chieftain who, gazing at the sun, exclaimed in his pidgin English: "Me lookum old big fella fire. He high up too much. He alla same one fella island. He fly long long. He no come down."

Almost the very opposite of such a hypocorism was Epicurus' surprising estimate in 300 B.C. that the sun might be "two feet in diameter." If this idea seems inexplicable for a renowned Greek philosopher and physicist, remember that some Eskimos today still believe that when the sun sets in the western ocean he is paddled by kayak back to the eastern horizon at night just beyond the northern skyline, thus accounting also for the northern lights of their region.

If you put your imagination in the primitive circumstance of living on a flat earth where the sky is nothing but a magic ceiling inhabited by mysterious supernatural actors in an endless drama, you can appreciate the difficulty of being factual about the size and height of the sun. And so the achievement of Anaxagoras in calculating the sun to be "a great hot stone" as large as the Peloponnesus not only startled the court of Pericles but caused the eminent philosopher himself to be exiled for blasphemy. Yet Anaxagoras had come remarkably close to the right dimension if we allow him the assumption of a flat earth. For he had measured the angle of the sun's altitude as seen from widely different places and had figured its distance by triangulation or parallax as 4,000 miles, which is nearly the earth's actual radius and, had it really been the sun's height over a flat earth, would have given Anaxagoras just such a solar parallax as he actually measured.

Aristarchos of Samos, the astronomer, later timed the half-moon periods as accurately as he could without a telescope and concluded that the sun was "twenty times as far away as the moon," but it remained for Poseidonius, of all the ancients, to come closest to the right distance figures for both the moon and sun: 208,000 and 70,000,000 miles respectively. Both estimates are less than 25 percent too low, which is indeed impressive in view of the fact that Poseidonius was only timing eclipses and measuring shadows on the moon and earth without a telescope, and probably with no instrument more advanced than a homemade measuring stick or a diopter (primitive theodolite).

Only in the age of modern astronomy opened by Copernicus and Tycho have we come to realize that the sun is not really "on fire" in the familiar combustive sense and that, as some engineer recently figured out, if the sun were made of coal burning in oxygen he could not have stayed alight for more than 2,500 years. Quite plainly, something much more profound and basic than fire is blazing in that patriarch of worlds in our corner of the Milky Way. Yet even the relatively enlightened theories of eighteenth- and nineteenth-century astronomers could hardly have gotten below the surface of the solar mystery while the anatomy of the atom was still unknown, for the secrets of stars and of atoms have repeatedly turned out to be essentially the same secret, and, as we will presently see, there is a common flesh to all matter and the simplest of keys may fit locks of widely different make.

Looking at the sun through a smoked glass, one is apt to think of him as a simple sphere of definite size — a visible size which by strange coincidence so closely matches the moon's apparent dimensions that in some solar eclipses (when the moon is at her nearest to the earth) the moon more than covers the sun's disk while in others (when the moon can be 14 percent farther away) she doesn't quite do so and leaves a thin ring of direct sunlight showing completely around her. This coincidence is almost duplicated in the fact that both sun and moon rotate in the same period: about 27 days. Yet the sun is far from being a simple sphere and not only turns much faster at his equator than his poles but actually has as many sizes as he has layers, all of which are gaseous and, with one exception, normally invisible.

The surface of the sun that we see as brilliant light is known to astronomers as the photosphere, from *photos*, the Greek for light. Magnified through a modern spectroheliogram, it has a fibrous woolly look in hydrogen light and a cerebral or breadfruity appearance in the light of calcium, and in almost any kind of filtered photograph it looks strongly granulated. Yet surprisingly, although these sun grains turn out to have diameters ranging from about 180 to 1,000 miles, each grain lasts only a few minutes. This effect was described by the papal astronomer Secchi a hun-

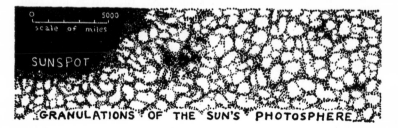

GRANULATIONS OF THE SUN'S PHOTOSPHERE

dred years ago as resembling "grains of rice bubbling in a milky fluid," but lately his rice pudding has been deduced to be really composed of fountains of hot gases that continuously jet upward from deeper layers until they cool off and fall back like bubbles in a boiling cauldron.

The flaming visible surface appears to have a certain solidity just because it maintains its average size, shape and pattern, yet it is really a thousand times more vacuous than a candle-flame on Earth, and even the concentrated moiling gases hidden a thousand miles below it are a hundred times thinner than earthly air. From there on down into the deep heart of the sun, however, the pressure and density increase steadily, reaching the compactness of water about halfway, and in the center itself the highly compressed gassy matter is ten times as dense as steel, the pressure 100 billion times that of earthly air at sea level and the temperature something like 40,000,000° F.

Thus the sun's body is extremely variable and, although nothing but gas, the gas is inconceivably hard, hot and heavy at the center and nearly as unimaginably complex and dynamic in its massive turbulence, especially toward the outer and more volatile layers. In fact, it has been possible for man to deduce and to measure the sun's awesome activity only because the extreme heat and pressure of the solar interior break down all material elements into relatively simple masses of protons, electrons and alpha particles, while the spectacular chromosphere and corona layers outside the photosphere, though normally invisible because of the photospheric glare, can be plainly seen and photographed when the photosphere is blocked off as in a total eclipse.

The general solar circulation, as now accepted by most astrophysicists, adds up to a whirling interchange of elementary particles caught between the twin pressures of heat from within and weight from without, complicated by the sun's aforementioned nonuniform rotation and focused around magnetic hurricanes thousands of miles in diameter that are but eddies of much greater magnetic tides (sometimes called magneto-hydrodynamic waves) extending probably all the way through the sun and out the other side.

These hurricanes, commonly known on Earth as sunspots, were

once described as "flying birds upon the sun" by an ancient Chinese stargazer who must have spotted some extra-large ones which can be plainly visible to the eye without magnification through smoke or sunset haze. But they are now recognized to influence the earth in more ways than the high priests of the Middle Kingdom could possibly have divined, being two-way vertical vortices that have no familiar counterpart but behave something as volcanoes might if their active craters were as big as the Pacific Ocean (or up to a hundred times bigger), flaming white-hot and spinning, with violent whirlpools in their centers forming funnels thousands of miles across and sucking deep into them vast masses of incandescent hydrogen at a mile a second. The surrounding parts meanwhile belch out ions of calcium, iron and nickel which are hurled millions of miles upward into the vacuous raging corona on the "top of the sun," where their temperature and speed are rapidly increased a thousandfold before the terrific blast of light and "shock waves" of solar magnetic forces that send them out to the planets and far beyond.

If this wild arena of unearthly violence seems terrifying in its magnitude, it is no less awesome in its relentless deliberation. For days in advance, the sunspots' approach is heralded by premonitory increases in radiant heat at the exact points where they are going to erupt, this extra radiation accompanied by the lashing

MAGNETIC LOOP FLARES
ON THE SUN

out of tongues of flame hundreds of thousands of miles high into the corona where they float ominously and literally on the updrafts of sunbeams for hours, sometimes many days. These scarlet streamers are composed of glowing veils of gaseous calcium and often look (in telescopic, time-lapse movies) like bubbles as they billow upward larger and larger, probably following lines of waxing magnetic force which has been measured to increase locally at such periods by more than a thousandfold (up to 4,000 gauss). Sometimes they look like gnarled trees with blazing rain pouring downward from their branches in beautiful magnetic curves that have been clocked at speeds up to 400 miles a second, sometimes like delicate bridges arching from surge to surge, or columns, or odd-shaped flocculi that, though made of a kind of fire, have an ice-bergish propensity for remaining at only 10,000° F. despite the 2,000,000° F. corona all around them.

After a day or two of this weird outer drama, tremendous masses of glowing gas begin to heave on the sun's main surface like budding volcanoes directly under the flaming veils, shortly bursting apart to reveal the open craters we see as sunspots. These look dark because they are relatively much cooler than the rest of the photosphere, which also explains their lower pressure and consequent mawlike action of sucking down hydrogen into their whirling centers like so many celestial bathtub drains. But the most remarkable aspect of their deliberation is the fact that, although at least a few sunspots are nearly always visible, they are far from haphazard. They never appear at the poles and seldom at the equator but always begin close to the sun's 30th parallel of latitude, normally in pairs as in a minuet, a positively charged spot a few degrees of longitude behind a negative spot, often with a corresponding pair charged in the reverse order on the opposite side of the equator. From there they develop slowly and primly as they dance toward the equator with little hope of reaching it, attaining maximum size at about the 20th parallel and normally fading away before they get much beyond the 10th. The life of individual sunspots may thus last anywhere from a few days to several months, only one that I know of having survived as long as a year and a half. But about every eleven years there is a climax of their collective activity, after which their size and numbers decline again only to rise to a new maximum in another ten or twelve years when the order of magnetic polarity of the spots is reversed, the sun's north and south magnetic poles exchanged. The whole 22-year period between similar states of polarity constitutes a complete magnetic cycle.

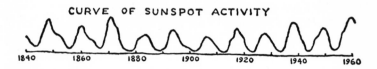

CURVE OF SUNSPOT ACTIVITY

1840   1860   1880   1900   1920   1940   1960

Just why the period averages 22 years and what happens to regulate it are, of course, even harder to deduce in the case of the sun than comparable mysteries inside the earth, but recently astronomers have evolved the now prevailing theory that the magnetic disturbances that regularly develop in the sun may be closely related to his nonuniform spinning. For the great disparity that permits his equatorial day to amount to only 25 Earth days while his polar day lasts for 34 is bound to create latitudinal shear surfaces in the vast, moiling solar gases. These must inevitably influence his magnetic lines of force and, it is believed, mold them into wavy doughnut forms that twist and writhe about his middle latitudes, something like jet streams about the earth, and on both sides of his equator.

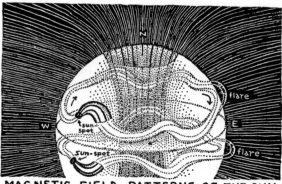

MAGNETIC FIELD PATTERNS OF THE SUN

In any case, since the highly conductive plasma of the sun is material that slides easily parallel to lines of magnetic force but cuts across them only with difficulty, it is understandable that the flow of swirling matter tends to follow the same toroidal lines around the sun — intermittently breaching out of his fiery surface in visible sunspots and spraying ions at thousands of miles a second through his corona to coast to Earth in thirty hours, flowing into Earth's magnetic mantle (the Van Allen belts) and to its magnetic poles, touching off northern and southern lights and rumpling the inner surfaces of the ionosphere. This flow is enough to vibrate all magnetic needles on Earth and disrupt radio communication (which reflects off the ionosphere) and in several known cases to garble telegraph messages and throw power plants out of kilter from Rome to Nome. Such an effect is in addition to the far-reaching influences (on weather and life) of the radiation drop, which, when a big sunspot directly faces the earth, can reduce our share of sunlight by as much as 4 percent.

If it strikes you as hopeless, trying to reckon intelligible cause and effect in this mysterious magnetic and thermal hurly-burly, it may be helpful to know that at least a basic beginning was made some quarter of a century ago in one of the famous early fruits of the atomic age: the theory of the synthesis of helium inside the sun, a masterpiece of astrophysical deduction created by the two German physicists Carl Friedrich von Weizsäcker and Hans A. Bethe. By postulating a complicated but evidently natural sequence of interchanging protons and neutrons among the frenzied nuclei of hydrogen, carbon, nitrogen and oxygen at 40,-000,000° F., they showed how helium is continuously born to the accompaniment of nuclear "binding losses" in the form of radiation from within the sun. Not only does this steady creation of radiant energy largely explain the sun's enduring power, but the fact that the ever-growing mass of helium is light enough to rise to the relatively cool photospheric surface makes clear how the radiation is restrained and controlled, for the inert helium, a "rare gas" on earth, is not chemically susceptible and does not absorb radiation but confines it like a blanket that thickens every year. In this way it increases the sun's internal pressure and heat and magnetic energy, and starts new kinds of nuclear transformations that produce still more energy — thus prolonging for indefinite billions of years the vitality and brightness of our paternal star.

The fact that the sun is only an ordinary star, though larger than most if you count all the dwarfs, makes this scrutiny of his make-up the more important, for what goes on in the sun must be a fair sample of the kind of activity to be expected all over the heavens. Indeed, far-fetched though it seems at first glance, if we understand the sun we understand the average star.

Another, even more fundamental, step in this understanding was taken when Sir Arthur Eddington, the great astrophysicist, discovered a definite relationship between mass and luminosity — in other words, a simple rule for the tonnage of a star that must be behind every ton of starshine. He saw that the sun's light could not be attributed to size alone, for there are dark clouds in space much bigger than the sun which show no glim or glow in them at all. But a concentrated mass, he reasoned, is different. Mass (felt on Earth as weight) creates pressure which produces heat which makes light. His chain of logic put into mathematical form showed why the sun, a million times more massive than the earth, must be dazzlingly luminous; why other bodies with only a tenth of the sun's mass can glow but faintly; and any with less than a hundredth must be too dark to be visible except to their closest neighbors and would not therefore be considered real stars.

But if the lower limit of a star is a mass too slight to produce the internal pressure needed for glowing, there is an upper limit also where the star mass is so tremendous its internal pressure exceeds that produced by gravity and it must explode. Eddington deduced the upper limit as a natural consequence of the accepted rule that radiation pressure increases as the fourth power of the temperature. According to this seemingly drastic law of nature, when any mass has increased enough to double its internal temperature, its radiation pressure must have risen sixteen (double to the fourth power) times, which explains why stars are not infrequently seen exploding, and none has been found with a mass as much as a thousand times the sun's. The obvious limits thus placed both on the amount of stellar gas needed to create starlight and the quantity that will stay in one piece makes the mass of any star definitely critical and well accounts for the sun's similarity in mass to most of his companions.

A good illustration of how the balancing of pressures actually works inside a star is astronomer Fred Hoyle's calculation that if the sun were made of metal and rock like the earth, his internal heat and pressure, being vastly greater than the earth's, would vaporize and condense this molten material so fast that the collapse of the sun "would be visible to the naked eye." Yet even then the sun would not shrink indefinitely, for the shrinkage would naturally raise his temperature and pressure still higher and, when he had shrunk to about half his present size, "the internal pressure would become sufficient to support the overlying layers" and the collapse would stop.

The extremely high temperature thus needed inside a star to balance its pressures naturally ensures that its surface will be relatively cooler, for the same reason that the earth's surface is cooler than its compressed interior, and this has a damping effect on the star's energy flow or radiation outward, incidentally budgeting its strength and greatly prolonging its life. Were the sun's surface not thus kept cool but permitted to get as hot as his center, he would be "a million million times as bright" as he is and would vaporize the earth in a few minutes, although he would have to pay for this prodigal splurge by burning himself out in a relatively early end.

It is true that the synthesis of helium inside the sun adds to his supply of energy and enables him to maintain his size, but the sun or any star would go on radiating light for a long time, even if he were made of nothing but water vapor or cheese or old brick ends. For his radiation comes from his mass and is only budgetatively affected by the chemistry of his material. Indeed, according to Hoyle, if he were made of rubble, the sun would not only go on shining, he would shine at "about 1,000 times" his present rate, because "a sun composed of rock rather than largely of hydrogen would require a substantially higher internal temperature to maintain the pressure balance."

You may have been wondering, in connection with all this, how in the world our amazing sun ever got lit up in the first place. Where do suns come from anyhow? And, incidentally, how did the planets get involved — including the earth and moon?

These questions all naturally go together, for there is hardly any doubt left that the whole solar system was created simultaneously and that something similar happens in the case of other stars. The best modern theory seems to be that all stars originate from elemental gas, and that the sun, like his far-flung brothers, was born of a cloud of hydrogen and a few other gases probably mixed with dust. Under the same cloud was the earth conceived and formed along with Jupiter and all the rest of the solar congregation, even, no doubt, some members that are now missing. This primordial building material of the universe is still barely detectable throughout space in the form of extremely thin haze or gas that nevertheless amounts in its total to about 2 percent of the mass of all the stars and planets of the Milky Way, and it apparently continues to coagulate into clouds here and there.

The most acceptable theory as to what makes the elemental atoms of gas and later the molecules and microscopic dust grains (averaging less than $\frac{1}{100,000}$ of an inch in diameter) collect into these dense birth clouds is that the pressure of light does it — for, especially in the case of fine space dust, light acts something like gravity, causing every two neighboring particles to attract each other on the average by "a force varying inversely as the square of the distance between them." Light does this by pushing its way outward from all stars in all directions with a strength that, although too small for ordinary observation, is plainly manifest in comets' tails, as we have seen. But the one direction from which light cannot push a dust mote is the direction of another mote whose shadow falls upon it, a fact which inevitably reduces average light pressure between particles, in effect drawing them together.

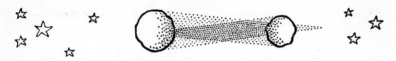

Of course this method of cloud production is slow, being (as surely as anything can be) the work of one of the great elemental "mills of God" so famous for "grinding slowly." Yet calculation shows that each passage of a million years brings noticeable changes, and a hundred million years makes literally worlds of difference. For one thing, there is a natural acceleration in the process because the nearer each particle gets to its neighbors the greater must be the relative shade upon it; and the denser the whole cloud has come to be, the less chance the subdued light inside it has of resisting the inward pressure of the full starlight outside; while every increase in density and mass inevitably builds up gravity toward a noticeable quantity.

Eventually, of course, there must arrive a point where the gravity is as strong as the light pressure. In the case of a dust cloud with the same mass of material as the sun, this works out to be when the diameter of the cloud has shrunk to some 6,000,-000,000,000 miles, or about 60,000 times the distance from Earth to sun. Quite an extensive cloud, you'll agree, yet from then on it will be settling together faster, ever faster, until in a few hundred million years from its beginning it has formed tremendous lumps into which so many particles have fallen that their size and mass and pressure and heat have built up so high that they begin to glow — and they are stars!

Don't get the idea that this apparently simple sequence of starbirth and sunbirth is without its complexities, however, nor its ramifications free of controversy. For although it has recently become a widely accepted theory among astronomers, there is plenty of room for argument, especially about its details. As no

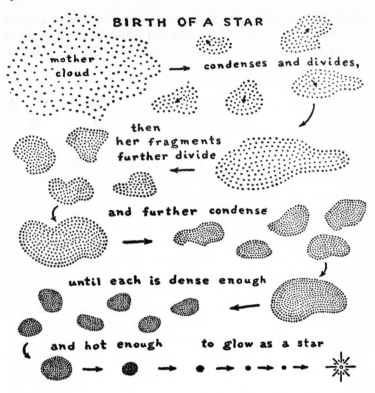

BIRTH OF A STAR

mother cloud → condenses and divides,

then her fragments further divide ←

and further condense →

until each is dense enough ←

and hot enough to glow as a star →

one can yet be very positive about what churns the Milky Way, so it is out of the question, with our present knowledge, to be dogmatic about the stirrings of the cosmic dust that spawned it, even though similar creative gyrations are right now apparently going on in plain sight of us in space clouds all over the sky where baby stars are being rocked in their inscrutable cradles of immensity. Fact is, star motion is tantalizingly slow. Yet great things are surely taking place among the stars, and the momentum of our galaxy must have been imparted in some degree to the primordial cloud which was to become the household of the sun, and the laws of thermodynamics, of magneto-hydrodynamics and of turbulence must have created eddies in it around the central mass which could form knots or nodes that might ultimately turn into the focal cores of planets and moons.

At least that is the gist of the most convincing hypothesis of the birth of the solar system, ironically published by Weizsäcker in Germany in the critical war year of 1943, when death rained from the earthly sky upon every side yet could not destroy the smallest detail of his celestial concept. It is a beautiful abstraction, this theory, and rings true for the musician and the poet as well as the chemist and the mathematician, and the steady accumulation of astronomical facts ever since has generally supported it.

Weizsäcker started with Immanuel Kant's famous eighteenth-century thesis that the original, nebulous rotating sun ejected rings of gas from its equator by centrifugal force and that these rings, which looked something like Saturn's, only much bigger and fatter, eventually broke up into separate puffs and condensed by gravitation into planets. The idea was further developed and popularized in 1796 by Pierre Simon de Laplace, the French mathematician, but sixty years later was disproved by James Clerk Maxwell, the English physicist, who showed conclusively that gravity would have been far too feeble to lump any sun rings into planets, just as it is now too feeble to produce the slightest detectable clot in the paper-thin rings of Saturn.

Although this rejection of the Kant-Laplace presumption led to a return to favor of the older theory (originated by Georges de Buffon) that the sun must have had a near collision with some other large body, with the planets evolving from the splash of tidal impact, Weizsäcker was able to clear up virtually all the many discrepancies in both theories by using modern chemical analysis and a much improved perspective on the matter of turbulence. By these means he demonstrated in geometric detail how worlds grow like raindrops from collisions of tiny particles in the sky, yet in elegant cellular patterns that make one think of plankton in the sea, our earth maturing only through an almost endless series of seeming "accidents" or cataclysms that try the imagination to conceive of.

Weiszsäcker's model of a prenatal solar system shows the sun clot gathering in the center while all around it the gas and planetary dust revolve, each molecule, each crumb describing its own orbit according to the classic laws of Kepler. But putting himself mentally and mathematically into the average flow of these heterogeneous seeds of worlds, Weizsäcker saw that there was a definite rhythm in the tide and laws for the traffic just as inviolable as with Saturn, though considerably more complex. While collisions kept reducing the number of individual particles, the particles that least often intersected the orbits of others naturally survived in the greatest numbers, and these least-intersecting orbits turned out to form a pattern of separate bean-shaped cells that girdled the central mass like a necklace. Although each particle's orbit, of course, had to be elliptical in relation to the dominating proto-sun, it was bean-shaped in relation to the average motion of its fellows as looked at by a hypothetical observer riding in his mind's eye around and around inside the great swirling cloud. These bean beads, furthermore, tended to be five in number (occasionally six) like the petals of common flowers because of the way their shapes fitted together, and each string of five had a similar string outside it, each necklace being about 1.7 times as big in diameter as the next inside, the whole concentric array

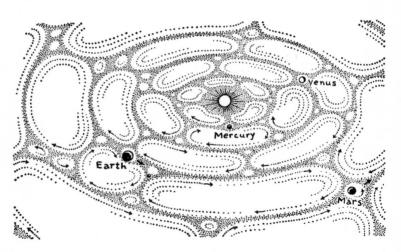

forming a simple geometric progression from the sun core all the way out to the uttermost reaches of solar influence.

In case you are wondering what all this has to do with the birth of planets, you need only look awhile at the way the mass is moving — the many bean-whirls individually rotating in the same direction while collectively they revolve in files around the sun with little counter-rotating eddies between the beans like related groups of thunder cells and geared tornadoes that have actually been observed on earth. You can see that the particles inside each rotating bean cell seldom collide because they are all going along together in the same general direction and at almost equal speeds like cars in a single wide lane of a turnpike. It is obviously the particles at the outside edges that have most of the collisions, for there they meet opposing traffic and the slightest deviation outwards is almost certain to produce a head-on crash. That would seem a bad thing on first thought to an earthly mind, but look again and you will see that these are not the crashes of death. They are actually the crashes of life! For here at the crossroads is where dust meets dust, and the beginnings of solid substances are molded that will ultimately become home and life to us all. Every collision adds its mite to some concentration of mass, and all the growing seeds between each two bean necklaces eventually unite into bodies the size of meteorites, then asteroids and finally into some sort of an integrated protoplanet with perhaps a few proto-moons around it, and each protoplanet grows and grows, cataclysm by cataclysm, even as the face of our well-preserved moon testifies she did too, until the solar family matures into the shape we see today.

While each body evolves in this extraordinary process, it must inevitably also spin, being subjected to the continuous torque of the lesser particles pelting against it at different angles on its opposite sides — this amounting to a vast shearing action that grinds each budding world like grist in the solar mill, incidentally sorting one world from another and grading them like eggs according to their densities, in this case both internal and atmospheric densities. The cooler outer reaches of the sun's influence, for example, permit the hydrogen and other plentiful gaseous in-

gredients of the protoplanets to condense into liquid or solid
masses heavy enough to attract by gravity more and more of similar
abundant substances, which thus build the bulk of Jupiter, Saturn,
Uranus and Neptune. The hotter inner regions near the sun, on
the other hand, cannot hold more than a little of these more active
and volatile elements, retaining instead mostly materials of high
boiling point (metals and rocks) which can solidify despite the
heat.

That is why the earth and its neighboring planets made of iron
and nickel are so small — because the meager supply of metal was
exhausted before they got big enough to compete gravitationally
with the huge outer planets, which were collecting all the hydrogen within reach. And that is why there is almost no hydrogen
on Earth now except in the compound forms of ice, water and
water vapor. The "critical mass" (minimum body with enough
gravity to hold it) for hydrogen is about the size of Uranus or
Neptune. What little free hydrogen may still remain in the earth's
atmosphere is believed to be still steadily escaping outward, its
atomic vitality easily overcoming terrestrial gravity and enabling it
to drift away to the major planets or beyond. The critical mass
for helium is about Earth size, which explains the rarity of that gas
on earth. And the critical mass for oxygen, nitrogen, carbon
dioxide and water vapor is the size of Mars, which accounts for
the borderline atmosphere there and the virtual absence of any
at all on Mercury or the smaller bodies.

Thus works the natural centrifuge of our nascent star, like a
cream separator or an egg-grader sorting out the stuff of the
worlds, sending each element to its appointed station, each future
spore of bone and brain — each fin, each foot, each feather. And
the distance intervals of the planets support Weizsäcker's conclusions better than they did Bode's Law; Uranus is just twice as
far from the sun as Saturn but each other planet is a little less
than twice as far out as its nearest inward neighbor — the average
being 1.7 times, almost exactly as in the abstract geometry of
the bean necklaces. The intervals of moons likewise conform —
Saturn's nine moons each average 1.8 times farther from Saturn
than the next inside, and Jupiter's moons are comparable.

Of course there are vast magnetic influences (particularly among ionized gases) and many other factors and irregularities here, just as in trees and animals and clouds — which diminish not in the slightest the perfection of the whole nor fail to add immeasurably to its beauty. Can't you see Pythagoras devouring this modern orchestration of his elementary music of the spheres? Wouldn't Kepler have been fascinated?

There most likely were even more maverick moons in the early days than now, and it is possible some of those that did not escape may have just boiled away when, according to some astrophysicists, the sun briefly flared up from the sudden heat of contraction as he first settled into his present state of condensation. This may well explain why, of all known moons, our own is now the nearest to the sun, none of Venus' or Mercury's having withstood that initial "bath of fire."

Almost beyond a doubt there were also some very eccentric planets in those days, swooping about like comets, now skimming deep into the corona and close to the sun itself, now careering far out toward the other stars. One of these, it is generally allowed, may well have collided with Kepler's missing planet that could have revolved up to then between Mars and Jupiter, and whose shattered residue is as likely a source as any for the asteroids and smaller ether-corns described in the last chapter.

One could go on and on conjecturing about the sun and his family, the clues are turning up at such a rate these days. And yet most of the mystery must remain untamed behind that baleful, benevolent glare that is virtually everything we could hope for in mortal life. Only recently, Charles G. Abbot, after a lifetime of observation, came out with the conclusion that the sun is definitely one of the variable stars, pulsing regularly by as much as 2 percent. These changes, he says, are obscured by the earth's moody atmosphere but would be obvious to an astronomer on the weatherless moon — with which we up here are quick to agree. Abbot has measured as many as 64 different cycles of solar fluctuation, the longest of which is the sunspot cycle. One corresponds to a "212-day cycle noted in some studies of human pulse rates." Another matches a recognized weather period of "about six and a half days." Still others have been correlated with recurrent mental ailments, cholera, meningitis, gestation eclampsia, and even the suicide rate.

Radioastronomy has provided probably the most exciting recent data on the sun: ionic "noise storms" at radio frequencies from the almost invisible chromosphere and corona, and outbursts from sunspots that have increased "in intensity by a factor of ten million in a few minutes," while tending to repeat themselves every five days. What this may signify in solar potentiality is suggested by Hoyle's prognosis that ultimately the sun's complex nuclear processes will make him swell until he is thousands of times bigger and brighter than now, whereupon he will start his final decline until he is only a feeble ghost about a twentieth his present size, the type of star known as a white dwarf. Such drama might seem theoretical fantasy if it were not being actually observed nightly in other stars in various stages of their evolution all over the sky.

It is understandably not easy to take in the reality of even the simplest solar facts, like sunlight pushing part of the earth's ionosphere for 1,500 miles outward from the line of sunset to create a special kind of auroral glow similar to a comet's tail. I mentally gulp every time I realize that if I could drive a car at 60 m.p.h. steadily toward the sun, day and night without stopping, it would take me 175 years to get there; that if the sun's center were where the moon is, the earth would be only about halfway to his surface; or that the whole system is bearing us all at a relative speed of 12 miles a second toward a point in the sky near the star Vega, called "the apex of the sun's way." I have to stop and think to figure out why the shortest day of the year on Earth has neither the latest sunrise nor the earliest sunset, or whether that has anything to do with the sun's being three million miles nearer the earth at New Year's Day than on the Fourth of July. And what of the relationship between the sun's steady radiation loss of mass and his direct radiation feeding of plants and animals on earth?

Most wonderful of all to me is the realization that for all his terrible power, the sun is just an ordinary gentle star who rises in a loving manner, bringing life and joy to the world — that, in fact, he is perpetually rising somewhere on Earth, ever pushing his hopeful sunrise ahead of him as he trails his eternal sunset behind — that he literally twinkles to the fish in the sea as remoter stars twinkle to dwellers in the air — and that his mystic potencies have long demonstrated themselves for the common good, not just now or here but nearly always and everywhere, even unto the uttermost reaches of radiation.

7. the cousin stars

As I LOOK OUT OF SPACE upon the earth and see now with my eyes what it has hardly been possible to imagine for these billions of years, the strength of distance comes to me — the power of perspective welling upward through consciousness. I think I must be really coming to a larger view. Even the old familiar stars look different now, for I can see for the first time the earth's proper place among them and feel something of how insignificant is our ancient roost in the greater company of reality.

Astronomers have pointed out that if the earth suddenly ceased to be, it probably would not be missed by anyone anywhere — except (believe me) us space pioneers — because there would be no intelligent beings left (so far as we can tell) in the solar system to notice that our moon had turned into a planet to plod on alone in the earth's footsteps. And of course, the observers on other star systems are presumed to be much too far away to have either known or much cared about such a trifling sun parasite as our tiny jot. Even the sun itself would be of interest only to those stars near by (say, within a few quadrillion miles) where there might or might not be any minds capable of studying it. Farther off, to match the increasing numbers of likely observers would be a correspondingly decreasing visibility because of distance.

Yet as we believe our own world is not just scenery, so we must appreciate that the giant stars and their galaxies are not there for mere decoration either. One can't suppress the hunch that there is some sort of tangible meaning to it all — in fact, a growing and multiple meaning — and that if one could somehow find a hundred meanings there would still be a thousand deeper ones waiting to be found.

I think the study of astronomy must be to a man somewhat as the study of a man would be to a germ dwelling inside his body, and that you and I can no more grasp the whole sky than one of our germs could conceive of us. This, of course, is aside from the debatable question of whether the organic sky in turn may better understand us than we can understand germs or ourselves. The only sure way to the stars for us, it seems, is to look at them humbly, beginning on Earth with all our human limitations — to seek perspective along with its risks to body and mind as did Thales and Pythagoras and Aristarchos and Poseidonius and Copernicus and Galileo and Kepler and Newton and many a simpler soul, an Arab herdsman or a village pariah, the kind who for ages immemorial have been laughed at for walking into wells (as Thales once did) while gazing overmuch at the heavens. Indeed, it is the few stargazers and astronomers who survived the wells and the greater hardship of ridicule, even some, perhaps, who died in the wells, who have given us much of the freedom and knowledge of the world we now live in.

So let us take heart for the tenting sky. Is it not the surest example of God's "terrible majesty . . . who laid the corner stone thereof when the morning stars sang together, and all the

sons of God shouted for joy?" Certainly the stars we can measure
live on the most lavish scale that can be sensed by the human
mind. Imagine two golf balls roaming the skies of North America,
each somewhere within a thousand miles of the ground and anywhere between Panama and the Arctic ice. Averaging thousands
of miles apart, they would seem to have plenty of elbow room,
yet they are packed just as tightly as the 200,000,000,000 stars of
the Milky Way! And Milky Ways in turn are as numerous in the
sky as grains of sand on an ocean beach!

There is no way of grasping it adequately in terms of earthly
experience, but one can try to penetrate at least the nearer depths
of sky — to begin a comprehension of the inner shell of visibility
composed of the 5,000-odd stars that are all that the sharpest
human eye can see unaided. This shell obviously is not uniform
in distance, since many of the nearest stars are too dim to see
without a telescope, while others that look near are in reality
remote but unusually bright. It is a shell composed solely of
visibility, its stars limited to the first six visual magnitudes. And
these stars, commonly referred to as "fixed," are actually in
perpetual motion — motion that seems very slow because of the
distance but often amounts to hundreds of miles per second and
is not random but part of the almost incomprehensible flow of
that river of suns we see as the Milky Way.

Beyond this first shell lies layer after layer of stars of the seventh
and fainter magnitudes, each layer composed of many more stars,
each magnitude appearing about two and a half times fainter than
the last, the fifteenth magnitude exactly one hundredth as bright
as the tenth while ten thousand times more brilliant than the
twenty-fifth, and so on. Up to the twentieth magnitude, just
beyond the limit of visibility through the 100-inch reflector on
Mount Wilson, the stars number about 500,000,000, but several
billions can be individually seen through the 200-incher at Mount
Palomar — still more caught by long-time exposures on its most
sensitive photographic plates, each star of the last layer being no
brighter than would be the beam of a pocket flashlight aimed at
us from the moon. Yet even this vast number, extending to the
twenty-fourth magnitude, is only a small fraction of the stars in

our galaxy and its outlying clusters, many of which overlap each other so densely they are literally buried in light as billions of others again are shrouded in mysterious space clouds of utter darkness.

And all the while, year in, year out, thousands of astronomers and their assistants are listing and classifying new stars in the standard catalogs. One published in nine volumes in 1924 contained data on 225,300 stars, and a recent map shows every visible star out to an average distance of 2,100,000,000,000,000,000,000 miles from Mount Palomar.

When Ptolemy compiled his great *Almagest* at the Alexandrian observatory in A.D. 140, he called the stars by name. But in modern times it has become obvious that this could not go on indefinitely, since there are more stars than all possible names of reasonable length. And anyhow, it seemed a strain on nature to have to think up longer and longer names for fainter and fainter stars, like pasting bigger and bigger labels on smaller and smaller packages until the label outweighs the package. So astronomers soon stopped thinking up titles like Almerzamonnagied or Aschimeshinermis (names of real stars) and, after they ran out of Greek letters, then Roman, reverted to Arab numerals, which, being of inexhaustible supply, are even more plentiful than the obviously finite number of all seeable and potentially seeable stars.

It is quite appropriate anyway, I think, to use Arab numerals for stars, since the Arabs, herdsmen almost to a man, sleeping in the open with their heads on their saddles, named more of the early stars than did the Greeks, and even a lot of the Greek-named stars got renamed by the Arabs during the golden age of Islam when the Abbasid editions of the *Almagest* became the foundation of cumulative scientific knowledge.

Though not quite as varied as the wind names of the world, star names to me have a fascination and beauty peculiarly their own, and are probably the most ancient and classic of all the features of the real Arabian nights. Consider Algol (*al gol*, the ghoul), who highlights the evil head of Medusa in the constellation of Perseus and was thought to have demonic powers because he pulses every third night; Thuban in the Dragon's tail, who was the North Star when the Egyptian pyramids were built; Markab and Algenib at the shoulder and rump of Pegasus; Algorab of the Raven; Arneb of the Hare; Mizar and Alioth of the Great Bear. Many have Greek names like great Arcturos or bright Sirius of the Greater Dog, Procyon of the Lesser Dog, or Castor or Canopos, or Job's dainty Pleiades, which make me think of Chopin's preludes, or the rainy Hyades, or Coma Berenices (The Hair of Berenice), a faint cluster that delicately represents lovely tresses. Some sound French or German like Fomalhaut of the Southern Fish or Japanese like Nunki of Sagittarius the Archer. One is suggestive of an Oriental sneeze: Rho Ophiuchi! But most of them are obviously Arabic: Suhail, Alatrab, Zarijan, Nijad, Salib, Mebsuta, Mibwala, Zaban, Unuk, Ghurab, Ruchbar, Sabik, Sagma, Ajmal, Theemim, Phegda, Huzmat . . . I could go on and on indefinitely. It is like reading Sinbad the Sailor's almanac, this roll-call of the orbs. Can you feel the rhythm in it? Merach, Almach, Megrez, Furud, Urkab, Iclil, Jahfalah, Zavijava, Zubenesch, Mabsutah, Difda, Murzim, Chenib . . . drifting at random across the scarcely charted ocean of silent suns. It seems a pity that they ever switched to initials — Alpha Librae, Beta Capricorni, Gamma Virginis, Iota this, Mu that — or mere numerrals: Catalog No. L886–6 or C.D.–36 ° 15693. But the actual heavens have turned out to be so far beyond human comprehension that nothing less abstract than pure mathematics could seriously hope to keep up with them. On earth it would be like stripping Chicago down to 42 ° N. 88 ° W., its bare address its full title — the irreducible essence of identification.

The stars themselves, however, naturally hold far more of wonder than their names. Although they are fundamentally much alike, being balls of glowing gas about 80 percent hydrogen and 15 percent helium and nine tenths of them between one tenth and ten times as massive as the sun, their variety in appearance, volume and density is startling. There is a remote star

called S Doradus in the larger of the Magellanic Clouds that is 400,000,000,000 times as bright as the dimmest star known — and if you could line up the two an equal distance away (even in a diffusionless vacuum), you would not see the dim one at all because of the extreme contrast in luminosity. The volume of another and virtually nameless star quite near us, an invisible infra-red member of a family unit called Epsilon Aurigae, is great enough to contain most of our solar system, including the 5½-billion-mile circumference of Saturn's orbit, and is about 100,000,-000,000,000 times as big as the smallest star known, which has a diameter of only 2,500 miles and is literally smaller than some moons. Such giants as this E Aurigae component — now known as E Aurigae I (for Infra-red) — are sometimes described as "red-hot vacuums" because their material, though hot, averages thousands of times thinner than earthly air and is normally invisible, so that you might fly through them for days in your insulated space ship without even realizing you were inside a star. At the other extreme are white dwarfs with a density 60,000,000,000,000 times greater, where any mountains would instantly flatten from their own weight of 600 tons per cubic inch, where it would take a powerful jack to raise a grain of sand and the faintest wisp of cigarette smoke would clunk to the ground like a shovelful of bird shot.

A large percentage of the stars are definitely irregular in one way or another. Like people, stars are apt to express themselves in their social relationships. Nearly half do not dwell alone as does our bachelor sun but have somehow picked up a mate to dance with around and around a common center of gravity. At least 2 percent are believed to be triplet or quadruplet suns. Some turn out to be quintuplets like Epsilon Lyrae or sextuplets like Castor or Mizar, or a cluster of some larger number that circle in very complex orbits around each other. Many have thick turbulent atmospheres of their own besides those of their probable planets and in some cases even of their moons. Some throb rhythmically as if from an internal sequence of atomic interchange. Some tick almost like clocks, some flash a kind of code in dots and dashes, some seem to breathe, some just change their color and brightness slowly and irregularly, some seem to smolder, some fume or smoke or spit, some actually explode.

How rich we are that we can look on these worlds with the perspective of modern science, with precise knowledge garnered and established by thousands of trained astronomers over hundreds of years with the help of billions of dollars' worth of equipment — that we do not have to wonder as did former men whether stars are jewels dangling from celestial drapery or peepholes in the astral skin of creation!

The explanations for stars and their behavior go back over the horizon of antiquity in many forms, but that the profundity of these perennial asphodels of light was recognized from earliest times is established beyond doubt by cuneiform inscriptions and hieroglyphics in which the sign for God was always a star. It is written that a strange star over Bethlehem literally introduced the new-born Christ to the people of the earth. Sabianism or star-worship is the oldest known religion and is, of course, tied in with the fact that certain stars were guides to herdsmen and farmers in their seasonal activities and to sailors and explorers navigating the trackless seas and deserts of the world.

We still allow that "Sirius rising with the sun (about July 23) marks the dog days well begun," because this Dog Star, worshiped by the Egyptians as the "Bringer of the Nile" and known to Job as Mazzaroth, was once thought to produce the heat (and high water) of summer by adding his fire to the sun god's. Ancient sailors used to swear by the zodiacal sign of Gemini, the twin stars (Castor and Pollux), and so do we — by Jiminy! The curious and powerful concept of the zodiac (the sequence of constellations in the sun's annual path) seems to have originated in Asia Minor or Armenia. Certainly it represents the kinds of animals and views of the heavens then seen in that region. But the Chinese had a modest four-sign zodiac of their own, comprised of *Tsing Lung*, the azure dragon; *Heung Woo*, the dark warrior; *Choo Neaou*, the red bird; and *Pih Hoo*, the white tiger.

The HARE   PERSEUS   The SWAN   The TWINS

Everywhere the animistic pantheism naturally created constellation symbols, and gradually established the eighty-eight constellation titles that serve modern astronomy today. These range through all sorts of odd things that were once thought to have magic powers: *Musca*, the fly; *Norma*, the carpenter's square; *Indus*, the Indian; *Reticulum*, the net; *Pyxis*, the box or compass . . . They include household furniture, from *Mensa*, the table, to *Fornax*, the kitchen stove; several parts of a ship like *Vela*, the sail; *Carina*, the keel, and *Puppis*, the poop; eight occupations (not counting *Virgo's*) from painter to snake charmer; a dozen tools and inventions, including some surprisingly modern ones like *Antlia*, the air pump; *Telescopium*, the telescope; *Microscopium*, the microscope; *Sextans*, the sextant; *Octans*, the octant; and thirteen species of living mammals, eight of birds, and a full dozen assorted reptiles, arthropods and fish. Hardly to mention also the the mythical creatures and the many legends that have accumulated about these seemingly endless celestial hosts.

Our Big Dipper, for instance, seems to have once been that

Greek nymph named Callisto. She was an outdoor girl and had talent in the song and dance and also, it is said, used to go hunting — for what sort of game one asks not. But it appears unlikely to have been four-legged game, because Greek legend indicates she aroused so much jealousy in Queen Hera, matron of the gods, that Hera, having determined to cool her off, turned her into a polar bear and banished her to the Arctic skies. And to keep her from getting too earthy again, Hera also stipulated that the Bear constellation could never retire below the horizon as most other stars do. And that, they say, is why the Big Dipper trudges round and round the pole, never escaping Hera's watchful eye — at least not as viewed from anywhere north of the latitude of Greece. So poor Callisto knows now only too well what can come from getting in another woman's hair. Indeed, the locks of Berenice were placed right under her nose, just to remind her. And she must have many a wistful memory as she circles eternally around the pole, accompanied also by the small but sobering memento: her baby son Arcas, the cub bear or Little Dipper whose tail in our time contains the North Star.

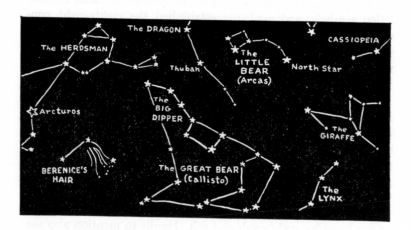

Speaking of the North Star, which is more specifically called Polaris, I think it is worth some scrutiny as a sample of what the sky holds in store everywhere. Of course, Polaris is a fairly

ordinary star except for the chance fact that at present the earth's
axis is aimed within one degree of it, yet it has its secret life to unfold to modern astronomers. Even in a small telescope it becomes
two stars, one of which in larger magnification turns out to be
a "brilliant supergiant" that has been spectroscopically analyzed
as "double" in turn, having a close but invisible companion.
The supergiant itself has also recently been found to be variable,
pulsing with a heartbeat of four days, and its unseen mate
(according to the spectroscope) circles around it once every
30 years at a range of a few hundred million miles, while the
visible and much remoter cousin takes several millenniums, even
though it is only 18½ seconds of arc away by visual angle. And as
if this were not amazing enough, the largest telescopes have spotted
two more members of Polaris' family at the delicate angles of
43" and 82", thus relegated to such slow orbits that it has not yet
been possible to prove that they will ever complete a circuit
around the central giant. Most significant of all to me, however,
and requiring an almost celestial effort of mind to comprehend,
is the fact that these five stars (or are there still more?), along with
their possible unseen planets, moons, asteroids, comets and
meteorites, occupying many thousands of times as much space
as our solar system, are all contained in the gentle twinkle of
Polaris, the tip of Arcas' innocent tail, that has been showing the
north to unsuspecting seafaring men for some thousands of years

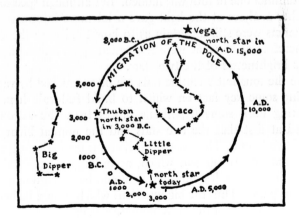

and still today guides everything from submarines to flying freight-
ers to intercontinental missiles on their journeyings of peace or
war about the earth. The fact that Polaris is only temporarily
the North Star is, of course, attributable to the earth's precessing like a wobbling top, its axis describing a slow circuit about
a bigger axis every twenty-six thousand years or so, within which
time Vega takes its turn at being the North Star and the Southern Cross hovers over New York betwixt less orderly and perhaps
less misleading eons that I like to think Job envisioned when he
declared God "stretcheth out the north over the empty place, and
hangeth the earth upon nothing."

♈ ♉ ♊ ♋ ♌ ♍

Algol, the pulsing demon of Arabia, is another star with a story
which not only awed the ancients but posed one of the greatest
riddles modern astronomers have ever solved. As the most famous
of the variables, its message of dots and dashes was early decoded
to mean that Algol is really a binary, consisting of twin stars
revolving around each other in the remarkably short period of
2 days, 20 hours, 48 minutes and 53.8 seconds, the dash being
accurately interpreted as a deep eclipse of the brighter star as the
dimmer one passed in front of it, the dot a slight reduction in light
as the dimmer one in turn was hidden. But although spectroscopic
and other analyses of the light gave a lot more information, the
astronomers were still uncertain as to how total were the eclipses
and therefore as to what were the actual sizes, luminosities and
relative brightnesses of the two stars.

Since the toughest scientific nuts are often cracked by variously
assuming some key fact on which to build full-scale hypotheses
for testing until some hypothesis proves true, the astronomers
assumed at first that the two stars had the normal binary mass
ratio of two to one. That was in 1911, and it made the bigger twin
half as massive as our sun which, according to well-established
mass-luminosity graphs, indicated it should be much dimmer than
it obviously was. Thus the big question: which should be believed,
the mass-ratio table or the mass-luminosity graph?

The nutcracker was wielded by two astronomers named Richard A. Rossiter and Dean B. McLaughlin at Ann Arbor Observatory, who had the rare imagination to figure out a way to get the missing masses by calculating the diameter of Algol's brighter twin, even though the most powerful telescopes showed the whole of Algol only as a single pinpoint of light. Their key step was to clock the star's roll through the sky, to measure the rotational velocity of its equator in miles per second by a method used previously only on the sun. They reasoned that if they could somehow observe first one edge of it, then the opposite "limb," measuring how fast one side was coming toward them and the other going away, by its doppler (wave frequency) effect on the spectrum, they could get an accurate result. But the sun, whose disk can easily be blocked off to reveal any segment separately, is a very different matter than a distant star. How could they possibly cover up part of a mere point of light?

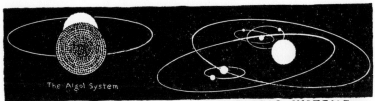

The Algol System

SIMPLE AND COMPLEX MULTIPLE-STAR SYSTEMS

The answer was: *they* couldn't. Yet Algol could. That is where the imagination came in. Rossiter and McLaughlin correctly visualized that the eclipsing stars would cover each other's edges one after the other as they crossed over, just as the moon makes a crescent out of the sun immediately before and after a total solar eclipse. Even though Algol was much too far away for them to hope ever to see the crescents, they could calculate the exact moments when Algol's light must come from the crescents and thus accurately record it, limb by limb, in the spectroscope. In this remarkable way they finally succeeded in finding the star's speed of rotation. As they had already surmised its period of rotation (day), which must match its interval of revolution (year) in such a close stellar partnership, it was a simple matter to calculate its diameter (2,550,000 miles), which is now probably better established than the dimensions of any other star except the sun.

With that elusive key in hand at last, the mass ratio between the two stars was easily determined as five to one. And a short while later, the reason for the original wrong assumption in this ratio appeared with the discovery of a slight biennial weaving motion in Algol's course through the sky, which led to the detection of a third member of the family, one that is so much heavier than the other two that they both revolve around it in a period of just under two years. It now became clear that the light coming from Algol during its dash intervals, when the bright twin is covered by the dim one, is not the light of the dim twin alone (being much too bright for that) but mostly the light of the sly aunt or third member, who is aloof enough (20,000,000 miles away) to shine continuously without interference.

You might not think that such painstaking detective work in unraveling the mysterious twinkle of an inconspicuous star would influence life on Earth much, yet the lives not only of men but nations have hung and will again hang on lesser things. Think of the case of Orion, the mighty Nimrod of our winter sky, and his string of hunting dogs, who may have influenced the outcome of World War II. I am not referring here so much to Procyon, "the water spaniel at the stream" (Milky Way), as to the big dog Sirius and his little white-dwarf companion (known since 1844 but first seen by accident when an optician in 1862 was testing a new big object-glass), now designated by the subtitle B. If you feel like smiling when you contemplate this dog-star puppy, you'd better be serious because, made of stuff that weighs eighteen tons a pint, it is not to be taken lightly, and even its name sounds like a schoolmaster admonishing a giggly pupil, "B Sirius!" or, more customarily, Sirius B. Stranger still, the mighty mite (almost as heavy as the sun but shedding only $\frac{1}{360}$ as much light) was not only the first invisible star to be generally recognized (by the big dog's limping gait) but was the one star in all the heavens, as we shall understand later (page 585), which could help Einstein most in proving his general relativity theory. The acceptance of Einstein, of course, led, among other things, to major efforts in atomic research and to the A-bombs that so decisively raised the siege of Japan.

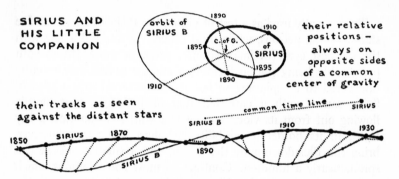

SIRIUS AND HIS LITTLE COMPANION

orbit of SIRIUS B

their relative positions — always on opposite sides of a common center of gravity

their tracks as seen against the distant stars

If modern research has already loosed "the bands of Orion," perhaps it will some day also "bind the sweet influences" of the Pleiades. In the meantime, it is appropriate at least to consider this delicate confluence of stars, since the very word "consider" derives from "con" and "sider," meaning a gathering of stars. Astronomers have worshiped and admired these graceful daughters of Atlas ever since, as the legend goes, they were pursued and frightened by Orion and ran away through the starry meadows to hide in the soft mane of Taurus the bull, where they still are and where, in the telescope, you can actually see the veily nebulosity around them. The Pleiades were mentioned in Chinese literature in 2357 B.C., when Alcyone, brightest of them, was very near the "point" occupied by the sun at vernal equinox. The Romans named them Atauria, "the darlings of the bull." Other peoples at various times have called them "the rosette of diamonds," "the hen and chickens," "the swarm of fireflies," "the shining drops of dew," "the seven virgins." Their date of setting was the ancient signal for the spring sowing of grain.

In South Africa they became "rimestars" because their coming
heralded the autumn frosts. The Great Pyramid is closely associated with them, and Greek temples were oriented to their position
as early as 1530 B.C., later including the Parthenon.

★   ★ ★★
★ ★

Traditionally used as a test of vision, the Pleiades appear as five
stars to some persons, while most others see six, and a few with
the sharpest eyes (or imaginations) seven or more, the seventh
presumably being purple Pleione, a strange potent star recently
discovered to be spinning so fast it has flattened into a kind of
flying saucer with a dark red ring of hydrogen continuously
flowing out from its violet core, a fact which is doubtless a key
factor in its borderline visibility. Modern binoculars, however,
bring the Pleiades out by the dozen, and a small telescope can
sprout nearly a hundred. Contrary to most constellations which
only *appear* to be together, like an airplane brushing the moon, the
Pleiades are an open cluster of young stars moving as a real unit
through space, their mysterious and beautiful mane clouds along
with them, perhaps dominating the life or weather on some of
their planets and moons. Their queen Alcyone, blazing with the
light of three thousand suns, in fact would be the tyrant of our
nights were she as near as Alpha Centauri or Sirius but, being
twelve million diameters of the earth's orbit away, her regal glance
is tempered by its 325 years of travel to our sight. Which, of
course, is part of her power of fascination, for it is admittedly,
a strain for a human mind to grasp that the same light we see to-
night from these celestial sisters, including shy Merope, sweet
Taygeta, Sterope and little Pleione, had already been moving
toward us for a century and a half when George Washington
was elected the first president of thirteen newly united states.

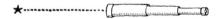

Less of a consideration than the Pleiades but of its own special
interest is the nearest star to our sun, collectively known as Alpha

Centauri (of the constellation Centaurus), which, as you may have suspected, likewise turns out to be multiple and its main member (Alpha Centauri A) the closest replica of the sun so far discovered anywhere. Although the fact that the center of this system is composed of two medium stars was noticed by telescope way back in 1689, it was not until 1915 that a faint eleventh-magnitude star was discovered two full degrees away circling slowly around them both and obviously part of the same family. And this little reddish dwarf that is only the size of a medium planet but a thousand times heavier is the closest known individual star to the sun (in distance) in the whole heavens, a mere 25,000,000,000,000 miles away! Now famous on earth as Proxima Centauri, it is an insignificant little thing that would not have been noticed but for its nearness, and it may well go unnoticed still by any stargazers of Alpha Centauri A or B since it apparently describes an elongated orbit that averages something like 800,000,000,000 miles from its two big brothers and takes many thousands of years for each circuit. Even though it periodically flares up to double its brightness, it averages less than 1/10,000 of our sun's brilliance, and is barely a speck in our biggest telescopes.

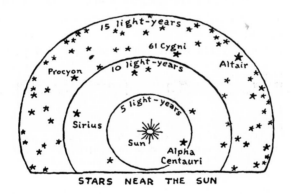

STARS NEAR THE SUN

That there must be many such dwarfs roaming the skies seems evident from the fact that at least five (or 25 percent) of the twenty nearest-known stars are definitely dwarfs and several others are stunted in various degrees. Stars still unknown, of course, are apt to be dwarfish also, like the shy red pigmy twins discovered in 1948 by Dr. Willem J. Luyten only six light-years away, which makes them at present the nearest-known stars to the sun except for the Alpha Centauri family, even as they drift off at a languid 26 miles a second. Both these stars, incidentally, are enveloped in huge cloudy atmospheres of incandescent hydrogen and calcium gas. And the fainter of the two, only 1/60,000 as bright as the sun, demonstrated a startling flare-up on December 7, 1948, increasing to twelve times its normal brightness, then subsiding, all in twenty minutes — a unique and unexplained "atomic explosion" estimated by Dr. Luyten as equivalent to "a billion atomic bombs." Luyten, by the way, is the world's leading small-star fancier, having discovered some 5,000 dwarfs, including nearly 400 white ones among which is the smallest star known: about 25 light-years from Earth and only half again as big as our moon though weighing 40 percent more than the sun.

Any of these dwarfs may just possibly be ready to explode, because they are of such dense material that their atoms quite likely had to collapse in their shrinking process, perhaps even combining electrons and protons into neutrons under the terrific pressure and leaving them in an unstable state. Certainly today's astronomers will remember the dwarf WZ Sagittae, which exploded in 1913 and again in 1946, on each occasion brightening about a thousand times, then fading away to a tiny white spark — and such flare stars as the nearby red dwarf Kruger 60 B, which periodically

Two photographs of the star system Kruger 60
showing smaller star B normal (left) and
flaring (right) only 135 seconds later

lights up with such astonishing suddenness. There has been a growing consensus on the nuclear temperament of dwarfs, many astronomers concluding that the majority of them are just senile stars made of "degenerate gas" living economically like old people on pensions who presently will die, their corpses thereafter slowly turning from white to red and finally into "black dwarfs" to

cruise endlessly and invisibly on and on through space as countless millions may already be doing.

Some "dead" dwarfs might even become planets, according to
the definition of a planet as a nonglowing body on an orbit around
a star, but obviously their great density would make them vastly
different from anything in the solar system, and any animal life
that grew upon them would need something less gravity-sensitive
than legs to move around on. However, the common run of
multiple stars in the sky may also develop much greater planets
than ours, as is suggested by the dark body "fifteen times as massive as Jupiter" recently spotted hovering around the near-by binary, 61 Cygni. And there may be many such borderline planets,
almost massive enough to glow, in the bigger star houses — to say
nothing of planets with irregular and eccentric orbits moving
around complex multi-suns which light them up on both sides at
once so they know no night, have never seen twilight and
probably know nothing of stars except their own local suns. Some
double stars are thought to be so close together that their atmospheres actually overlap, permitting small intense stars to revolve
inside the outer limits of large diffuse stars. Beta Lyrae is an
overlapping binary in which the smaller star receives a steady
stream of incandescent hydrogen gas from the larger one, letting

THE SPOUTING BINARY OF BETA LYRAE

it overflow in turn through an endless red wake into space. Others,
such as Capella, the classical Goat of Auriga, may turn out to be
two that touch each other only once in their revolutions — in

Capella's case, of 104 days' duration — forming a brief intermittent "double sun" of incandescent gas shaped like a dumbbell. Besides the instability of such a condition, with its friction of clashing gases which obviously cannot go on touching and separating with unchanged rhythm indefinitely, such a system would seem pretty unfavorable to life. Certainly any planets circling the embracing stars would be bound to pass through zones of widely differing gases and temperatures, their creatures perhaps subsisting on oxygen on their version of Tuesdays, but having to breath methane on Thursdays and a blend of ammonia and formaldehyde on Friday nights, to say nothing of putting up with a terrific ordeal by fire every summer — a flame bath that would drive the very rocks to ruth as the neighbor sun swept its closest and all the moons flared up like hot coals, sprouting bright comet tails across the sky.

Other seemingly inhospitable stars are the radioactive ones that put out hard x-rays or deadly gamma-rays, either of which would soon tear apart any planetary molecules that had approached the complexity which appears essential for what we call life. And there are the hot, shrunken Wolf-Rayet stars that eject gas streams at velocities up to 2,000 miles a second, and the cool "carbon stars" that, when their surfaces fall to 3500° F., "must shower out a rain of soot." And of course, a whole assortment of pulsating ones that throb, not from eclipsing partners like Algol, but from some mysterious internal chemical rhythm, only dimly understood, which amounts, in the case of red-giant stars, to a continual series of lesser or greater explosions that are usually irregular both in timing and intensity. The best-known of these is famous Mira Ceti, the huge "miracle star" appropriately situated in the constellation of the Whale, which, like Moby Dick, is wont to disappear altogether for months at a time and was considered sacred by Fabricius, the Frisian pastor who discovered it in 1596.

A slightly different kind of variable that explodes in predictable proportion to its rhythm is exemplified by U Geminorum, a star that abruptly flares up a hundredfold in brightness every 97 days. It is obviously related to the star AB Draconis that puffs up to fifteen times normal once every fortnight and to a broad class of other U Geminorum explosive types that follow the same rule of keeping a strict proportion between change in magnitude and interval, all multiplying their brilliance at each flare-up by about 3 percent more than the number of days from one outburst to the next. Thus: 100 times brighter each 97 days; 60 times each 58; 15 times each 14, and so forth.

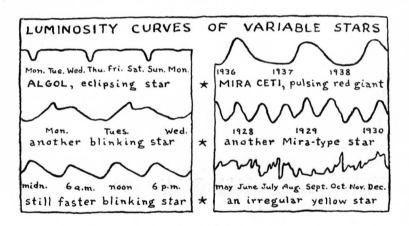

Still another kind of variable is the Cepheid, named after its best-known representative in the constellation Cepheus, whose periods are short and very regular and with an amazing uniformity of relationship between interval and absolute (not relative or apparent) brightness. The central supergiant star of Polaris, for example, is a Cepheid of four-day period. Some astronomers think that Cepheids are really huge single stars in the act of breaking into two, their regular fluctuations of magnitude caused by the fact that their elongated birth-shapes reveal alternately brighter and dimmer surfaces as they spin. Others theorize that they are spherical "geysers of fire" expanding and shrinking every few days. But their surest trait is that those whose interval is one day long turn out to be all of the same actual brightness and those with a ten-day period about four times as bright, with others ranged proportionately between. It is almost as if these strange worlds were ancient beacons on a mountain with people on it gathering fuel so steadfastly between fires that the longer they work collecting brushwood the brighter the succeeding blaze in exact proportion. And the wonderful thing about the Cepheid's fixed relationship between time and absolute brightness is that it provides astronomers with an accurate way of measuring distances to remote stars even millions of light-years off in space. Before 1912 there was no known means of getting the range of any but the closest stars, those few so near that by surveying them very precisely at six-month intervals (time for the earth to move to the opposite side of the sun), their distance could be calculated by parallax or geometric triangulation. But now if an astronomer can just spot a Cepheid and take its pulse, he knows immediately how much light it should radiate and therefore, by the brightness or dimness of its appearance (using a simple equation), how far away it should be. And the fact that Cepheids happen to be dazzlingly yellow supergiant stars widely distributed throughout the sky and so bright they can be picked out individually even in foreign galaxies has led to their wide acceptance as the "milestones of the universe."

A still more spectacular kind of variable is the temporary or surprise star, which suddenly lights up where there was apparently nothing before and blazes brightly for a few weeks only to fade back out of sight all in the same year. The first such star ever recorded burst into visibility in the constellation of Scorpio in 134 B.C., and, according to Pliny the historian, was spotted by Hipparchos of Nicaea, the greatest astronomer of antiquity, who called it the "nova" because it was "new" and different from all others previously seen, in fact, as he said, "one born in my own age!"

Up to then, the world had regarded the fixed stars as absolutely sacred and changeless, but this mysterious object dramatically demonstrated that stars on the contrary may come and go, and it served to stimulate Hipparchos into creating the world's first exact and comprehensive sky catalog, which listed the number, brightness and position of every star he could see "in order that even the least of these should not pass unnoticed" — a task which impressed Pliny as "a presumptuous scheme even for a god" but which started the earliest program of systematic celestial observation on Earth, and for which modern astronomers will never cease to be grateful.

As the centuries passed, other novae appeared from time to time — the star of Bethlehem could well have been one — and at present, by international synoptic collaboration and electronic comparison of regularly photographed sky sections, they are turning up at an average rate of one every ten days. Even though many fewer than one percent become bright enough to be visible to the naked eye, spectrography reveals nova light to come from gases first bursting outward, then collapsing inward at speeds of thousands of miles a second, the confused spectral lines shifting toward violet, then red, in striking contrast to the sharp steady lines of the calm normal star. The atoms are obviously subjected to such violence that they lose electrons and exhibit the characteristic spectral signature of ionization with shifting lines that has come to mean "nova." This, of course, is strong evidence of the explosive atomic nature of the phenomenon, and is often corroborated, when the nova is not too far away, by actual sight of the dissipating gases, or even (as in the case of Nova Hercules in 1934) of separating pieces of the star itself during the years following the outburst. The outburst, moreover, having come to be associated with white dwarfs, is now believed to signalize not the blooming of new stars but more likely (as hinted on page 176) the death agony and collapse of old ones.

Even if you don't consider a flare-up of a hundredfold in brightness an explosion, there is a type of nova called the supernova, which suddenly increases a billion times in brightness and whose gases have been measured to shoot out at more than a hundred thousand miles a second. That is an explosion by anybody's definition and, incidentally, it is the biggest kind of explosion ever actually seen anywhere, unless you count the "explosion" of the universe itself, which is probably something on a rather different order, as we will see in the next chapter. No supernova in our Milky Way galaxy, however, can yet have been studied with modern methods, because none has occurred since 1604, five years before Galileo's telescope. But a number of remote ones have been seen and photographed in other galaxies, like the supernova of 1885 in our neighboring Andromeda galaxy (1,500,000 light-years away) and one whose light reached us in March 1950 from a galaxy seven times farther off, where it must have originally exploded some 10,000,000 years before the animals of earth had ever dreamed they could evolve such creatures as men. There is even some evidence of a double supernova having occurred within the last few millenniums in the large Magellanic Cloud.

The first humanly documented supernova seems to have been the one described in conservative Chinese annals as the "guest star" of A.D. 1054, which appeared "several fingers southeast of T'ien-kuan [Zeta Tauri]" and was probably the most stupendous material outburst in all history. The spectacle amazed humanity and was recorded in pictures on both sides of the earth, even in Indian rock drawings in northern Arizona, where it was depicted rising beside the crescent moon in what was later calculated to be exactly the right circumstances for an hour before dawn on the morning of July 5, 1054, perfectly matching the Japanese and

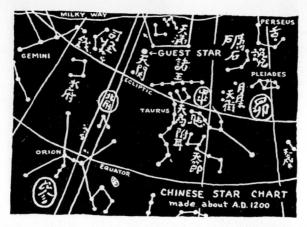

Chinese records. Like the almost similar supernova observed by
Tycho Brahe in November 1572, this one for a time outshone all
other stars in the sky, its iridescent yellow glare plain to see in
broad daylight. It could well have been the brightest celestial
object, other than the sun, ever to be beheld by historic man. Even
though it occurred twelve years before William the Conqueror
landed in England and faded from prominence within a few
weeks, lingering in faint visibility for less than two years, the mark

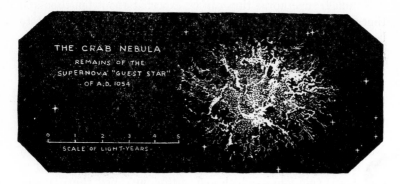

of this holocaust is still vividly evident in the famous Crab Nebula
of Taurus, a luminous space cloud which looks like an explosion
to this day and has been measured to be about 4,000 light-years

away, five light-years in diameter and still slowly expanding at 680 miles a second.

Among the possible causes of supernovae, one that has been discussed a good deal is the hypothesis that they are set off by collisions between stars. While such a dramatic happening could well burst the rind of helium just under the surface of either or both stars, releasing catastrophic amounts of radiation from the extremely hot interiors, calculation shows that it could not happen anywhere nearly often enough to account for the two or three supernovae known to occur on the average in each galaxy each millennium. Thus the famous "dark-star menace," which in popular imagination used to threaten the end of the world almost without warning any time, was effectively dispatched by Sir James Jeans, who estimated that the stars are so far apart there would be only one prospect of the sun's hitting another star in 600,000,000,-000,000,000 years. As most of those scientists who think the universe had a beginning place it at about 6,000,000,000 to 10,000,-000,000 years ago, we could expect only one or two collisions per 100,000,000 suns since the dawn of creation, which works out to only one crash in the whole Milky Way each 2,000,000 years — quite a modest enough batting average to soothe most anybody's jitters.

Although supernovae thus can be expected about ten thousand times as often as stellar collisions, they are rare enough not to be a source of worry and besides, any near ones will doubtless give us millions of years of forewarning once their probable atomic causes are well understood. On the credit side there are many possible benefits that may come from supernovae: one being the use of remote supernovae as milestones in gauging the distances of galaxies too far away for seeing Cepheid-variable stars. Another benefit, revealed by spectroscopic study of the Crab Nebula among others, would be the scattering (if not the creation) of the atoms of heavier elements like iron and nickel forged in supernova explosions — which some astronomers now think are just what makes possible the spawning of such dense planets as the earth or which, in any case, certainly add immeasurably to the complexity and variety of the raw material of stars in general.

Speaking of starbirth, although a celestial blessed event is veiled in far more obscurity than even its human counterpart, probably occurring nowhere but deep in the densest space clouds, something was discovered recently that happened 1,600 years ago in the potent Orion Nebula and may be the birth of two stars. A photograph taken in 1954 of a certain small region of the great cloud showed two stars that were not visible in a similar picture taken in 1947. The two apparently newborn babies have been tentatively classified as of the so-called T Tauri type, named after a famous variable in the Bull constellation and thought to be in the squirmy, nebulous condition of stellar infancy. There has not been time yet, however, to ascertain whether the accouchement conformed to the dust-accretion hypothesis described in the last chapter for, if it is actually starbirth, it is man's first peek at it, and no one so far has gotten around even to weighing the youngsters, let alone to checking their individual characteristics.

Aside from their behavior and dimensions, perhaps the most remarkable differences between any two stars are those revealed by their colors, which after all are but natural symptoms of their temperature and stage of incandescence. The range in our neighborhood stretches all the way from purple Pleione to ruby-red Beta Pegasi and the famous cool red giants Betelgeuse and Antares, flanked by pale rose-tinted Aldebaran or the garnet of Mu Cephei. Bluest of the blue might be Delta Cephei, or the potent sapphire of Rigel or hot Spica. Green: emeraldine Beta Librae or Castor or the small companion of Antares. Yellow: twinkling Albireo, golden Arcturus, or the jacinth of Capella, if not our sun. White: the diamond dog-star Sirius or dazzling Vega or doughty Deneb. If we'd include an orange star, it might be Beta Capricorni. And there are invisible infra-red ones like the supergiant of Epsilon Aurigae I and semivisible ultra-violet ones like exuberant Zeta Puppis and little Gamma Velorum of the Wolf-Rayet type. To say nothing of innumerable combinations like the carnelian and emerald revolving around each other called Gamma Andromedae, the contrasting blue and gold binary, RW Persei, or the violet and topaz Siamese twins, Beta Lyrae.

Although many of these colors appear so pale you can hardly decide whether they have any tint at all, and some are noticeably changing, they outline the vast order of stellar relationships that astronomers have been laboriously piecing together out of the apparent chaos of the skies. The now generally accepted classification of stars grew out of an idea that came into the mind of Walter Baade at Mount Wilson Observatory in 1943, when he discovered that many distant regions of the sky contain much higher percentages of giant red stars than exist around here and started working out the basic stellar relationships between age, size, temperature and color. Eventually he sorted all known members of the heavens into five main populations, as follows: Population 1, the oldest stars, particularly dim and dying dwarfs and the cool red giants like Antares, mostly to be found in remote globular clusters that swarm around the dust-free outskirts of the galaxies; Population 2, elderly and less remote stars, probably including many variables and unstable ones such as novae; Population 3, the great middle-aged majority of stars like the sun, inhabiting most of most types of spiral galaxies; Population 4, younger stars, such as Sirius, located near the nourishing, dusty central planes of galaxies; and Population 5, infant bluish stars, like hot Rigel, along with the still unborn star babies that have yet to emerge from the space clouds that spawned them.

The theoretical explanations behind such star classifications developed out of the new nuclear physics, which gives us our first real insight into stellar evolution. All stars, now explain the physicists, burn fairly steadily in their youth and early middle age like our sun, bigger ones at a faster rate, smaller ones proportionately slower, until they have used up about 15 percent of their hydrogen. Then they start to express themselves individually. Like people whose "life begins at forty," the larger ones increase their already fast pace, becoming dazzling blue giants to burn themselves out before they are much past their prime. These spendthrift stars usually turn out to be inhabitants of galactic arms, where nourishing dust clouds favor rapid growth. Smaller, slower-starting ones, however, as if to demonstrate their contrary theory that life begins after fifty, launch even more spectacular careers in their old age. Gradually increasing their rate of spending hydrogen, they swell up to 50 or 100 times their original size, thereby cooling off and becoming red giants. When their hydrogen is 60 percent gone, their internal pressure begins to drop, letting them shrink in an uneven, unstable way that often produces pulsations, irregular variability, perhaps eventually a nova splurge of greater or lesser degree before they finally collapse with their last hydrogen into the form of a dense white dwarf to fade quietly out of sight for good.

This sort of thing now appears to be going on constantly and continuously all over the sky and expresses the first reasonable cycle of life that man has been able to divine for the world of stars after countless centuries of looking and wondering and theorizing. It is a significant breakthrough into a macrocosmic existence that had long been considered hopelessly beyond human reach. For stars until quite recently were no more distinguishable one from another than water droplets in a cloud, and their motions had almost no recognizable pattern. But now we have also projected our consciousness right into their family lives by an ingenious mathematical condensation of the time dimension, so that you can see synthetic time-lapse movies of stars based on their calculated courses in which all motion is speeded up by a factor of many billions, bringing the heavens to life as vividly as fireflies on a summer night. It is a God's-eye view of the firmament with binary star couples and lively trios moving about like dancers on a ballroom floor. Globular clusters of thousands of stars show the

movements of individual members as clearly as swarming bees, each one following his own graceful orbit, often moving alternately inward and outward from the central blaze or spiraling devotedly around it under the complex druglike influence of gravity. One would think on first glance that the stars in the dazzling center of such a cluster must be actually stuck together in a contiguous fiery mass, yet the telescope discloses there is so much space between even the most densely packed stars that any of them can have dozens of planets and that it would take light a full year to reach from each to the next.

♎ ♏ ♐ ♑ ♒ ♓

Thus the lessons of perspective in the great outer world around us, the heavens that no stretch of earthbound thinking can hope to comprehend — the world of worlds in which even our seemingly immutable signs of the zodiac represent but a fleeting local viewpoint! For Libra and Aquarius are at most but finite earthly illusions. They cannot but look a little different even today as viewed from near-by Procyon and will surely look a little different again from Earth in every coming millennium. Simple projection of known star motions shows that in less than 25,000 years our fat Great Bear will have turned into a lanky giraffe, Sagittarius' quiver will be empty and Orion will have lost his belt if not his trousers. While these ideological symbols, of course, are only small twigs on the celestial family tree, they contain fertile seeds that will bloom and bear and bloom again as the world matures through future ages. Could there be any example better than Virgo, chaste deity of the equatorial sky, who carries greater secrets than the ancients could have guessed? For known even now only to the ravenous eyes and antennas of the great telescopes is a famous field of thousands of galaxies hidden in her inscrutable womb — actually the densest concentration of these potent "island universes" within fifty million light-years of here, even though admittedly but a sampling of the untold billions that drift beyond and all around them, filling every cranny of visibility in the growing seeable cosmos.

8. the foreign galaxies

BEFORE I CAME OUT INTO SPACE, I assumed that
the drastic shift in perspective would do something for my mind
and imagination, if not my soul. But I had little inkling of how
deeply the mystery of distance would affect me up here, or of how
moved I would be by the relentless presence of these worlds and
worlds-of-worlds strewn all around us, above, below and on every
side.

Yet the shock of space awareness here has been different only
in degree from the lesser shock inflicted upon nearly every thinking man on Earth by the doings of the rocket engineers and, even
more profoundly, of the astronomers. Certainly to all of us who
grew up supposing the sun the brightest light in the world, it
has been a jolting and humbling experience to discover instead
that the great sun is really only a street lamp in a suburb of a
large star city. Then that the city in turn is but a shiny grain
of sand on the shores of a vast ocean of unknown extent which,
for all its size, has turned out to be less than a drop of dew in
a much greater continent of reality.

But that is just the sort of progressive revelation that the unfolding horizons of modern astronomy have been bringing to all mankind. And one's awakening to the galaxies and to the uncountable swarms of galaxies naturally makes one wonder: is the arrangement of the heavens a majestic example of chance, or is there really some sort of pattern signifying an over-all system behind the appalling array?

Of the latter there can hardly be any doubt, as has been intuitively sensed from the earliest times and scientifically established by measurements of increasing scope and variety ever since. For from the ancient astronomical Tables of Tirvalore in India to the 200-inch reflector of Palomar, order has prevailed in man's view of the firmament, albeit a subjective order at first — the plausible incorporation of noble figures into the zodiac, with here and there a sinuous reptile called Hydra or Draco slipped in to swallow the scattered misfit stars, and for a long period an original theory (probably conceived in India) that both Earth and sky were invisibly held up by a mystic herd of elephants upon the back of a giant tortoise, which stood on a star-spangled serpent. Such a celestial team evidently seemed both necessary and natural to ancient minds, and it was only when some genius or jester asked "What holds up the serpent?" that the philosophers got to work on profounder hypotheses of cosmology.

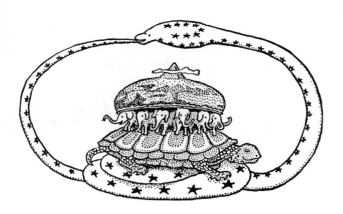

When their stirred imaginations finally accepted Tycho Brahe's ritual of systematic observation, progress seems to have naturally entered its present acceleration, the pool of known facts to have begun to expand more rapidly and measurements to take on sharper precision. Where Hipparchos and Ptolemy considered it an achievement to measure angles as fine as 5′ (one sixth of the moon's diameter as seen from Earth, a twelfth of a degree), Tycho, the last great naked-eye astronomer, got it down to 10″, thirty times more precise, and by the end of the nineteenth century astronomers had subdivided angles as small as 0″.001, one thousandth of a second of arc or the width of a penny from two thousand miles away. Today at Palomar they are pushing 0″.00001, with the big mirror polished to a tolerance of a millionth of an inch and rotating with its giant tube like a balance wheel in a Swiss watch that is comparable in size to an ocean tramp steamer.

THE RADIO TELESCOPE

Radioastronomy has blossomed even more suddenly into a major branch of the star sciences, having sprung up out of the discovery of radiation from the Milky Way as late as 1932 by Karl Jansky of the Bell Telephone Laboratories. Huge steerable parabolic reflectors up to hundreds of feet in diameter and even bigger linked-antenna interferometers are already in use in various parts of the world, and the National Radio Astronomy Observatory being built in West Virginia includes a 600-foot radio "tele-

scope" ideally secluded in a valley away from the habitudes of hurricanes and tornadoes (particularly hazardous to such sail-like surfaces) and sheltered by surrounding mountains and special laws
against interference by any earthly radio broadcasting that might
otherwise encroach on their Hertzian solitude. Taking advantage
of the fact that hydrogen in space naturally radiates energy on a
wave length of 21 centimeters, the new breed of radioastronomers
is already at work measuring the shapes, speeds and courses of the
clouds of hydrogen in the Milky Way and beyond it and in
general supplementing the optic astronomers, who are often frus-
trated by the dust that blocks off the light they need.

It has been estimated that more than 99 percent of our Milky
Way galaxy is actually hidden behind these mysterious dust clouds.
Some of them appear black like the famous Coal Sacks of
Cygnus and the Southern Cross or the mysterious Elephant's
Trunk cloud. Others are glowing white in reflected starlight like
the great stormy Orion Nebula in the middle of the Nimrod's
sword, which is probably in the act of giving birth to a new star
cluster. Some have strange shapes like the Horse's Head Nebula
of cold dark dust being squeezed by hot glowing gas, or the
Ring Nebula illuminated by a bright star, the Rosette, the Dumbbell, the Trifid, the Owl, or the beautiful Veil in Cygnus whose
fine filaments (100,000,000,000 miles thick) are thought to be
jetsam from an ancient supernova still drifting through the rare-
fied interstellar gas. There is even a mysterious, barely visible,
broadcasting cloud in Cassiopeia that was once called a "radio
star" and is the strongest source of radio waves in the Milky Way,
but of which almost nothing is known except the spectroscopic
revelation that it is "an irregular cloud of gas with violent internal
motions and high excitations," very likely including unimaginably
vast cosmic thunderstorms that require centuries to discharge their
equivalent of lightning from positive to negative centers of static
potential. And there must be still less noticeable clouds of interacting dust and gas similar to any or all of these, which form
Taurus' mane about the Pleiades and feed our sun's corona and
in general compose the basic surround of galactic space, the milt
of stars — being altogether a much greater thing in the sky than

is commonly realized because of their preponderant invisibility.

Yet enough of the Milky Way has remained unobscured for it to have commanded attention from earliest times as the most extensive phenomenon in the visible heavens — the mysterious "Great Serpent" of the Akkadians, the "Night Manna" of the Egyptians, who believed Isis sowed it with grains of wheat, and known variously to others as "the Sky River," "Stream of the Shepherd's Hut," "River of the Divine Lady" and "Jacob's Road." Anaxagoras in 550 B.C. intuitively referred to it as "that shining wheel, men call it milk," for Greek mythology had attributed it to the milk spilled from Hera's breasts after she had angrily jerked away from the bastard Hercules, who had suckled her in her sleep. Later Greeks were to know it as "the Circle of the Galaxy," after *gala* (milk), and Romans "the Via Lactea" or Milk Run to Heaven which the departed could enter at Gemini and, if they made their way successfully, leave finally through the Door of Sagittarius, somewhere beyond which must begin the Elysian fields.

Even the Orientals and aborigine Americans seem to have independently accepted this girdle of stars as a divine pathway. The Japanese named it "the Silver River of Heaven" over which on the seventh day of their seventh month the celestial shepherd boy (Altair) and his spinning maiden (Vega) meet each year upon an invisible bridge, and the Iroquois Indians called it the "Road of Souls." The Ottawa Indians, however, considered it the wake of a divine turtle swimming along the bottom of the sky, and the Patagonians believed it the heavenly trail on which their worthy dead friends were enjoying an eternal rhea hunt, while in the Punjab it was the wake of an ark, the African bushmen knew it as "the Path of Glowing Ashes" and the early Britons unaccountably dubbed it "Watling Street."

Aristotle gave a learned scientific explanation of this hazy band as "glowing vapor," but it was Pythagoras whose earlier intuition had seen it, possibly for the first time on Earth, as "a vast assemblage of very distant stars" — stars that could only be confirmed as actually existing more than two thousand years later when Galileo finally turned his telescope upon them.

The present view of the Milky Way is changing so rapidly that it is hard to keep up with either the new evidence or the new interpretations, but the body of well-established facts has also produced quite a vivid and understandable picture that every modern education should include. In it our home galaxy is revealed as a discus-shaped mass of two hundred billion stars spinning in a turbulent whirl of gas and dust, its fiery center hidden from our optical view by the intervening shrouds, although the outer silhouette can be seen edge on fairly clearly in the faint form of the Milky Way.

The reason we view it edgewise as this dense band of myriad suns is that our own little sun happens to be near the outer rim of the great disk, whose center is hidden directly behind the faint constellation we know as Sagittarius in the southern summer sky. When you gaze in any direction other than toward the Milky Way, naturally you see practically nothing of our galaxy for you are looking axlewise or perpendicular to its plane through only part of its thickness, or a mere 5,000 light-years of distance, containing scarcely 100,000 of its stars in your general line of sight, only a few hundred of which could be visible without a telescope. But your spokewise, rim-eye view along the plane of the Milky wheel, especially when directed toward its hub in Sagittarius, exposes your eye to a thousand times more stars, one behind another for 80,-000 light-years, so that even though most of them are dimmed out by dust or made unresolvable with distance and lack of angular separation, their combined light overwhelms the intervening void with the glow of unimaginable glory that has been on its way to your eyes since before the last ice age.

If that soft flush of milkiness is still hard to visualize as a whirlpool of rampant suns, remember that its violence is on a time scale unknowable to human minds except through the abstraction of celestial mathematics and that the eye is a poor instrument for viewing it even with the aid of a telescope. In fact, were it not for radio telescopy, infra-red photography, spectroscopy and the difficult construction of deductions from such remote clues as our sister galaxy in Andromeda (a million and a half light-years beyond our own and the most remote thing visible to the naked eye), we would know hardly anything about the Milky Way, and its many spiral arms would be little more than confused clouds without demonstrable pattern or meaning.

As it is, however, we have already patched together a pretty complete model and find that our sun is on the inside of about the fourth arm out from the galactic center with a couple more fainter ones still farther out, the arms being difficult to count exactly because they are wavy and often branched and crisscrossed, apparently because of their propensity for passing through each other. Although they are all formed largely of dense luminous hydrogen and dust studded with blue supergiant stars, the clouds are arranged something like beads on a necklace, and we are fortunate in being in a clear region between beads from which we can see at least the very nearest part of our galaxy: the famous North America-shaped cloud and the spawning Orion Nebula close by in the same arm as ourselves along with big blue stars like Rigel, Vega, Altair, Spica, while a giant double-star cluster in Perseus lies in the next arm outside ours and the beautiful

Lagoon Nebula of flailing hydrogen in the nearest arm inside. Beyond these neighbors the veils get too thick for optical vision, but the longer-waved radio telescopes "see" to the very center of the galaxy, where a vast sphere of hydrogen 20,000 light-years in diameter is whirling about much faster than the rim regions we inhabit. The radio-eye view of this galactic nucleus understandably has a radar texture to it, yet it clearly sees clouds of hydrogen turbulently puffing and spiraling out of the sphere at speeds up to 100 miles a second, while deep inside there is a mysterious doughnut ring of denser hydrogen a mere 3,000 light-years in diameter, spinning at nearly 200 miles a second and harboring so much empty space inside it in turn that it makes one think of the eye of a hurricane — even to the weird little coin-shaped eyelid of whirling hydrogen (a few hundred light-years across) in the very center.

The significance of all this is something astronomers have barely begun to guess at, but you may get an inkling of galactic dynamics in the knowledge that the arm we are in carries the sun and Earth through one revolution of the Milky Way whirlpool every 230 million years as compared with only 120 million for the stars and clouds halfway between us and the center and with still greater angular velocities for those in the nucleus itself. Such estimates are important in calculating the galaxy's centrifugal force, which obviously must balance its gravity as long as it maintains itself. Gravity in turn is a direct indication of mass, which in the case of the Milky Way thus figures out to be 70 billion times the mass of the sun, almost 98 percent of it accounted for by stars and their satellites and the remaining 2 percent largely just loose hydrogen gas. The weight of the dust particles that often cloud the gas is only a negligible percentage of the total heft of this ethereal presence in "empty" space which, thin though it is, contains at least one atom of hydrogen in its every cubic centimeter for as far as it has been measured within the galaxy. Even a billion light-years beyond the Milky Way and well removed from any galaxies or hermit stars, traces of this basic hydrogen are believed to continue, perhaps comprising in their total immensity a good deal more than half of all the matter of the universe.

The true make-up of our Milky Way galaxy, however, cannot be grasped by considering only its vast starry disk and its all-pervasive hydrogen, for a very significant part of it is the swarm of some hundred globular clusters of stars, mostly far from the disk plane and forming a loose spheroidal skeleton around the central nucleus with the disk rim as its equator. It was astronomer Harlow Shapley who first understood this skeleton and in 1918 made the boldest hypothesis since Copernicus demonstrated that the earth revolves around the sun: pointing out that the sun in turn, far from being in a central position, must be moving around the galactic nucleus like any other humble star. And he identified and located the galactic nucleus at the center of gravity of all these massive clusters that stand out like ethereal vertebrae around the Sagittarial half of the sky.

One such compact cluster more than 30,000 light-years away in Hercules is actually visible to keen unaided eyes, while several others can be fetched by ordinary binoculars. And the curious thing about these clusters — each a remote buzzing blaze of some hundred thousand cloudfree stars — is that, while they are obviously part of the galaxy and move with it, they are normally aloof enough to be regarded almost as semisatellites or separate midget galaxies in themselves, their spherical and elliptical shapes seemingly modeled on similar-looking galaxies, a million times larger and more complex, that are now known to be floating in large numbers in all the corners of far-flung foreign space.

If the globular clusters are not true satellites but part of the basic galactic structure, as is indicated by their comparable presence in the Andromeda and all other observable galaxies, there are other recently appraised clustered-star systems, remoter and a hundred times larger, that do qualify as satellites of the Milky Way. These average about 100,000 light-years off and contain some ten million stars each, which makes them a special caste of galactic moons — comparable in relative size to the moons of Jupiter and

Saturn and, as would be expected from their distance, revolving majestically around our galaxy every two billion years!

Then what about the famous Magellanic Clouds near the Southern Cross, which even in the largest telescopes look almost like pieces of the Milky Way hurled off into the void and which have recently proved to be less than twice the galactic diameter away while steadily receding at better than 100 miles a second? Could such star systems possibly be considered satellites of our home galaxy?

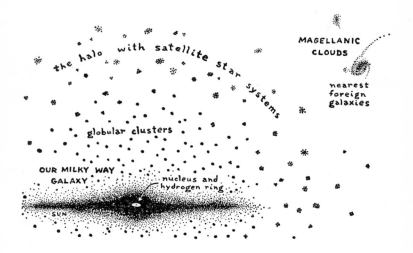

Indeed, these "Cape Clouds" of Magellan were considered just that by many astronomers after World War I when it had first become generally accepted that they were really outside the Milky Way, but during World War II it was realized that the big Cloud for certain, and probably both Clouds, are well above the average in size and mass among all galaxies in our neighborhood. The big one quite unobtrusively stretches across 30 degrees of sky. In other words, even though they may have a combined total of only twenty billion stars as against the Milky Way's two hundred billion, these Clouds are much bigger in relation to us than is any moon in relation to its planet and, since there is no evidence that they are circling around us, they are deservedly ranked as full peers among the score of members of our local clan of galaxies.

The big Cloud probably is the same "white ox" the ancient Arabs knew as *El Bakar* in their southern sky and which Anghiera, on reports from Portuguese seamen, once compared to the "mild effulgence" of the Milky Way. But it is to Pigafetta, returning years later from the famed round-the-world voyage of Magellan, that the world generally ascribes the discovery of these nearest of outside firmaments, and they have long since established themselves as symbols of alien mystery amid the exotic Antarctic constellations of *Dorado*, the goldfish; *Tucana*, the toucan; *Pavo*, the peacock; and the chameleon, phoenix, flying fish, flamingo, water serpent and bird of paradise.

And what of the rest of our local galactic gathering — who are its members and what, if anything, do they have in common? At the far end of the group is our twin, Andromeda, about ten times the distance of the Magellanic Clouds and a good ten times bigger, a great whirlpool disk tilted quarter-face to us (15 degrees from edgewise) and almost a mirror duplicate of our Milky Way though probably a little larger.

She has her similar aureole of reddish globular clusters, and the dusty clouds strung along her spiral arms are besprinkled with bluish stars. There are even two little handmaiden galaxies attending her in the manner of our Magellanic pair, although they are closer, smaller, and neatly elliptical. Then in several parts of the space between and around the two major galaxies of our clan float spiral systems of assorted sizes, three congregated at a range of 1,300,000 light-years in the constellation of Leo, others in Triangulum, Draco and the Little Bear, and four irregular galaxies of the Cape Cloud type in scattered places, with here and there half a dozen smooth ellipsoids. Two of the latter, called Fornax and Sculptor (after their associated constellations), are so low in density they are almost transparent as they drift along a cozy 400,-000 light-years from us, which is less than three times the distance of the two Clouds. But some of the others are more than two million light-years away and so aloof that it is a question whether they are gravitationally tied to the rest of the family or are just

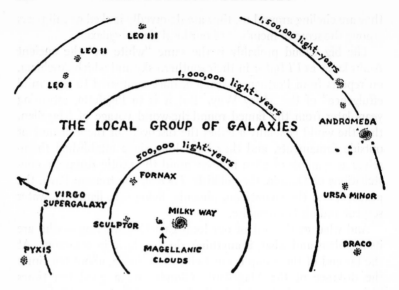

THE LOCAL GROUP OF GALAXIES

strangers who happen to be passing by. The less remote ones, even though their distances be about equally incomprehensible, are more definitely united by this same mysterious force that binds the moon to Earth and which both Newton and Einstein have described according to the perspectives of their own ages. In any case, it is generally agreed that the whole collection of great systems must obediently revolve around an unknown gravitational center somewhere this side of Andromeda, which, under the same influence, is now drawing toward us to the tune of 200 miles a second or just fast enough to have come a thousandth of the way during the 1,500,000 years it took her light to reach our eyes.

If this is a rough model of our own tribal stamping ground in the outer galactic cosmos, the larger picture of the knowable universe must bring in a vastly more complex and imagination-humbling pattern. Indeed, as we stretch our ken out to ten million

light-years, then to 50 million, our local group containing Andromeda and the Milky Way dwindles down to one of the smallest
of a dozen widely scattered associations of galaxies. The largest
is that ellipsoidal swarm of many thousands of galaxies discovered
this century centering in the direction of Virgo, and being in
reality a kind of Milky Way of Milky Ways that extends (invisibly
except to the most powerful of telescopes) across the entire sky
edgewise for more than 120 degrees from Cepheus to Centaurus.
Beyond it several other supergalaxies soon appear: one in Hydra,
one occupying both Pavo and Indus and another edgewise southern supergalaxy mostly in Eridanus, which, exceeding that celestial
river, covers about 50 degrees of sky from the larger Magellanic
Cloud almost to Orion. Having now reached outward to 100
million light-years, we find a further large association of galaxies
in Perseus, then a big one at 125 million in Coma Berenices and
still another at 180 million in Hercules. In the next 300 million
light-years beyond that, at least nine more such super organiza-

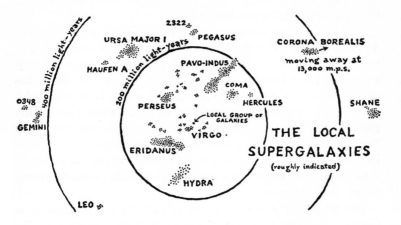

tions, each of hundreds of galaxies, appear like foreign nations
of the cosmos. These are usually scores of millions of light-
years apart with more numerous smaller aggregations in between
them and of course thousands of nomad and hermit galaxies
darting about without any obvious plan.

It is hard to hold any realistic perspective in the face of such immensities. Are we ourselves perhaps part of the great Virgo nation which seems to be loosely joined to our little supergalactic tribe as to other small ones relatively near ours? There is good reason to think so, even though a substantial part of Virgo's body has been measured to be chastely receding at a brisk 700 miles a second, for Virgo as a whole is full of vital activity with differences of speed among her separate galaxies ranging to a maximum of 1,500 m.p.s., and it could well be that the Milky Way is as a corpuscle floating in a remote extremity of her vast circulation. Even the intervening gaps that at first seemed to be millions of light-years of nothing turn out to have dwarf galaxies sprinkled through them with faintly luminous filaments bridging the void from one to the next. Astrophysicist Fritz Zwicky of Palomar announced in 1952 that such intergalactic bridges, far from being exceptional, are probably the rule, and he listed hundreds of them he had already discovered, including a gracefully curved one that stretches "sharp as a lighted boulevard" for 72,-000 light-years (430 quadrillion miles)!

Gerard de Vaucouleurs, one of the French pioneers of the Virgo supergalaxy, has described this federation of Milky Ways as roughly similar to our own private Milky Way in shape and with an uncounted population of galaxies that "may run into the tens of thousands." He calculates its disk as about 40 million light-years across, by ten million thick but with much more irregularity than our Milky Way and lots of subclustering, as in the case of the "local group." There has even been measurement of rotation in its nearer parts, suggesting that its flattening, like the Milky Way's, comes from centrifugal force, and that the whole stupendous thing is one great whirlpool of whirlpools.

The alignment of our galaxy in relation to the supergalaxy is curious. It is not only closer to the rim than is the sun to the rim of the Milky Way (making our galaxy even more rural than our sun) but is turned so nearly perpendicular to it that the north pole (axial projection) of the Milky Way is found within 5 degrees of the center of the Virgo system. In other words, our galactic axis forms virtually a spoke on the super wheel, holding almost the exact opposite of the relationship that exists between the axes of Earth and sun, which are roughly parallel. It is good exercise not only for the mind but the ego thus to project our imaginations into larger and larger orientations of the sky, for we find the Copernican revelation repeated again and again — not only by Shapley, who moved the center of motion outward from sun to galaxy, but by others who have since pushed it farther to the supergalaxy and undoubtedly will continue to bear it onward step by step as man's consciousness expands indefinitely through the material cosmos.

Another way of getting a large-scale view of creation is by looking at it with a statistical eye, considering it not just as it is here or there or in any particular place but as it is everywhere on the average. This is a practical as well as hopeful approach to the largest thing we know of, because the most significant fact about averages is that they get more reliable as they are built on larger and larger numbers. Just as the risky roulette wheel can roll on to become the rock-ribbed foundation of Monte Carlo, so the apparently random irregularities of local galaxies and super-galaxies may turn into patterns of meaningful regularity if we can see them in big enough perspective.

That is exactly why several and sundry mathematicians have recently been trying out various mechanisms of chance to see what kinds of universes would result. At the Statistical Laboratory of the University of California, for instance, they began simply with a single roulette formula: divide space into equal cubes and spin the wheel once for each cube, putting a galaxy into all cubes where the wheel indicates zero and nothing into the cubes that draw any other number. But the simple universe that results from this kindergarten creation is not much like the one we see around us. Most obviously, it is too randomly scattered, showing almost nothing of the real universe's strong tendency for galaxies to be bunched in clusters.

So they tried a more complex formula. They assumed that galaxies always come in clusters, counting the occasional lone galaxies as clusters of one. Then, spinning the wheel for each cube of space as before, this time they let each zero pick a "cluster center." Thus, once the space was seeded with centers, they could spin for each center in turn to decide how many galaxies would be associated with it, and again for the galactic pattern around each center. By trying many such mechanisms and combinations of mechanisms, even adding extra steps to provide clusters of clusters, a great variety of distributions of galaxies in space could be produced. Obviously the many variables involved (such as sizes of roulette wheels, assignment and order of designations, etc.) soon become so complex that any appreciable thoroughness in covering them requires a large electronic computer, while analysis of galaxy patterns actually observed in the sky is about equally difficult. Both, of course, must be understood completely, in order to match the statistical anatomy of nature with an abstract formula of probability. This must include, among other things, an allowance for the disparity of time, since the pattern on a photographic plate of galaxies represents widely different periods of history (according to the distance traveled by the different rays of light) which must be sorted and somehow reckoned into the whole. And inevitably there must be made many such minor adjustments as the blocking of remoter galaxies by ones nearer in both space and time, the relative motion of our own galaxy, and so on.

No important breakthrough has yet been made by this weird modern approach, but the wheels are grinding and the transistors sparking over it and something will turn up sooner or later. It is surely wonderful that man's mind can probe by this abstruse method into the remote galaxies and their clusters that are lying out there upon space like handfuls of shining seed sown upon black soil. For there are actually thousands of times as many galaxies now knowable through our greatest visual and radio telescopes as all the stars ever visible to the naked eye, and each of these galaxies on the average contains literally billions of stars. What this means even in our own corner of creation can scarcely be appreciated by the calculation that if every star in our Milky Way alone had a name or a number it would take a hundred thousand fat telephone books just to list each star once. Or if someone were merely to count these stars at the rate of one per second day and night, month after weary month, the job would take more than three thousand years!

If one galaxy can be that tremendous, while its stars are trillions of miles from each to the next, how hopeless is it to grasp the infinitude of galaxies and their great tribal clusters; still more so their foreign nations. If the entire known universe were proportionately reduced to the size of the earth, for example, all its stars would disappear. For on such a scale the largest stars would be scarcely a millionth of an inch in diameter and far too small to see in any ordinary microscope. Only an electron microscope would have a chance of revealing them. And these stars would stand only a few tenths of an inch apart and a galaxy of them would be like a very faint cloud of diamond dust several hundred feet across. Outside such a galactic cloud there would be nothing but emptiness for maybe a quarter mile in all directions. Yet within another mile would appear various other clouds, perhaps flattened and tilted at odd angles to each other. If you flew through them in a fast airplane, these glittering galaxies of submicroscopic dust would drift past you every few seconds on the average. But you would soon notice that sometimes there would be none at all for almost a whole minute, while at other times you would be virtually dazzled by a dense concentration of them, several to the second. In other words, galaxies actually live in great irregularity in the sky, and the clusters and metagalaxies (as the Milky Ways of Milky Ways are sometimes called) perhaps even more so. And you would notice all sorts of vast and wonderful patterns among these organizations of organizations of organizations as your airplane roared onward hour upon hour across the eight-thousand-mile breadth of this tiny model of the visible universe.

Of course, you would be moving much too fast to measure distance in light-years or even in the astronomer's longer units called parsecs — a parsec being the distance of a star whose direction varies by ⅓,₆₀₀ of a degree according to whether it is viewed from the earth or the sun, the great radius of our earth's orbit subtending that tiny angle some nineteen trillion miles away, giving such a star a parallax of exactly one second of arc at the range of a parallax-second or parsec. Thus one parsec equals 3.26 light-years and one light-year equals almost six trillion miles. You would find it impractical even to use the thousand-times bigger units of kiloparsecs and would have to resort to the million-times bigger megaparsecs and then convert them back again in your statistical surveys to ascertain the average number of metagalaxies per cubic kiloparsec. As no human in the visible future is likely to move at anything approaching such a relative speed, there remains plenty of freedom to speculate, as does Fritz Zwicky at Palomar, that space really "may be divided into cluster cells that fill the universe just as bubbles fill a volume of suds."

But then one can mentally condense time as easily as space, which brings up the question of change and evolution in these endless but apparently fixed worlds all around us. Is there really any kind of growth or decay in galaxies? Or metabolism of a metagalaxy? If it takes more than two hundred million years for the Milky Way to rotate just once, can we possibly tell its life or say where it is going?

Yes, we can make at least a beginning of an answer, for there are plenty of theories about this difficult question and a definite consensus is forming. Most astrophysicists agree that the evolution of galaxies and groups of galaxies is from the diffuse and formless gaseous state toward condensed and complex solidity — from simple undefined clouds of random atoms toward structural symmetry and developed form. Weizsäcker, for instance, definitely classes all celestial objects as either clouds, rotatory forms, or spheres, and explains in detail the sequence of development from one to the next by means of natural forces, including turbulence. He shows how any primordial state of uniform distribution of matter throughout space, if indeed uniformity ever could have existed, would have had to be not only absolutely calm but paradoxically highly unstable, because as soon as the slightest irregularity or local change occurred anywhere, this prime event would inevitably have set up waves of pressure, involving gravity, radiation and magnetism, all of which are basic mediums of energy that by their nature must disperse outward, spreading what is scientifically describable as turbulence.

Obviously, this is the modern physicist's expanded version of the ancient symbolic postulate, "The earth was without form and void . . . and the Spirit of God moved upon the face of the waters." And we can safely accept turbulence as inevitable from the first event that ever happened in this eventful world, an event that could have been anything from a stupendous creative explosion to a slow condensing of uniform hydrogen. Or if you accept time as a finite illusion and events as a continuous process without beginning, then still must turbulence be ever present as one of the eternal realities of nature.

In any case, we see turbulence all around and even inside us in varying degree from the grandest reaches of space to the wind and the bile. And it may well exist inside the electron. Turbulence is the shearing effect of disparate velocities, the divergence of streams into eddies and subeddies. It is elemental dynamic form, the stress wave, the music of fluid motion. And the study of it teaches us much of how and why the diffuse gases that still permeate space have been and continuously are turning into stars and habitable worlds.

This process was already under way in the first local thickening of the primordial hydrogen, and it is ever advancing by a kind of cosmic condensation, a progressive aggregation of the gas atoms into denser regions or cells which at first are extremely nebulous and irregular, only gradually forming definite clouds. As Sir James Jeans explains it, "any gravitating gas filling a very large volume" is bound to break up into individual "gas balls." It is a phenomenon a little like the condensing of water vapor in earthly air into microscopic droplets to make the common cumulus cloud. But in the cosmic case there may be nothing as solid as dust for the gas atoms to cling to and form around. For presumably, if there was a creative beginning, there was a time before atoms had ever joined together to make dust — even before there was any such thing as a distinction between elements or a molecule or a liquid or a solid — and all these building materials of the palpable worlds had somehow to be fashioned out of raw hydrogen and its constituent parts, the simplest of all substances in the material realm.

It does not seem necessary to speculate here about the universe before the time of protons and electrons, because that pre-ionic world, if it existed, was hardly a material world at all in any understandable sense. And are we not carrying rashness far enough just to guess how hydrogen formed everything physical we have ever heard of? The mere concentration of hydrogen into regions, abetted by turbulence, could logically have produced enough pressure and eventual heat to create stars, which in turn might well have cooked up the other elements out of hydrogen particles, which by the chance and complex collisions of nature would sooner or later have made all the kinds of molecules there are. Once the heavier elements formed into solids, making dust inevitable, dense dark clouds would gather, and the assembling of planets must have started, for creation had moved into its present productive phase.

Then while stars were being condensed out of the clotting clouds in the manner already described in the chapter on the sun and the patterns of turbulence were paving the way for terrestrial life, the galaxies and great metagalaxies were likewise forming according to the dictates of turbulence. Knowing that the lives of individual eddies are very short, few of them lasting long enough to travel much farther than the length of their own diameters, one might well ask how anything as huge and permanent as a galaxy could arise from an eddy. Yet it is precisely the eddy that is accepted as the most plausible source of galaxies. For in fact, as Astrophysicist George Gamow puts it, "the standard size of a galaxy would correspond" (in a turbulent universe) "to the smallest size of an eddy which can be held together by its own gravity." And even though it must take still larger eddies to produce clusters and great nations of galaxies, any decrease in eddy stability on that scale should be more than made up for by a corresponding increase in the potency of gravity. However, as gravity is an involved subject, we must bide awhile before returning to delve deeper into this curious tendency of the cosmos in Chapter 13.

And so the great star systems, molded by the majestic flow of universal forces, roll on according to their own immutable laws — for example, eddy speeds varying as the cube root of their size (the Kolmogoroff Law, which holds good right down to molecules), and turbulence varying in direct proportion to the density, width, speed and fluidity of each flow (rule of Reynolds). And as the irregular clouds gradually contract under gravitation, the law of conservation of angular momentum accelerates the tempo of their turning like a spinning skater pulling in his arms, giving the clouds a more definite and symmetrical shape. This shape normally tends toward spirality with the two arms being drawn progressively closer and closer to the central body, and the great mass of star-strewn gas assuming some such double spiral as that of the Andromeda galaxy and the Milky Way. This general form prevails among a good three quarters of all known galaxies. Weizsäcker says it happens for the same reason that cream poured into a stirred cup of coffee takes on its strikingly similar sort of dynamic symmetry, the outer parts of the cream quickly forming arms that trail behind the faster-turning center, until they are spooled into a simple ring to look like the Vincent Van Gogh-style galaxies, designated type *Sa*. How the majority of galaxies can have arms still open and unspooled is a mystery unless, as astronomer Jan Oort speculates, "perhaps one side of an arm collects material while the other side evaporates it."

Even harder to explain is the type of open spiral that has a straight bar across its center extending for its full diameter, apparently a sort of rotary lawn sprinkler made of stars that in most cases is strewing fiery wakes behind both tips like a flaming stick thrown end over end. The rather amorphous large Magellanic Cloud and some other irregulars incidentally seem to be starting to form such bars, but just what kind of magnetic or other stiffening force could turn any cloud into a barred spiral seems hardly to have been guessed at. A clue may be lurking in the apparently embryonic arms sometimes observed inside the nuclei of barred galaxies or in the recent plasma experiments in which protons and electrons are shot into an intense magnetic field — a process that sometimes produces miniature barred spiral forms of a strikingly similar shape.

Undoubtedly, each particular type of galactic spirality is determined in large part by the turbulence of the immediate surround, particularly by any collision or near-collision — just as a dancer may be set to whirling by brushing elbows with another moving in the opposite direction. Indeed, the average energy of galactic rotation has been found to equal the average energy of galactic random motion, just as is required by the general law of classical statistical mechanics. All galaxies are to a degree thus interdependent even at great distances, because they are part of the same connected ocean of turbulence, and the amount of spin or contrapuntal shear in any one of them bespeaks its adventures. Those whirling or grinding the fastest naturally have been thinned out by centrifugal force into hurricane-shaped disks which have wide clear eyes at their centers — eyes clear of clouds, at least, for the dust is held away from the centers in the same manner as are Saturn's rings, leaving only stars in the center floating in clear, invisible gas. The most dramatic example of this I know of is the famous Sombrero galaxy in Virgo, which looks something like a large light bulb surrounded by a dark dusty brim (page 189).

The stars, being centers of dense, hot matter, naturally react very differently from the diffuse dust. It is they which are believed to form the relatively invisible skull bones of galaxies while the conspicuous illuminated clouds are mere wigs which, even as in humans, should properly be of less importance than what they disguise. Thus when a condensing galaxy is set to spinning by adjacent turbulence, it is the delicate plumage of dust and gas that makes the most dramatic response, spreading and tapering to a disk, while many of the inconspicuous stars and clusters of stars stubbornly remain outside as the spherical skeleton.

THE EVOLUTION OF GALAXIES

primordial clouds of stars

loose spirals

barred spirals

tight spirals

ellipsoids

spheres

Or if the galaxy has not been disturbed, its clouds may calmly stay with its symmetrical star systems to form one of the well-known elliptical galaxies that make up about a fifth of all that are known. Even the spiral disks, however, must eventually disperse their energy through friction and radiation, slowing down to more and more globular shape as the superficial hairdo returns at last to the natural configuration of the skull.

In this way the great outer sky becomes explicable as the home of the overpowering variety of galaxies we see: the playful young irregular ones like the Magellanic Clouds, which have hardly begun to feel the great formative influence of gravity and magnetism; the lovely adolescent open-armed spirals obviously in the first flush of their new-learned ballet; the older tight-armed whirlers doing their polished pirouettes; the disciplined ring-tailed galaxies that might have illumined Van Gogh's "Road with Cypresses"; the elliptical elite in their smooth formality; the prim spheroids like the Blue Jet galaxy M 87 (Messier 87) in Virgo haloed by its thousand globular clusters settling toward crystallized complacency. The vaster orders of metagalaxies and cluster continents seem much less definite, in fact are still largely beyond reach of our growing perspective, though they are apparently galumphing grandiosely in their own unassailable largo — the giants inexorably sorting the pigmies according to cosmic hierarchies of fragmentation that accelerate as they reach smaller and smaller units — the separate members of a ten-thousand-galaxy nation often colliding and sweeping one another up like a great monopolistic industry its small competitors, even as our Milky Way may be doing with such vapid neighbors as Sculptor and Fornax.

Galactic collisions, of course, occur very frequently compared to star collisions, because galaxies on the average are only about a hundred of their own diameters apart (still closer in clusters), while stars are separated by some millions of star diameters even in the middle of galaxies. Yet for the same reason, galactic clashes are not very catastrophic since the meeting bodies pass right through each other like blending puffs of cigarette smoke with practically no stars ever coming within a billion miles of one another. Instead, most of the clash is between the hydrogen and other gas molecules, usually including dust clouds, which are thus swept almost completely away from large star fields, causing great magnetic stress that can be heard in many parts of the sky (out to some six billion light-years) as the strongest radio signals known to be arriving from anywhere beyond Jupiter. One such source in Perseus, designated NGC 1275 (New General Catalog 1275), has turned out to be a head-on collision of a tightly spooled spiral and a large sprawling galaxy with wildly distorted arms. Another even louder signal has been appropriately diagnosed as a kind of swan song from Cygnus, transmitted by the unusually hard crash of two large galaxies that are so tightly inter-meshed at present it is hardly possible to say whether either one is spiral or elliptical. Several lesser encounters have been dis-covered in various stages of clashing, sideswiping, milk spilling or just swishing close enough to each other at 1,000 miles a second to draw out graceful whorls of visible bridge material, not to mention presumed ionic and magnetic arches millions of parsecs in length.

TWO GALAXIES IN PERSEUS
COLLIDING AT 2000 M.P.S.

NGC 1275

The only foreseeable outcome of all this macrocosmic evolution, according to the consensus of cosmologists, is the ultimate consolidation of all matter into collapsed galaxies made up of "dead" stars, the so-called "heat death" ordained by the supposedly immutable law of entropy, under which all energy must eventually be distributed evenly everywhere, with nothing warmer or cooler than anything else and only tepid corpses of worlds floating listlessly, perhaps at greater and greater distances apart, thus rendering any encounter between them less and less possible.

White-dwarf stars like Sirius B are already practically dead and have little to look forward to but continued cooling off until they are red dwarfs and finally black ones drifting invisibly onward to an unknown future — perhaps very slowly decaying into some kind of ash or exhalation to be recirculated eventually back into the still-far-from-understood basic metabolism of the universe. It has been estimated that a good 20 percent of all stars are now in the corpse stage, buried in vacuous darkness here and there among their gay comrades even as the cemetery dwellers of earthly cities, and that the larger systems are settling into their own forms of rigor mortis. Globular clusters, for instance, may be the only remains of once-giddy young eddies of gas that condensed into spinning nebulae and eventually into small elliptical galaxies or satellites of galaxies that somehow wasted down to these cores. Gamow points out the fossil role probably played by all star systems in perpetuating the dynamic forms of primordial gas clouds, that, like pre-Cambrian seaworms, have long since been replaced by more durable solids faithfully delineating each detail of their departed bodies.

★ ∞ ★ ∞ ★

But even fossils do not last forever. Nor, for all we know, do universes of fossils. Nor perhaps even fossil universes of the third or higher orders. Which brings us to the ultimate material questions: what part of what whole is our universe? What is the over-all event that it seems to be part of? Where do space and time lead to? Is the universe resting in equilibrium, or is it going somewhere or doing something?

If you assume these questions to be beyond the scope of the human mind, you may be surprised to know that many scientists, including Einstein, have been doing solid work on them and, in the opinion of some, have already nibbled at the answers. Although we must wait until Chapter 13 before going into the basic nature of space and time, it can be said here that in the days of World War I Einstein concluded that, although a lot is obviously happening in the turbulent sky, the universe as a whole must be unchanging. In order to reach any conclusion, however, he had found it necessary to assume that gravity was opposed by a great antigravity force of repulsion, which he named the "cosmological constant" and designated by the Greek lambda, Λ, a kind of mathematical joker in the pack of eternity.

And then, only a few years later, in 1922, two major revelations convinced Einstein that cosmic repulsion was not a sound or necessary postulation after all. He frankly referred to Λ as "the biggest blunder of my life." For not only had the Russian mathematician Alexander Friedmann discovered a flaw in the jungle of equations, which might permit the theoretical "static" universe to swell or shrink despite Λ, but also Edwin Hubble, the American astronomer, had found the first observational evidence that the real universe is in fact swelling very rapidly, though not necessarily very evenly.

This Hubble did through the aforementioned doppler principle, measuring the recession of galaxies spectroscopically by the reduced pitch of their light frequency. In this remarkable way, he and his successors proved conclusively that although galaxies themselves are not measurably expanding, the distance between them is increasing on the average all over the sky. The effect of this is to find greater and greater speeds away from ourselves as we measure more and more remote galaxies, the amount being expressed by Hubble's "distance law," which says that the distance of any galaxy in millions of light-years multiplied by 105 gives its recessional velocity in miles per second. In other words, the whole known universe is literally flying apart, its outward motion reaching a major fraction of the velocity of light at the extreme limit of visibility and radio detection in every direction — amounting to an explosion the violence and magnitude of which could hardly begin to be approximated by the wildest human imagination!

Of course, it is only the scale of this cosmic phenomenon that conceals it from our earthly sense and permits us the paradox of celestial peace under "fixed" stars in a bursting universe. For galactic recession is now as accepted among astronomers as the circling of the moon about the earth. Indeed, mathematics thrives on paradoxes and can usually assimilate the implications of anything that can be measured. So the most obvious logical inference from cosmic expansion soon resulted in the hypothesis of a Belgian prelate, the Abbé Georges Lemaître, that all the receding galaxies must have once been massed together in an immensely dense primeval nucleus, a kind of unhatched egg of the universe. As developed further by Sir Arthur Eddington, Paul Adrien Maurice Dirac, George Gamow and other physicists, each cubic centimeter of such a nucleus (which Gamow calls *ylem*, from Aristotle's word for primordial substance) must have "contained at that time a hundred million tons of matter" composed mainly of photons and neutrons in an unorganized ionic state of stupendous pressure at a temperature of nearly a trillion degrees. Being a state of an assumed infinite universe, this so-called nucleus, of course, also had to be infinite in volume, and therefore cannot be imaginable as having been contained within any surface or limit. You might think of it as the manifestation of a supreme compression of endless matter, or perhaps as the peak of some cosmic wave of unimaginable dimensions that reached a node and rebounded. If time existed before the ylem, Gamow suggests calling it "Saint Augustine's era" after the man who took up the question of "what God was doing before He made heaven and earth." But it is doubted whether any material trace of such a period of prehistory could possibly have survived in any form as highly organized as hydrogen, and the survival prospect of even microscopic quantities of Augustinian heavy elements, if there ever were any, is considered less than unlikely. To put it mildly, according to the Lemaître theory the universe's material slate was wiped clean at the time of the Big Squeeze — now judged to have been roughly around the years eight to ten billion B.C., which nicely fits the well-substantiated estimate of the earth's age as close to five billion years — and we are today in a completely new cosmic generation freshly fledged and individual unto ourselves.

And the little men of the new earth, probably like beings on any planet anywhere anywhen, are trying to make what they can out of all the stimulating complexities that keep sprouting around them, including the fundamental abstract questions that obviously lurk behind the surface foliage. E. A. Milne, for instance, says the radius of the exploding universe is simply the velocity of light times its age. Dirac, for his part, has offered that the mass of the universe is the square of universal time measured in units of the interval required for a light ray to cross the diameter of an electron. And Gamow has declared that the temperature of the universe can always be approximated by dividing 25 billion degrees (F.) by the square root of the number of seconds since the day of ylem. He goes on from there to explain that although radiation was much more important (being incomparably more massive) than matter in the hot early days of the universe's explosion, by the time the universe was 250 million years old and had cooled off to an average temperature of some 150° F. below zero, the reign of radiation gave way to the reign of matter. No longer content to remain hidden and dissolved in radiation, matter at last began to condense and gravitate, and the new relative massiveness of matter was what made gravitation important and started the elaborate processes of gas concentration into clouds that ultimately spawned the stars and built the world we now know.

The wonder of all such reasoning made even Eddington confess, "The theory of the exploding universe is in some respects so preposterous that . . . I feel almost an indignation that anyone should believe it — except myself."

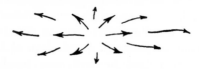

If looking backward from our explosion created the theory of the Big Squeeze, what can be found by looking forward? Are the receding galaxies bound to keep on accelerating with distance until they attain the speed of light and actually slip over the horizon of knowability because their radiation no longer has power to get back to us? The preponderance of thought seems to accept something of this kind as probably inevitable. And by figuring the momentum of galaxies the same way one figures the momentum of rockets fired up from the earth, it turns out that the galaxies are indeed fleeing from each other at seven times their escape velocity, which means they must have overcome intergalactic gravity by a wide margin and therefore cannot be expected ever to return together again.

The potential loophole in this calculation, of course, is that it is based on the assumption that galaxies constitute the main mass of the universe. So if the supposedly very thin hydrogen of intergalactic space should somehow prove to contain more than seven times as much mass as the galaxies, then the galaxies would not be escaping after all but would eventually slow down to a stop like a spent rocket and fall back to one another. This might produce a kind of pulsating or bouncing universe that would alternately expand and contract like a lung or a beating heart, as distinct from the so-called hyperbolic universe that must expand without limit. The latter universe, according to the "purest" mathematical requirement, must also have contracted (before the Big Squeeze) from "an infinitely thin state an eternity ago," the two sides of the Squeeze holding a mysterious mirror symmetry to each other — an implosion-explosion, involution-evolution balance that can be compared with the approach and departure of a comet and may ultimately provide the key to an understanding of time.

Still another possibility is the steady-state universe suggested first by the two English mathematicians, Hermann Bondi and Thomas Gold, then enthusiastically developed in a slightly different direction by Fred Hoyle. This theory proposes a new "cosmological principle: namely that the large-scale features of the universe are the same not only from every point of view in *space* but also from every point of view in *time*." In other words, although stars and galaxies evolve, the cosmos as a whole stays the same, its average density and energy maintaining a perfect, symmetrical equilibrium. To the question of what replaces the matter of the galaxies as they keep flying away from each other, the Bondi-Gold-Hoyle answer is: new matter is continuously and spontaneously being created everywhere at the benign rate of one atom of hydrogen in each quart of space every billion years or (which is the same thing) one atom in each cubic mile of space every hour. This creative pace was arrived at by careful calculation not only of the rate of "overflow" of matter through "the outer edge" of the expanding universe but of the rate of consumption of raw hydrogen in the condensation of primordial clouds into new galaxies. When the two rates turned out to be virtually equal, Bondi and Gold were convinced of the reality of hydrogen creation and soon began to explain the universe's expansion as an inevitable consequence of the creative pressure, while Hoyle modified the Einstein relativity equations to develop this providential interaction into a mathematical "feedback" relationship that automatically stabilizes "the mean density of matter" everywhere. The boldly postulated crea-

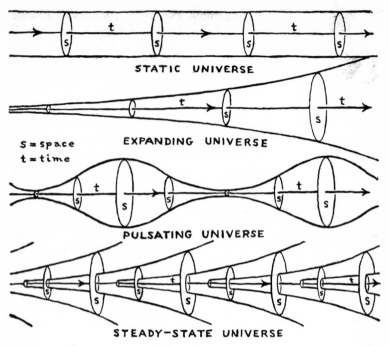

STATIC UNIVERSE

S = space

t = time

EXPANDING UNIVERSE

PULSATING UNIVERSE

STEADY-STATE UNIVERSE

SPACE-TIME RELATIONS OF THEORETICAL UNIVERSES

tion of hydrogen out of nothing has not bothered him or his colleagues a bit for, as he says, all cosmologies and philosophies require some kind of creation simply because the universe exists, and why should it be any harder to believe that hydrogen "just appears" continuously than that it was created all at once at a grand beginning eight billion years ago? Or, for that matter, why should the creation of atoms between galaxies be more mysterious than the creation of space between galaxies, which we have already accepted without undue fuss?

All things being mysterious in essence, the most serious obstacle to acceptance of the steady-state universe has turned out to be not so much its continuous creation as its dearth of evolution. For two American astronomers, Joel Stebbins and Albert Whitford, in 1948 carefully measured the reddening of light from distant galaxies through light filters of different colors and, to everyone's surprise, discovered that the light from very remote elliptical galaxies was reddened about 50 percent more than could be accounted for by the red-shift effect of recession, while the light from equally distant spiral galaxies had reddened only by the expected doppler amount. Obviously this disparate reddening of the elliptical galaxies could not be caused by any general factor such as dust in the intervening space, which should affect all equidistant galaxies impartially, so many astronomers have accepted the only other explanation in sight: that the excessive reddening of the old elliptical galaxies occurs because we see them now as they were a billion years ago when they were intrinsically redder from the light of supergiant red stars flaring up in that fitful period of their decay. The spiral galaxies on the other hand, nearer the prime of life, have presumably not changed their appearance much in a billion years, for they are growing as well as decaying and their virile dust clouds are still spawning new stars. It is rather the elliptical ones, crystallized, dust-free, sterile and fading, that are undergoing the "change of life" that spells a measurable decline — thereby demonstrating evolution on the grand scale. And such an evolution is supported also by the recent findings that remote galaxies recede faster than proportionate to their relative distance (under the distance law) and have more frequent collisions than nearer galaxies, indicating that when the light we see left those galaxies long long ago, the universe was expanding faster than now and its parts were in closer contact with each other. Though still not conclusive, such strong hints that evolution is not confined to the earth or even to the Milky Way but has its mystic counterpart in the farthest reaches of the universe have gained enough acceptance to impress even Fred Hoyle as "the most serious potential contradiction of the steady-state theory."

Perhaps these and similar issues relating to the tangible cosmos may remain unresolved for a long time, but the enigma of what lies beyond all sight and radio detection or any kind of physical measurement is even more profound, for it deals with a world entirely beyond the sensible — undoubtedly to a great but unknown extent beyond the capacity of the human mind. We can imagine that, when electronic amplification is perfected and applied to great telescopes erected up here on space stations well above the turbulent air, galaxies ten billion light-years away will come within visual range. But, according to extrapolation of the distance law, if they were ten billion light-years away when their light started toward us they would have to be more than twenty billion light-years away now (assuming they still exist as part of the material universe) and receding at more than the speed of light, which the accepted theory of relativity says no material object can do. So even visible objects, just by drifting along, may become only imaginary before their visibility is manifest. And anything any farther off might easily miss even being thought of!

As for the question of whether our universe is a closed system contained within any kind of material limits at all (perhaps what

THE BASIC GEOMETRY OF FINITE WORLDS

number of dimensions	bounded	unbounded
1	a line that ends	an endless line
2	a flat plane	a closed surface
3	a volume	an endless volume

geometricians call finite but unbounded) or whether it is in some geometric sense truly infinite — with a horizon but not an end — that is the kind of abstraction Einstein took on in his general theory of relativity, which deals with the curvature of space and helps modern cosmologists in their search for evidence as to whether our universe curves positively and finitely inward like a sphere or negatively outward like an infinite saddle. But we must hold off most of this abstruse and tantalizing subject until Chapter 13.

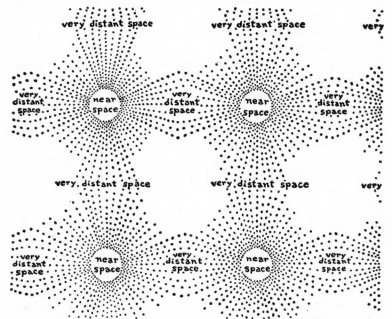

ONE MODEL OF THE ULTIMATE GRAIN OF THE UNIVERSE

Suffice it to say here that nature seems deliberately to be forcing upon us the doctrine of mysticism. For we appear to have been endowed only with finite minds that conceive of neither an end to space nor of space without end. In essence, we have been planted like seeds of blind faith in the midst of a basically nourishing medium that is nevertheless, to our present capacity, inconceivable.

Under such circumstances, it would seem arrogant in the extreme to let ourselves think we had seen or dreamed of even one millionth of one percent of the scope of all that lies around us. As every mathematician knows, the smallest percentage of infinity is still infinity. So how can we pretend to speak learnedly of the universe? Or think of astronomy as an exact science?

From where I drift, astronomy in the large is no more predictable than a card game, no more exact than a horse-race. It only seems exact in the narrow view. If you actually picked out one horse during a race and analyzed its gait by slow-motion camera over a distance of twenty yards, without any further knowledge of the race, probably horse-racing would appear as exact as astronomy is popularly supposed to be. By timing the animal's leg motions carefully, you could predict within a hundredth of a second when each hoof would next strike the turf — just as the astronomer predicts an eclipse. But if your perspective never took in more than a few cycles of the gait of one horse, obviously you would not know much about horse-racing.

Now a metagalaxy or the whole visible universe can be compared to a single horse in the race — or to a hoof of that horse — or perhaps only to an electron in a molecule in the hoof. Study of the metagalaxy over many centuries might give earthly astronomers just a hint that there was a hoof. But knowledge of the entire gait of the horse would probably have to await very advanced space travel and telescopic development beyond our wildest plans, to say nothing of hundreds of millenniums of recorded observation. Conception of the horse's position relative to other horses, of the final outcome of the race or of the race's significance to the community around it would be so far beyond the potentiality of humanity that it could not be considered of our world. Only some ultimate synthesis of soul knowledge could pronounce the winner or begin to comprehend the reaction of the inconceivable public at large.

As it takes perspective to gain perspective, it will be a long bootstrap climb upward from man's present celestial outlook to one as relatively comprehending as that of a baby attending the circus. Indeed, the frankest acceptance of modern cosmology's limitations is vital to our progress through this firmament paved and ceiled with mystery from before the eldest dawn until long after the youngest night, from higher than the zenith to lower than the nadir, even from far far beyond all the horizons of radiation or gravity or thought.

Ylem and self-seeding hydrogen and every other swig of the Bacchanalia of current cosmic hypotheses seems to me to suffer from an insufficient allowance for the unknown — for the limitless complex of possibilities beyond measurement or sense. In actual fact, why could not the universe be expanding just because eternity is nonsymmetrical? Or because what we see is only part of some great supercosmic bubble that is unaccountably in ferment, perhaps literally an eddy of some much vaster turbulence or willfulness? Or maybe even an ingredient in the outer dynamic equivalent of a stew or a storm or a web or a wish in the unknowable macrocosm? After all, the wagon wheel feels only one small part of the road. Yet all the road is there.

Far from a depressing thought, this enhumbling of the known is relatively and really an enlargement of the whole and an enhancement of our total potentiality. For "day unto day uttereth speech and night unto night sheweth knowledge," and the wisdom of the stars is the wisdom of man who, in spite of himself, is indirectly but materially made of stars. Even man's glorious going forth into space is as nothing to the greater glory of space's coming to man in return — to acquaint him with "the ordinances of heaven" that, better than Job, he may someday "set the dominion thereof in the earth" and in all habitable creation.

fields in space,
deeps of time

9. stuff of the worlds

IF MY STATION HERE in the black heights is good for stargazing, I think it may also offer a fresh perspective upon the fine texture of the smaller things of the universe. For we have a fairly complete little world of our own out here, populated with eighteen men, two women, four hamsters and a canary. To say nothing of probable bird lice and God knows how many other species of insects, microbes and viruses.

True, it is not as independent a world as the earth itself, but still, it is provisioned with ample atmosphere for its needs, with circulating liquids, and structural solids of many kinds, including all the common elements, most metals and virtually every important alloy and planetary compound — not to mention the intermittent meteoric intruders that suggestively rap and spark upon our outer shell like the symbolic knuckles of nature reminding us that she is at least as eager as we for a wider opening of the door of knowledge.

When I was a child I used to think that little things were simpler than big things, but one day, wandering in the woods, I suddenly understood that the smallness of an acorn may not really make it any simpler than the oak, for it as surely contains oaks as the oak contains acorns. And ever since then, whenever space outside our world of sense seems more important or more impressive than space within the atom, I can remind myself that the differences are only relative and almost certainly illusory. Are not the crystal world of the snowflake and the symmetrical lattice of metal as real as a comet or the Milky Way? And what of the wild microscopic jungles of yeasts and bacteria that have been making bread and cheese and wine since long before man could understand fermentation? Who are we to tell our genes what they may grow or our flesh its rate of metabolism? Can an emperor banish a case of sniffles? Is the elephant master of the mouse?

To grasp the meaning of size, one must consider the fact that outer space after all is made of nothing but inner space even as great Babylon was built of little bricks or a whale is outnumbered by its billions of invisible cells. Nor is inner space closer to our reach than outer space, paradoxical though this may appear, for its true dimensions and dynamic laws are even less understood than the more classic forces of the universe outside. In actuality, both kinds of space pervade our entire world, and as truly as the great suns of the remote sky radiate with the vibrations of their atomic parts do the orbits of our inmost structure add up to the amazing complexity and bulk of this material universe.

If we arrange a scale of sizes to give precise form to our thinking on this basic aspect of space, it turns out that a simple logarithmic spectrum or sequence of a hundred and fifty intervals just about covers our whole knowable world if we let each unit interval on the scale represent ten times the volume of the unit just below it and one tenth that of the unit next above. In linear dimensions thus each unit would come out $\sqrt[3]{10}$ or 2.15 times as long or wide or deep as the one below. And if we set the size of a grapeseed at magnitude 50, a third of the way up the scale, and the size of a solar system at magnitude 100, two thirds of the way, the entire deduced universe appears approximately at the 150 mark and the smallest size we could reasonably expect to measure (perhaps of some still unknown field entity) is somewhere around the zero point. Some physicists, indeed, would go so far as to say that such are the actual approximate limits of material reality: that there is in fact no distance as short as a quintillionth of an inch and literally no room for anything outside the finite but unbounded universe. In any case, the spectrum nicely encompasses and correlates our whole consciousness of space, with some to spare, balancing the macrocosm against the microcosm so neatly upon the pivot of Earth that we can mentally dance up its entire staircase ten steps at a time for a skip check of the key size stones of creation.

Starting down near step 10, for example, we are at about the size of an electron or proton, and perhaps other basic components out of which all atoms are made. At step 20 (10^{10} or ten billion times larger of volume) we can begin to see the inner shell of a small atom, at step 30 a molecule, at step 40 the virus or borderline of life, at step 50 a grapeseed and at step 60 a man. From the individual man we jump to step 70 for the sum bulk of all mankind (several billion individuals) conceived as concentrated into a cubic kilometer — and, passing the scale's asteroid-sized mid-point, to step 80, which is about the size of an average moon. Then on to step 90 for the sun, a medium star, to step 100 for a smallish planetary system around a star, to step 110 for a binary or multiple-star system (about one light-year in diameter), step 120 for a globular cluster of stars, step

Volumes in powers of a minimal unit volume	Object examples	Linear distances	Diameters in meters
150	possible universe (?)		10^{27}
	spherical "horizon" of knowledge		
140	a group of supergalaxies	one billion light-years . .	10^{24}
	supergalaxy		
	minor group of galaxies	one megaparsec	
130	large galaxy	one million light-years . .	10^{21}
	small galaxy		
	galactic satellite cluster	one kiloparsec	
120	globular cluster of stars	one thousand light-years .	10^{18}
	distance to Regulus		
	distance to nearest star	one parsec	
110	multiple star system	one light-year	10^{15}
	inner reservoir of comets		
	orbit of Pluto		
100	orbit of Jupiter	one billion kilometers. . .	10^{12}
	orbit of the earth		
	outer corona of the sun		
90	the sun (an average star)	one million kilometers . .	10^{9}
	Jupiter (a large planet)		
	the earth		
80	average moon	one thousand kilometers .	10^{6}
	large asteroid		
	medium asteroid or mountain		
70	all mankind (a cubic kilometer)	one kilometer . . .	10^{3}
	great pyramid		
	whale		
60	man (a cubic meter)	one meter	1
	grapefruit		
	cherry	one centimeter	
50	grapeseed (a cubic millimeter)	one millimeter . . .	10^{-3}
	flea or grain of sand		
	ovum or dust particle		
40	bacterium	one micron	10^{-6}
	virus		
	protein molecule		
30	sugar molecule	one millimicron . . .	10^{-9}
	atom	one angstrom (10^{-10}m.)	
20	inner atom	one thousand fermis . .	10^{-12}
	atomic nucleus		
10	elementary particle	one fermi . . .	10^{-15}
0	possible field entity (?)		10^{-18}

130 for a large galaxy, step 140 for a group of supergalaxies and step 150 for the deduced possible finite universe.

This scale is a fair approximation of reality according to our present state of scientific knowledge. It shows that a thimbleful of water is only midway between an H_2O molecule and the oceans, so that if you should dump a thimble of water into Liverpool Harbor today and wait a few years for thorough diffusion, you probably could not dip a thimbleful out of the Strait of Magellan or Tokyo Bay without its including at least a few molecules of the same water. It reveals that as the sun is to the moon, so does the mountain loom above the elephant and the whale appear to the rat, the flea to the amoeba, the bacillus to the virus, or the protein molecule to the atom.

But of course, these comparisons are only a starting point for the study of form and function, which relate in many curious ways to size. Perhaps you think a small model can be made to behave just like a full-scale machine. But have you ever wondered why pumpkins grow upon the ground instead of dangling on vines like grapes? Why bones are 18 percent of a man but only 8 percent of a mouse? The great Scottish biomathematician D'Arcy Thompson went so far as to say "the form of an object is defined when we know its magnitude," and he developed Galileo's famous "Principle of Similitude" to show how the geometrizing of God applies without exception to everything in nature. Galileo was probably the first man to observe that trees on Earth cannot grow more than about three hundred feet high nor animals more than about a hundred feet long, while terrestrial buildings and conveyances are similarly limited by the fact that their supporting surfaces, having only two dimensions, cannot increase as fast as their weights, which, having volume, must expand in three dimensions.

For this basic reason, all engineers know that under conditions of earthly gravity a plank that nicely spans a brook cannot be made to bridge a great river simply by increasing each of its dimensions a thousand times, not even if its wood be replaced with the strongest steel. For the solid rhombohedral weight would grow a thousand times more than the surface area and the span would inevitably bend and break under the burden of itself long before it attained the desired size. This is why great bridges must be so strictly limited in weight, so artfully designed to place their maximum strength precisely where strength is most needed, so delicately attuned to the graceful dictates of material magnitude.

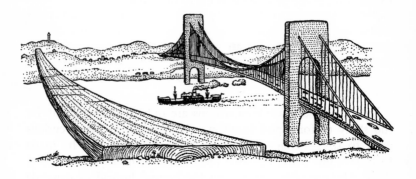

For the same reason, a paper model of an airplane that flies beautifully may turn into a flop when similarly made five times longer and out of cardboard. And it could well become a vehicle of tragic death in full-scale metal if it were not carefully adapted to its increased relative weight. There is no end to applications of the basic principle of similitude, which limits falling raindrops to a quarter-inch in diameter, keeps stars between 10^{32} and 10^{35} grams in mass, and prevents the elephant (if he ever should jump) from jumping higher than the flea. Great worlds, we have found, collide on the planetary scale not with a thud but a ponderous splash, and on the stellar scale with a long-drawn flash. Yet because gravity and other natural forces have very different values on different scales, a raindrop is not made round by the same influence that bulges the earthly oceans.

Indeed, things as small as raindrops begin to follow noticeably the principles of the lesser worlds where electromagnetism ultimately replaces gravity and where friction and surface tension and molecular vibrations grow rapidly from minor annoyances to overwhelming forces as we approach the utterly fantastic realm of the atom. That is why a moon can burst and crumble so easily through its weak surface, while most cells of your body, similarly round, are virtually indestructible within their tough integument, knit together by practically nothing but surface energy.

The surface of a great tree, by contrast, is quite relaxed in its widespread leaves, which are made necessary by its having far too much mass to be able to absorb enough sun energy through a simple spherical surface. Thus its form and beauty are geometric aspects of its magnitude, as is the human lung an effective means of greatly increasing the oxygen-absorbing surface of your body.

Such complicated solutions to the energy problem become less and less necessary as bulk diminishes. Insects do not need lungs, nor do algae require leaves. When an animal is smaller than a flea, its body tends quite noticeably toward the spherical, the shape with the simplest and smallest surface — a shape that is in large measure due to the increasing importance of surface tension as size diminishes. It is here in the upper microscopic size range that surfaces get to be the major structural members of all creatures and objects, right down to the world of molecules. Moreover, surfaces include internal ones such as the inner surface of a cell as well as its outer, both of which are intense zones of energy. A particularly surprising manifestation of surface tension is the fact that waves and ripples on the ocean move more and more slowly as they diminish in size down to a wave length of about three fourths of an inch, but below that critical point the relative power of their surface forces begins to move them faster and faster the tinier they become!

Surface tension is perhaps best described as the kind of energy

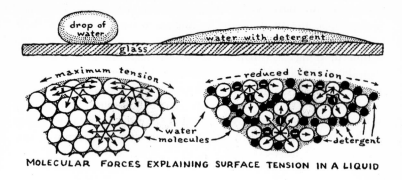

MOLECULAR FORCES EXPLAINING SURFACE TENSION IN A LIQUID

that gives exaggerated strength to any interface between a liquid, a gas or a solid and enables some bugs to walk on water, imprisons others in a drop and makes possible the capillary action of wicks and blotters. It was first described by Laplace as "the cumulative effect, the statistical average, of countless molecular attractions." More specifically, it is now known to result from the fact that the molecules at a surface are pulled harder toward the sides of their fellow molecules than toward the remoter alien molecules opposite them, thus giving them a kind of biased or polarized energy that might be compared to the fervor of patriotism at a national frontier in time of war. This surface stress naturally reaches its maximum influence in the size range of the colloids, between the magnitudes of bacteria and viruses, where the clannishness of these small-village-size gatherings of molecules attains a peak of intensity — where matter behaves in such a different way that a special field of study called colloid chemistry has arisen to deal with it. We must encounter these peculiar little gelatinous particles, in fact, whenever we look at the basic nature of life, for not only are colloids among the most complex of phenomena in the known inorganic world but the human body itself has been described as consisting essentially of "bundles of colloids soaked with water and strung around a bony framework to give form and support."

Although surface tension is a vital force below the range of $\frac{1}{500,000}$ of an inch, and films of oil knit together by it have

been measured to be as thin as ½₂₅,₀₀₀,₀₀₀ of an inch, the
surface energy of a spherical body close to molecular size varies
almost in proportion to its radius and tends to vanish when the
radius of a drop or particle is less than ½,₅₀₀,₀₀₀ of an inch
— just as the pressure of group loyalty may diminish in the
case of human gatherings of subfamily size. Smaller than this,
any material particle increasingly takes on the character of an
isolated individual molecule and eventually of a single atom,
where surface may no longer have much more meaning than does
the surface of a solar system.

BROWNIAN MOVEMENT

actual track of a
microscopic grain
floating in "still" water,
its positions plotted
at 30 second intervals

Long before this range of fineness is reached the macromolec-
ular vibration known as Brownian movement must be reckoned
with. Studied a little over a century ago by Robert Brown, the
English botanist, the mysterious quivering motion he descried
among crushed pollen grains in water and which others have
seen in milk, ink and in floating flakes of smoke, has since proved
to be due to the natural bombardment of molecules upon bodies
so small that these impacts do not average out. It is a basic
restlessness of matter in the size range that is still too large
to reveal the unimaginably frequent molecular collisions yet small
enough to feel their varying residual effects. Beginning just below naked-eye visibility, the motion is more and more noticeable right down to its maximum violence in the bacteria and
colloid magnitudes, where particles are slightly smaller than one
μ (mu) or micron (a millionth of a meter or about ½₂₅,₀₀₀
of an inch) in diameter.

In his famous book *On Growth and Form* D'Arcy Thompson
wrote that, in addition to their random quivering, Brownian
particles exhibit a straight back-and-forth motion as well as a
rotation that increases in rapidity with smallness, particles 13

μ in diameter turning on an average through 14° a minute while the 1μ particles rotate as fast as 100° a second. "The very curious result appears," he summed up, "that in a layer of fluid the particles are not evenly distributed, nor do they ever fall under the influence of gravity to the bottom. For here gravity and the Brownian movement are rival powers striving for equilibrium."

Along with this revelation of gravity's dependence on magnitude has come our new understanding of such concepts as the lower limit of flight. For just as there obviously is an upper limit to the size of birds and airplanes, which must in general double their airspeed to stay aloft after each quadrupling of their length, so does flight become more and more uncontrollable as any winged creature approaches the lowly size ranges of the hectic Brownian activity. The semimicroscopic fairy-fly, for example, probably the smallest living earthly flyer, has wings (or are they propellers?) only a millimeter long, made of nothing but a few hairs that whip the sticky molecules of air like eggbeaters in syrup. Although his weight is so slight in proportion to his surface that he probably notices no more pull of gravity than a man would notice while living on an asteroid, the fairy-fly must in effect fly through a kind of dust storm of swirling nitrogen and oxygen granules that are a ponderable obstacle to progress. And the invisible blizzard, of course, would mount relatively with any diminution in his magnitude, soon swallowing up the last traces of gravity and turning flying into swimming and swimming ultimately into digging at some stage far below the magnitudinal level where less-belabored progress could by any stretch of meaning be classified as flight.

With an effort of imagination we can thus picture a corpuscle or a molecule as living in the midst of a vast, bustling crowd, where temperature is expressed only in the average speed or excitement of the individuals around, and light shows itself in giant rainbows sweeping continuously over the surging populace in dazzling floods of pure color. From here, continuing on downward past this vibrant molecular range into atomic dimensions, we find great fields of electromagnetic pressure dominating the "planetary systems" of electrons and other atomic particles so completely that, according to modern calculation, the electrical force between a proton and an electron is 10^{39} (a thousand million million million million million million) times the gravitational force, the latter being far too feeble at this level to be measurable by any means yet known.

Thus the very laws of nature (in effect) turn out to change with magnitude, introducing almost incredible regions of the very big and the very small that are far stranger than anyone realized a century ago and that have scarcely begun to be understood even today. Although there are striking similarities between a plasma of whirling particles viewed through a microscope and a galaxy of whirling stars viewed through a telescope, this is probably just a rare parallel of form between one thing and another some 10,000,000,000,000,000,000,000,000,000,000,000,-000,000,000,000,000,000,000,000,000,000,000,000,000,000,-000,000,000,000,000,000 times bigger. Certainly it does not similarly happen that the wild beauty of a Himalayan glacier is noticeably suggested by the stylized charm of a magnified snow crystal, even though the glacier be materially composed of 1,000,000,000,-000,000,000,000,000 such symmetric gems of frozen H_2O. For not only is each individual crystal unique unto itself, but its very time-space relationship is so different from that of something a septillion times bigger that a glacier and a snow crystal must be to each other in many unobvious ways quite literally alien worlds.

In the magnitudes where life is apparent, time-space disparities, of course, express themselves quite eloquently in various rates of living. Not only does the velocity of a fish or a bird or a running mammal tend "to vary directly as the square root of its linear dimensions" by Froude's law of the correspondence of speeds, but the rhythm and tempo of its limbs and organs must change inversely with size in accord with Galileo's earlier principle of similitudes. The shortened pendulum of mouse muscle thus quickens to its smaller task, the whale's 10-pound heart pumps at a sedate eight beats a minute, the mayfly's lifetime may be bounded by a day and the marriage of the hummingbird is consummated in the wink of a human eye. One can measure such differentials also in oxygen consumed per body ounce per second or in relative production rates of carbon dioxide, both inverse to magnitude, while obviously they all abide by the general physical law of conservation of angular momentum which enlivens Saturn's inner ring, "fixes" the stars and in effect allows the quantitatively slower speed of a flying propeller to be much too fast to see.

As speed is the quotient of distance and time, here might be an appropriate place to introduce a time scale to match our scale of sizes: another simple logarithmic spectrum to show the basic temporal range of our world. This scale, as you can see, holds some fifty units of duration, each unit ten times as long as the unit just below it and extending about equally upward and downward from its mid-point: one second. Thus the scale's bottom is below a single proton revolution and its top somewhere above practically every estimated age of the universe. Since human consciousness has little natural awareness of time's shorter intervals, you may possibly be startled to notice that there is fully as much time difference between the durations of a light vibration and of a sound vibration as between a minute and a million years.

Before going deeper into the mysterious inner nature of our world, it may help to step back into the well-worn sandals of Leucippos, who lived in Abdera in Thrace in the fifth century before Christ, and consider his meditations while strolling upon a gray Aegean strand. He is said to have wondered aloud to his young pupil Democritos whether the water of the sea, which appears continuous in structure, could really be composed of

TIME SCALE OF THE UNIVERSE

Durations in seconds	Ages or periods of time
10^{25}	unknown outer limits of time
10^{20}	possible age of the universe (?)
	age of the earth (5 billion years)
	one revolution of the sun around the galaxy
10^{15}	age of younger mountain systems
	duration of human race (a million years)
	written history
10^{10}	age of a nation
	a year one revolution of earth around sun
	a month
10^{5}	a day one rotation of the earth
	an hour eating of a meal
	a minute taking of a breath
1	a second a heartbeat
	blink of an eye
	vibration period of audible sound
10^{-5}	a flash of lightning
	duration of a muon particle
	time for light to cross a room
10^{-10}	vibration period of radar
	time for an air molecule to spin once
	vibration period of infra-red radiation
10^{-15}	vibration period of visible light
	vibration period of x-rays
10^{-20}	vibration period of gamma rays
	time for a proton to revolve once in the nucleus of an atom
10^{-25}	unknown inner limits of time

separate, extremely tiny grains like the beach, which, at first glance, likewise appears continuous.

"I can divide it into drops," he observed, "and then I can divide each drop into smaller drops. Is there any reason why this process of subdivision cannot continue forever?" If it continues without end, of course, there will be no end of drops or smaller things — but at some degree of smallness the things must pass from the known into the unknown, then from the knowable into the unknowable or, depending on definition, from the tangible into the intangible, mayhap even from the concrete into the abstract, yet not — heaven preserve our reason — not quite from the something into the nothing.

In any case, it was the kind of question Greek philosophers liked to discuss, for they were strangely drawn to the fundamental mysteries. But no one knew of any experiment by which to test it. Instead, by deep intuition alone, Leucippos, and later Democritos, concluded that there must be a limit to the subdivision of any material — that somewhere there must be "parts which are partless" and that the world is therefore made of ultimately indivisible or "a-tomic" grains that are nothing but themselves in a state of constant motion and which, by being

at various times and places packed densely together or spread
thinly apart, compose and decompose the four classic elements
of fire, air, water and earth, besides all the compound materials
of the world.

Leucippos assumed that the forms of such atoms were infinite
in number since there was "no reason why they should be of
one kind rather than another" and because he observed an "unceasing becoming and change in things." Democritos more specifically defined them as identical in substance though different
in shape, order and position — three differences which he attributed to rhythm, interconnection and spin respectively. This
amazingly modern hypothesis included also the principle of conservation of matter, since the atoms themselves were considered
hard to the point of being absolutely indestructible, and all
chemical changes in all minerals, vegetables and animals were
therefore due to the unceasing aggregation and disaggregation
of these constituent grains in their limitless combinations.

A growing tree, to Democritos, must thus somehow join together the earth atoms and water atoms of the soil with fire
atoms from sunrays to produce the more highly organized material of wood — a line of reasoning quite close to the modern,
as it turns out, even though he underrated the air, which, as
we have recently discovered, gives all plants the great bulk of
their growing material in the form of oxygen and carbon. Certainly the Greek atomic school with its abstract imagination was
more advanced than the Chinese science of the period, which
did not consider air as part of the material world at all, having
adopted instead the five rather arbitrary elements of fire, water,
wood, earth and metal.

Of course, comprehension of the inner nature of anything as
subtle as wind or fire could not be expected before a long period
of accumulating odd facts and testing wild surmises. Even Galileo

two millenniums later, with his new microscope that made fleas look "as big as rabbits," was not able to contribute anything significant to atomic knowledge. It was not until the work of Christian Huygens, Wilhelm Leibniz, Robert Boyle and particularly Daniel Bernoulli, who published his kinetic theory of gases in the famous book *Hydrodynamica* in 1738, that the reality of atoms and molecules could be demonstrated mathematically as *pressure* — the combined hammering of a "practically infinite" number of invisibly small corpuscles composing a gas as they are "driven hither and thither with a very rapid motion," their myriad collisions literally adding up to a steady outward push in all directions. And heat, Bernoulli showed, was just another aspect of the same motion, the temperature always rising in direct proportion to the "increasing internal movement of the particles."

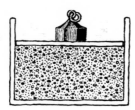

GAS MODEL FROM
BERNOULLI'S HYDRODYNAMICA

1738

This was a significant break in the old stagnation of alchemy, that shadowy pre-science with which soothsayers and witch doctors, borrowing freely from astrology, religious ritual and hieroglyphic symbols, had long influenced kings and generals, searching deviously for the elixir of life and the inner relationships between sunshine and gold, for the seeds of silver in moonlight. One enthusiastic alchemist is reported to have experimented two full years with a thousand eggs, trying to synthesize gold, methodically writing down the data of every tested combination in mystic symbols only he could understand.

By the 1770's, however, the growing list of known chemically irreducible elements numbered nearly twenty, and the fundamental stuff of the world was increasingly being sorted out. To the classic materials of gold, silver, copper, iron, mercury, lead,

♌ ♀ ♎ ♂ ♄ ☿ ☽ ♁ ♃
As Cu Au Fe Pb Hg Ag S Sn

tin, sulfur and carbon, a German physician had added flaky, metallic antimony in 1492 and another German described the reddish-white metal, bismuth, in 1530. These were followed by zinc, phosphorus (seen glowing in urine), arsenic and cobalt (named for the German mine goblin known as a *kobold*). In 1735 a strange heavy nugget from Colombia was designated as platinum; later, a lustrous metal was isolated as nickel.

It was not long after this that an astonishingly buoyant and invisible gas was discovered by Henry Cavendish in England while he was dissolving metal in acid. Described first as "inflammable air," then later named hydrogen, it paved the way for the age of ballooning, by which time another gas, much heavier and evidently endowed with the mysterious essence of life, had been separated from air by Carl Wilhelm Scheele of Sweden in 1771 and Joseph Priestley of England in 1774. Discovery of the latter vital element, soon to be named oxygen, inevitably revealed also the large inactive residue in air that we now know as nitrogen.

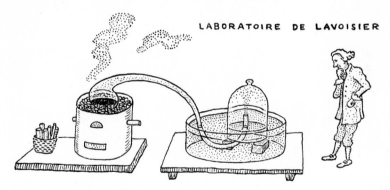

LABORATOIRE DE LAVOISIER

More important still, in the laboratory of a brilliant young French chemist, Antoine Laurent Lavoisier, who was studying combustion and the "calcination" (oxidation) of metals, all three of these strange invisible gases revealed their true places in the elemental scheme of nature. Learning from Cavendish that the burning of hydrogen produced pure water and knowing from his own experiments that combustion is the chemical joining of a burning substance with oxygen, Lavoisier correctly reasoned that water must be a compound of the two invisible elements, hydrogen and oxygen.

Unbelievable as it seemed at first, this conclusion threw so clear a light into so many old dark corners that it was speedily accepted by leading scientists everywhere. By the 1780's it had revolutionized related fields so completely that without any doubt it formed the keystone to a whole new edifice of science. Ultimately, it was to earn Lavoisier world fame as the father of modern chemistry, although by 1794 he had suffered the ironical fate of death under the guillotine at the hands of the fanatical Revolutionary Tribunal, whose members were incapable of appreciating the greatest scientist their country had ever produced.

Not least of his discoveries about oxygen, I must mention, is the fact that animal heat is generated by breathing, which produces a kind of living combustion whose rate is intermediate between the much faster burning of ignited fuel and the vastly slower rusting of iron or rotting of wood, all four forms of oxidation being essentially the same process at differing tempos.

Through still another of Lavoisier's far-ranging activities, the very words "oxygen," "hydrogen" and "nitrogen" soon became universally adopted, signalizing the introduction of a new standard terminology of science that he knew would be essential to orderly thinking if chemistry was to develop. Thus today the dominant or metallic element in a binary compound is, by common acceptance, always named first, and the second one is abbreviated with the suffix -ide, as in iron oxide (rust), sodium chloride (salt) or hydrogen sulfide (rotten-egg gas). Different quantities or bonding patterns are systematically indicated by such prefixes as mon- in carbon monoxide or suffixes like -ic, -ous and -ate in nitric oxide, ferrous ammonium sulfate, and so forth, each term part of the integrated system of nomenclature that renders its relationships obvious to anyone with a modicum of chemical acquaintance.

By the turn of the nineteenth century, the list of elements had been further enriched by the discovery of chlorine, manganese, tungsten, chromium, molybdenum, titanium, tellurium, zirconium and uranium. And by 1869, a total of 63 elements had been isolated and described, including one that Joseph Norman Lockyer had found the year before by spectroscope not on Earth but, surprisingly, on the sun. Called helium after the Greek "sun," this inert gas, which is the second lightest of all elements, was not to be found in our world until William Hillebrand of the United States Geological Survey came across it in the rare mineral cleveite in 1890.

☉ ☽ ● ○ ⊗ ⊕ ✳ ◎

Meantime, by a feat even more astonishing than learning about earthly material from our parent star 93 million miles away, three completely unknown elements were predicted in detail by a wild-haired Russian in 1869, simply through abstract deduction from the generalized relationships of the 63 already accepted elements. His name was Dimitri Ivanovich Mendeleyev, and he announced from Siberia, "There is an element as yet undiscovered. I have named it eka-aluminum. By properties similar to those of the metal aluminum you shall identify it. Seek it, and it will be found."

This sounded like an arrogant guess to most scientists at the time, even though a London consulting chemist named John

Dimitri Ivanovich Mendeleyev
1834 – 1907

Newlands had recently formulated an intuitive "law of octaves" to explain why the elements, when numbered in the order of their atomic weights, tended to repeat fairly similar properties at every seventh element like notes in the musical scale. But Mendeleyev had not reverted to the mystic methods of Pythagoras nor was he swayed by any suggestive analogy to the "seven planets" or the days of the week.

His music of the elements was tuned instead to quite modern concepts of observation, experiment and deduction. Ever since the famous John Dalton had established in 1807 that every chemical combination takes place only in its particular and precise weight proportions, the reality of atoms of different weights (as implied by Leucippos) had been accepted by science. The atoms of the known elements had been carefully weighed and measured by such means as hammering gold leaf to a thinness of one atomic diameter or spreading films of oil to their own definite limits, on the logic that no layer of material can become less than one atom or molecule (or other basic unit) thick and remain the same material. How could a layer of alarm clocks or chicks, for example, be reduced to half a clock or a half-chick in depth without a very drastic change in its nature? Thus a drop of oil one millimeter (about ½₅ of an inch) in diameter was found able to spread out over an area of nearly one square meter (a million square millimeters) before its film began to break, showing its molecules must be around one millionth of a millimeter thick.

This and more advanced types of reasoning had inevitably led Mendeleyev to realize that the most abundant elements (oxygen, silicon, aluminum, iron, calcium, sodium, potassium, magnesium, hydrogen, etc.) have small atomic weights and that those chemically similar to each other have weights either close in value (like platinum, iridium, osmium) or increasing in regular octaves (such as potassium, rubidium and cesium). From here it was just a matter of time for him to work out a Periodic Table of the elements that so clearly revealed harmonic relationships that he could confidently predict what several of the still undiscovered ones must be like. Even though Julius Lothar Meyer, a German chemist, had also (as often happens) independently conceived the same Periodic Law in almost identical form at about the same time, it was Mendeleyev's dramatic forecast of three unknown elements that won him immortal fame as the prophet of periodic chemistry who had enabled this strange new microscience to challenge respectable astronomy in oracular potency. For, sure enough, in the 1870's all of the Russian's prophecies came true as three new elements were discovered in France, Germany and Scandinavia on Mendelevian clues and named for their respective birthplaces gallium, germanium and scandium.

From then on the knowledge of our world stuff has rapidly accumulated. Chemists everywhere were awed to find that all the very active alkaline metallic elements forming group one of the Periodic Table (lithium, sodium, potassium, etc.) always united with oxygen in the strict proportion of two atoms to one, all the second group of elements oxidized atom for atom, the third group joined oxygen at the rate of two atoms to three — and each group in general became more acid and less metallic, going toward the seventh group of so-called halogens (fluorine, chlorine. . .). All of which expressed a mystic inner order of nature more beautiful than anyone could have anticipated — and which became increasingly obvious even though no scientist could yet say what gave elements their valence (combining power) or what an atom was really like.

⬤ ⬤ ⊙ ⊙ ⊛

Then as the number of known elements approached 80, the mystery was suddenly heightened in 1894 when two Englishmen, following a hint from Henry Cavendish, turned up a whole new group of invisible, impalpable elements that baffled even Mendeleyev. Later named the Zero Group, these queer inert, tasteless gases turned out to be the most unsociable of all elements and would not combine in any way with either the "ideal mixer," potassium, nor with fluorine, most violent of the nonmetals. Although helium, the first of them, had been known since 1868 as an unaccountable orange-yellow spectral line recorded in the sun's chromosphere during an eclipse and had been discovered on Earth by the aforementioned Hillebrand in 1890, it took William Ramsay to positively identify it as the "sun gas." Then he and his co-worker, John Rayleigh, liquified 120 tons of air and, using a microbalance that "could detect a difference in weight of one fourteen-trillionth of an ounce," painstakingly isolated the rest of what have come to be known as the "noble gases": argon (the lazy), neon (the new), krypton (the hidden), xenon (the stranger) and, working with an exclusive millionth of a gram of it, radon (the radiant).

With the discovery of this new family of aloof gases, whose very gaseousness seemed to be caused by their unsociability, the Periodic Table attained a kind of expectant maturity that might require only a few more key ideas to clear up the whole mystery of matter. At least that was how it looked to the British physicist Joseph John Thomson, who secured his place in history by making so bold as to divide the supposedly indivisible atom.

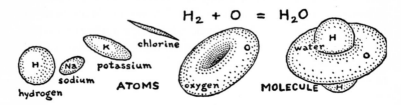

In the early 1890's, theorists had been still speculating about atomic shapes along the same macrocosmic lines used in ancient Greece. Hydrogen atoms were postulated as spherical; those of sodium and potassium were considered elongated ellipsoids. Oxygen atoms, on the other hand, were believed to be shaped like fat doughnuts so that two hydrogens could fit like cherries into the two ends of any doughnut hole to turn it into the neat three-part water molecule H_2O, Neptune's mystic trident out of which all the oceans are built. Even the stability of salt water could be plausibly explained with this model as a slipping of some of the bean-shaped sodium atoms or the pointed chlorines into the doughnut holes ahead of the cherries.

Ingenious as such mechanical postulations were, they could hardly begin to explain the real and increasing complexities of chemistry, and it wasn't until Thomson began to think of an atom as not a single particle but a conglomeration of much smaller entities, perhaps moving around in relation to each other, that a significant conceptual advance could be made. Thomson, of course, knew of Michael Faraday's classical hypothesis that the electrical charges of atoms are *always* a multiple of some minimum elementary quantity of electricity. But he went far beyond Faraday in considering these definite elementary charges as individual parcels of something that might somehow be extracted from atomic bodies and weighed and measured. He even accomplished the astonishing feat of shooting beams of negative charge units or "electrons" out of hot electric wires and through space between the positive and negative electrodes of a condenser so he could weigh these fantastic somethings by their deflection in a known electric field. And he found, to his amazement, that the mass of one electron is only $\frac{1}{1,840}$ of the mass of a single hydrogen atom! This would make an electron about as much smaller than a pea as a pea is smaller than the earth.

Since Thomson regarded an atom's positive charge as distributed uniformly throughout its body, which in turn was swarming with negative electrons, his atomic model could well be compared to a handful of peas or beans swirling about in a pot of soup. And this beanpot atom dominated physics for about fifteen crucial years until another great British physicist, Ernest Rutherford from New Zealand, demonstrated in 1911 that an atom cannot really be anywhere near as solid or substantial as a beanpot, but must be literally like a miniature solar system with its entire positive charge as well as virtually all its mass concentrated in an extremely small nucleus located in the very center like a sun, and the rest almost complete emptiness!

This new concept was even more revolutionary than that of the beanpot atom, and its demonstrable truth (particularly as explained by Niels Bohr, Rutherford's young Danish assistant) gave the scientific world a shock it has hardly yet recovered from. Using the heavy, positive, so-called alpha (a) particles emitted by such radioactive elements as the newly discovered radium or uranium, which are so concentrated and massive that they ram through electrons like bullets through snowflakes, Rutherford proved that the a particles can also pass through a sheet of "solid" aluminum foil with such strange deflections that the pattern of their scattering could only be explained by the fact that the positive parts of the aluminum were just about as concentrated as the a particles themselves: in other words, an atom's nucleus seemed to be millions of times smaller in volume than any whole atom. Describing later how amazed he was to find that a few of these enormously energetic particles should bounce back from the foil that the others penetrated like air, he said, "It was quite the most incredible event that ever happened to me in my life. It was almost as incredible as if you had fired a fifteen-inch shell at a piece of tissue paper and it came back and hit you."

Thus, by a series of classic experiments leavened with brilliant mathematical deductions, the atom was exposed and confirmed as a desolate waste of enormous emptiness — a microfirmament of space every bit as awesome in its vastness as the heavens outside us, and no less mysterious in its ultimate dimensions and significance.

The easiest way to begin visualizing even the simplest of atoms (that of hydrogen) might be to think of the central positive particle or proton as a very dense grapeseed (made of material much heavier than lead) with a puff of smoke, the electron, whizzing around it at an unearthly speed and at varying distances up to five miles, moving so fast, in fact, that you could never actually see it but only know by statistical records what space its total and ever-changing orbit must occupy.

Although such a scale model is not very satisfying, it is about as realistic as is possible using familiar materials. And if you can accept the fact that the dense grapeseed is really 1,840 times as heavy as the whole puff of smoke, you will realize the rough basic resemblance to the solar system, in which our sun is 768 times as heavy as the sum of all his planets. You also will notice that the smoky electron is removed by about the same number of times its own uncertain diameter from the grapeseed proton as are Mercury and Venus from the sun. Most significant of all, the electromagnetic attraction between proton and electron obeys the same Newtonian inverse-square law that defines the force of gravity between sun and planets.

All in all, it is not a bad analogy and, as we look at bigger and more complicated atoms than the hydrogen, with increasing numbers of electrons upon larger and larger orbits, to say nothing of correspondingly bigger and more complex nuclei, we even find a kind of Bode's Law of harmonic intervals that gives a strict and beautiful order to all matter and explains the "octaves" of the Periodic Table in a way that would have delighted Pythagoras or Kepler or Mendeleyev.

The harmonic basis of chemistry, of course, is not as simple as the music of a harp or a piano, where each note is produced by the vibrations of a string of different length or thickness. Yet each element is actually made by a different kind of atom, and

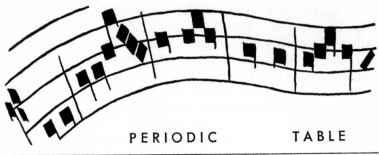

PERIODIC   TABLE

first octave	second octave	third octave	fourth octave

$$\triangle \quad \triangledown \quad \triangle \quad \triangledown$$

$$\Omega \; \wp \; \Omega \; \sigma \; \hbar \; \wp \; \mathcal{D} \; \Upsilon \; 4$$

Group

I 1. H (hydrogen)—— 3. Li (lithium)——11. Na (sodium)

II   ⊙   4. Be (beryllium)——12. Mg (magnesium)

III   5. B (boron)———13. Al (aluminum)

IV   ●   6. C (carbon)———14. Si (silicon)

V   ◐   7. N (nitrogen)——15. P (phosphorus)

VI   ○   8. O (oxygen)———16. S (sulfur)

VII   9. F (fluorine)———17. Cl (chlorine)

0 2. He (helium)——10. Ne (neon)———18. A (argon)

- 19. K
- 20. Ca
- 21. Sc
- 22. Ti
- 23. V
- 24. Cr
- 25. Mn
- 26. Fe
- 27. Co
- 28. Ni
- 29. Cu
- 30. Zn
- 31. Ga
- 32. Ge
- 33. As
- 34. Se
- 35. Br
- 36. Kr

these are lanthanons (rare earths)

58. Ce (cerium)	63. Eu (europium)	68. Er (erbium)
59. Pr (praseodymium)	64. Gd (gadolinium)	69. Tm (thulium)
60. Nd (neodymium)	65. Tb (terbium)	70. Yb (ytterbium)
61. Pm (promethium)	66. Dy (dysprosium)	71. Lu (lutetium)
62. Sm (samarium)	67. Ho (holmium)	

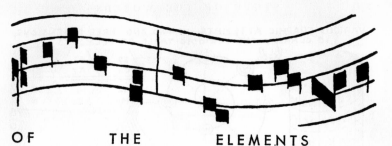

OF THE ELEMENTS

fourth octave	fifth octave	sixth octave	seventh octave
(potassium)——37. Rb (rubidium)——55. Cs (cesium)—— 87. Fr (francium) ·
(calcium)——38. Sr (strontium)——56. Ba (barium)—— 88. Ra (radium)
(scandium)——39. Yt (yttrium)——57. La (lanthanum)—— 89. Ac (actinium)

*58–71. Lanthanons: see opp. page

(titanium)——40. Zr (zirconium)——72. Hf (hafnium)	90. Th (thorium)
(vanadium)——41. Nb (niobium)——73. Ta (tantalum)	91. Pa (protoactinium)
(chromium)——42. Mo (molybdenum)—74. W (tungsten)	92. U (uranium)
(manganese)——43. Tc (technetium)——75. Re (rhenium)	93. Np (neptunium)
(iron)——44. Ru (ruthenium)——76. Os (osmium)	94. Pu (plutonium)
(cobalt)——45. Rh (rhodium)——77. Ir (iridium)	95. Am (americium)
(nickel)——46. Pd (palladium)——78. Pt (platinum)	96. Cm (curium)
(copper)——47. Ag (silver)——79. Au (gold)	97. Bk (berkelium)
(zinc)——48. Cd (cadmium)——80. Hg (mercury)	98. Cf (californium)
(gallium)——49. In (indium)——81. Tl (thallium)	99. E (einsteinium)
(germanium)——50. Sn (tin)——82. Pb (lead)	100. Fm (fermium)
(arsenic)——51. Sb (antimony)——83. Bi (bismuth)	101. Md (mendelevium)
(selenium)——52. Te (tellurium)——84. Po (polonium)	102. No (nobelium)
(bromine)——53. I (iodine)——85. At (astatine)	*these are actinons (the second series of rare earths)*
(krypton)——54. Xe (xenon)——86. Rn (radon)	

VARIOUS GRAPHIC ATTEMPTS, IN TWO AND THREE DIMENSIONS,
TO CLARIFY THE PERIODIC TABLE OF ELEMENTS

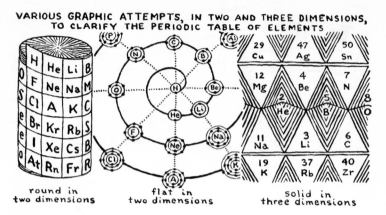

round in
two dimensions

flat in
two dimensions

solid in
three dimensions

the atoms range progressively in size and weight up the scale, octave by octave, totaling only a few more than the eighty-eight keys of a piano. And the distinctions between the atoms of the various elements are ascribed primarily to the different numbers of negative electrons revolving around each positive nucleus, which in turn must be composed of an equal number of protons, since all whole atoms are found to be electrically neutral. Thus an atom of hydrogen has one electron vibrating about one proton, an atom of helium two electrons around two protons, a lithium atom three and three, beryllium four, boron five, carbon six, nitrogen seven, oxygen eight, and so on up to the heaviest natural element, uranium with its 92 electrons. And even beyond uranium, modern alchemy has artificially constructed still more complex elements: number 93, neptunium; 94, the appropriately named plutonium, used in atomic bombs; 95, americium; 96, curium; 97, berkelium; 98, californium, which has recently been detected as a major ingredient of supernovae; 99, einsteinium; 100, fermium; 101, mendelevium; 102, nobelium; and so forth.

This amazing array of elements may be compared to the letters of the alphabet, which can be put together into never-ending combinations to form words. For similarly do the atoms join in even greater variety to compose all the wordlike molecules and genes of this material universe, which, in its dynamic entirety, is to be presumed a much more basic medium for meaning than any or all the languages of man.

Not only are atomic combinations more basic but they are also so much more complex that even the simplest compounds like water, salt, carbon dioxide and ammonia could not be understood until modern times. And the mysteries in such common substances as wood, leather, rubber, oil and milk are even today still in process of being cleared up. What makes a cloud form in a clear sky? Why is oil slippery, glue sticky, rubber bouncy? Why does one kind of metal ring clearly in a bell, another make a good watch spring, another carry an electric current, another take on magnetism?

All of these questions are being studied intensively in laboratories. All relate to fundamental states of matter or the shape, behavior and interrelation of molecules. A molecule is defined as the smallest particle any compound material can be divided into without changing into a different material and, as such, it is both the next stage larger than an atom and so fantastically rich in its varieties that it easily serves as the common building unit of our world.

Consider a molecule of octane, the familiar constituent of gasoline. Its formula is C_8H_{18}, which is an abbreviated way of saying that it is a flexible, centipedelike chain of eight carbon atoms in zigzag formation, each with two tiny hydrogen atoms attached like legs, and an extra one at each end for head and tail, making eighteen in all — roughly representable as

But if you break up the chain, as may be done in a cracking plant, you do not get two half-molecules of octane. For, strictly speaking, there is no such thing as a half-molecule of any material. Anything less than a molecule of octane cannot be octane. Instead the fractions of octane may include any of many lesser molecules or even single atoms of carbon. It is simple to figure out the possibilities by adding up the atoms in the smaller hydrocarbon molecules. Thus octane (C_8H_{18}) might be a sum of methane (CH_4), ethane (C_2H_6) and pentane (C_5H_8), or of carbon (C), propane (C_3H_8) and butane (C_4H_{10}), of menthane (CH_4) joined with hexane (C_6H_{10}) in the proportion of two to one, of two-atom hydrogen molecules (H_2) united with four times as many of ethylene (C_2H_4), of methane, ethylene and butane, or any of various combinations of hydrogen and ethylene, propylene, butylene, and so on. Furthermore, the nature of a molecule depends on the *arrangement* of its atoms, as well as on their kinds and numbers, so that an oxygen atom and 2 carbons surrounded by 6 hydrogens (for example) may form a molecule of alcohol or a molecule of ether, depending merely on whether the oxygen is beside or between the carbons.

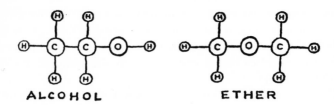

ALCOHOL   ETHER

If you are not a chemist, all this may appear fantastic, not to say confusing. But it is really simple, solid fact and not just theory or guesswork. Molecules in the quiet state can be seen clearly through electron microscopes and photographed. Even their constituent atoms can thus be definitely recognized and the precise ways they fit into one another. Besides "visual" observation, careful measurement, long experimentation and several lines of mathematical analysis have reliably predicted their behavior and proved their nature way beyond reasonable doubt.

In fact, one can literally subdivide a substance, say, water, into its ultimate grains with amazing ease. Put a drop of it in warm, dry air and, molecule by molecule, it will evaporate. If you had a sensitive enough balance-scale, and could read it fast enough, you could actually measure the water's weight from moment to moment and see that evaporation does not proceed continuously like an ebbing tide but jerkily in "jumps," whole molecule by whole molecule. Of course, the fact that each H_2O molecule weighs only .00000000000000000000000106 ounces shows how delicate this experiment would have to be. And the hopelessness of ever completing it for an entire drop of water is obvious from the fact that water molecules are only a hundred-millionth of an inch in diameter and therefore so numerous that if even those in one drop were placed end to end in a chain it would be twelve billion miles long or enough to reach to the moon fifty thousand times over!

One of the better ways of checking the size of molecules, incidentally, is by their collision rate as they bounce off one another in a gas, for obviously the smaller they are the less often will they hit each other and in a definite proportion. Naturally, such collisions cannot be counted except by some sort of statistical calculation, for not only are individual molecules almost inconceivably small and numerous but they move literally as fast as bullets. In the air of an ordinary room, for instance, the separate molecules of oxygen (O_2) and nitrogen (N_2) vibrate on their submicroscopic zigzagging courses at an average speed of around a thousand miles an hour — a third faster than sound. This relationship between molecules and sound is not accidental, for sound is nothing more than waves of disturbance among molecules propagated from each to the next by successive collisions between them. If all molecules traveled at the same speed and in the same direction, sound would have to move exactly at molecular speed, and it is only the fact that molecules move in all directions, including crosswise, that sound's net forward velocity works out at some 30 percent less. This 30 percent less, however, is a variable speed, for it is a fixed fraction of the collective rate of molecular and atomic motion — in other words, temperature — which, of course, is a varying quantity.

Perhaps a good way really to acquaint ourselves with molecules is to look at them where they are simplest and most scarce: out here in so-called "empty" space. And farther out, between the stars or, better still, between the galaxies, one might encounter scarcely a single star, planet or even a comet for hundreds of light-years in any direction. The rarity of molecules in such remote reaches may be hinted at by the remark of one astronomer that if so much as a faint whiff of cigarette smoke were diffused through each and every cubic mile of space, the stars would be invisible. In justification he had calculated that even the average of about a hundredth of an ounce of matter that is believed to be distributed as gas and dust through each hundred million cubic miles of space in the more crowded regions of the Milky Way is enough to cut the energy of starlight in half during every two thousand light-years of its passage. Which is the main reason why we cannot "see" many parts of our galaxy except through nonvisual (radio) telescopes.

Most intergalactic regions of space, of course, are clearer and presumably emptier than the Milky Way. And so an average molecule in all space would have to be a kind of tiny hermit world that could be compared to a peanut drifting somewhere deep in the Pacific Ocean with virtually no chance of encountering another nut (the nearest molecule) floating at random a few thousand miles away.

By transposing each thousand miles down to an inch, we would then have the proportionately reduced peanut representing the common hydrogen molecule (H_2) in space, something that in reality must have been created by an almost incredible fluke: the earlier collision of two smaller hydrogen atoms that met after months of flying about through millions of miles of real space (visualizable only as some such less improbable rendezvous as that of, say, two grapeseeds after a billion years of drifting in New York Harbor).

Yet this sort of thing must be repeatedly happening throughout the universe. And once two hydrogen atoms do meet at a permissive speed, they cling to each other like lovers in the natural magnetic embrace between each positive proton and each negative electron. While the nuclei (protons) of the two hydrogens keep their distance, being of similar (+) charge, there is room for the two electrons (−) to circulate around them both, perhaps in symmetrical figure-eight orbits. Thus the electrons are shared (probably alternately) by the protons — "in valence" as the chemists say — for it happens that two, and only two, electrons can revolve equidistantly and harmoniously around the immediate vicinity of an atomic nucleus. And this in turn suggests how the energy radiated by the hydrogen electron, vibrating back and forth between its two alternative positions in the hydrogen atom 500,000,000 times a second, broadcasts the common 21-centimeter waves that our radio telescopes receive from space.

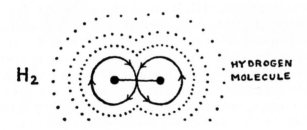

H₂ — HYDROGEN MOLECULE

It is in accordance also with the strange law of chemical nature, first proposed by Niels Bohr of Denmark in 1913, that all electrons tend to occupy "shells" around the atomic nuclei, the first shell (mentioned above) holding only two electrons, the second shell (farther away and larger) eight electrons, the third eighteen, the fourth 32 and so on.

Nobody has completely explained why electrons like to follow such rules, but there is no doubt that they do follow them and, in doing so, they throw light on the harmonic mystery of the Periodic Table, though not without adding still another beautiful enigma (the mathematical series of doubled squares) to those already uncovered: 2×1^2 equaling the first shell of two electrons; 2×2^2 representing the second shell of eight (used by heavier atoms); 2×3^2 the third shell of eighteen (by still greater atoms); 2×4^2 the fourth shell of 32; and so on.

AN EARLY MODEL
OF ELECTRONS
IN ATOMIC SHELLS

Thus an oxygen atom, for example, having eight electrons orbiting around its nucleus of eight protons, uses an inner first shell of two electrons plus six more in a second shell. But since the second shell needs eight electrons for harmonic completion, oxygen is inherently unstable by itself — and inevitably must be yearning for two more electrons which it will pick up whenever and wherever it can. This it may do by sharing the single electrons of some passing hydrogen molecule (H_2) or of any two hydrogen atoms in valence, thus creating the common water molecule H_2O. Or perhaps it will grab the two outer electrons of an iron atom to form ferric hydroxide (rust), or will join some other substance it chances to meet possessing a couple of likely electrons that can be seduced into any sort of oxide.

Thus do we begin to understand the strong and basic, almost sexual, craving of abundant oxygen to unite with other elements: to oxidize iron, copper, zinc, tin, aluminum, chromium, lead, magnesium, mercury, carbon, sulfur, sodium or other available materials; to burn, to ferment, to corrode, to ravish or devour or rot things away by combining with them chemically, after which they cannot be the same again.

And how many are the other elements that have it as bad or worse than oxygen! Only they are not as abundant, at least not on Earth. Carbon, the most versatile joiner of all, in fact specializes as the most essential chemical factor in the complexity needed for life. Sodium and potassium, each with one lonely outer electron, suffer from a built-in itch to find some body with an electron missing (like chlorine with its expectant seven electrons in the outer shell) and, until they join it, they are as restless as randy stallions.

This in essence is what all chemistry is about. Chemistry is the science of elemental combinations, of the behavior and inter-relation of molecules. And, as the study of biology is making increasingly clear, the phenomenon of sex undoubtedly had a chemical origin.

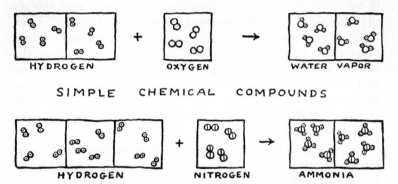

HYDROGEN   OXYGEN   WATER VAPOR

SIMPLE CHEMICAL COMPOUNDS

HYDROGEN   NITROGEN   AMMONIA

Now to get back to the simplicity of space, there is a constant struggle going on to determine what atoms will mate with what other atoms — a war between the vibrations that keep atoms apart and the magnetic forces that tend to draw them together. Although this conflict is at its minimum in intergalactic space, it has been calculated that atoms never anywhere get more than a few inches apart, and some physicists think that all the space between them, not to mention inside them, is also jam-packed with things that may ultimately be defined as matter. So the conflict of material forces is probably very real everywhere and needs to be understood if we are going to comprehend this impalpable, palpable world.

Besides the factor of atomic form already discussed (the electron shells), there is the factor of velocity. This can make all the difference in what joins what. Just as skaters in a roller-skating rink do not easily catch hold of other skaters moving at speeds much faster or slower than themselves, atoms in the void are more hospitable to the subtler approach. A violent collision of atoms will be as socially inconsequential as a corresponding clash of solar systems, for two speeding nuclei or suns have less than a ghost of a chance of touching each other, while the almost empty orbits of surrounding electrons or planets sweep through one another so swiftly that there is no time for any appreciable interplay. Even on those very rare occasions when some such intruding electron actually hits another, perhaps knocking both out of position, the effect is usually short-lived because ions (atoms with missing or extra electrons) are unstable and therefore so impulsive that they either sow their wild-oat electrons or are sown by someone else's at the slightest opportunity, quickly restoring equilibrium and normality to both sides.

More moderate atomic collisions, which do not involve any interpenetration of the electron shells, are comparable to the harmless bounding together of two billiard balls. Indeed, the atoms in real colliding billiard balls are believed to resist each other primarily through the negative-to-negative repulsion that arises when their outer electrons come into "contact."

It is only the very slow coming together of atoms that normally produces a deep and large-scale interaction between them. I mean, for example, the relatively slow bonding of two pieces of ice pressed together (which can unite them solidly even while immersed in warm water), the more leisurely setting of glue or cement or the still slower sticking of smooth, unoiled, metal surfaces as in long-idle machinery or old, unused hinges. Here something happens that must be a little like the action of one of those swinging gates that at first swings to and fro without locking but, when the motion has slowed down enough, suddenly drops its latch into place, with only a split second of rattling before all motion ceases. Of course, the outer shell of a slow-moving atom corresponds to the latch in this analogy, a shell of electrons that are repelled again and again by the similar charges of other electrons on both sides of their potential resting place in some nearby molecule. But this repulse is not quite as relentless as it seems at first and, if the shell of electrons has plenty of time to "swing" back and forth and to feel the varying pressures at different points on the molecule, it may suddenly discover some attractive gap and, still avoiding most of the worst repulsion, slip triumphantly into it.

The chances of attaining such a satisfying union, like a sound marriage, are normally enhanced by an unhurried courtship followed by some sensitive arranging and preparing. The congenial tempo of the whole affair, indeed, is of its essence and, from a larger view, is describable as not only a matter of speed but, even more, of temperature — the average excitement of hundreds or billions of molecules being what the word temperature actually means. It is by realizing this that we get an understanding of why temperature is such a critical factor in any chemical reaction — how it is the key to freezing, cooking, molding, cracking, welding and a prime clue to all the states of matter.

An apparently simple question here may help show what temperature and heat really measure. How cold is interstellar space? Strangely enough, this is a question that has no proper answer. Strictly speaking, the question itself does not even make sense. Temperature is only science's term for collective molecular motion such as exists everywhere on earth — underground, at sea and in the lower atmosphere. It is a statistical concept, the average of speeds of innumerable particles that continuously influence each other through perpetual collisions. But most molecules in interstellar space are no more collective than peanuts drifting a thousand miles apart. They react on each other probably less than our sun reacts on Alpha Centauri or Sirius.

For such independent particles, temperature (if the term can be used) means exactly the same thing as velocity, and it varies with every particle. The hydrogen atoms and molecules, impelled by starlight and obstructed by nothing, may be just as "hot" as the surface of the average star: some 20,000° F. On the other hand, grains of dust, being relatively large, rare assemblages of solid ice or maybe silicon or iron that cool themselves by radiating heat continuously, probably get fairly close to absolute zero, the limit of cold, which is 460° F. below zero. Thus we have in space a combination of a lot of independent particles of hot gas interspersed with a few bitter-cold chunks of dust with which they cannot really be said to mix, although it seems to be true that the rare collisions between dust and gas particles are what gradually builds up stars — the gas losing its velocity (heat) on sticking to the dust until a large enough body is amassed to generate heat by pressure.

The curious relativity of heat may be further illustrated by the apt phrase that an airplane (like a molecule) is coming in "hot" when it lands fast. Therefore, airplanes and molecules can be hot in relation to one object and cool in relation to another that happens to be moving along at nearly their own speed and direction, just as cars on a road are "hotter" to opposing traffic than to traffic going their way. This is the fundamental concept of temperature as *relative* velocity.

It is hard to imagine or appreciate the great difficulties men have had to go through to dig out such subtle bits of abstract truth. Almost up to the nineteenth century, heat was considered to be a mysterious, weightless fluid known as "phlogiston" or "caloric," which was created by burning and could flow invisibly from one body to another. But Benjamin Thompson of Woburn, Massachusetts, who became Count Rumford of the Holy Roman Empire and married Lavoisier's widow, had a profound flash of insight while directing the boring of cannon for the government of Bavaria in 1794. He suddenly saw a connection between the mysterious loss of energy expended in the drilling and the equally magical gain in "caloric" wherever the moving drill touched the metal. In short, he realized for the first time that "caloric" or heat is not an entirely separate thing-in-itself but is just energy that has changed its form. When Sir James Prescott Joule carefully measured and proved the equivalence of work and heat a century later, he established the first law of thermodynamics: the now well-known principle of conservation of energy. And this, logically, led to the famous second law (mentioned on page 214): the law of entropy or disorder which says, in effect, that random molecular motion (heat) can never be totally converted back into mechanical energy or work — that, in other words, there is bound to be some net flow of energy in any closed system from more orderly to more disorderly forms.

These thermodynamic laws come up frequently in any study of basic matter and help us to understand the strange behavior of substances in all their states from the maximum rigidity of absolute zero, where atoms and molecules are locked into the condition of least possible (not necessarily zero) motion, through solidity, plasticity, liquidity, gaseousness, atomic ionization or plasma, to the explosive fission of billions of degrees of heat where not only molecules and atoms have long since disintegrated but even the atomic nuclei (which we will look at in the next chapter) must burst violently asunder.

To bring all this down (or up) to Earth, molecules in their solid state can be compared to the leaves on a tree in summer. Green leaves obviously can move a little (depending on circumstances) but are securely anchored in their appointed places

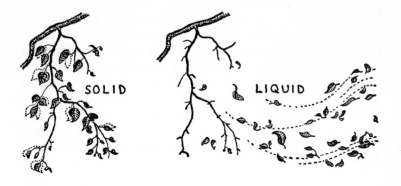

SOLID   LIQUID

according to a fixed, crystallized pattern. When something solid melts and turns into liquid, it is as if an autumn breeze (heat) comes along to flap the leaves (molecules) harder and harder until eventually they snap loose and start to flow through the air completely free from their former fixed pattern.

The basic idea of this process may well have been felt intuitively by Leucippos or Democritos, and it was Leonardo who wrote, "If heat is the cause of the movement of moisture, cold stops it." Certainly the dynamic nature of heat and its effect on materials were comprehended in essence as early as the seventeenth century, when Robert Hooke, the English physicist and colleague of Newton, wrote,

What is the cause of fluidness? Let us suppose a dish of sand set upon some body that is very much agitated and shaken with some quick and strong vibrating motion . . . By this means the sand in the dish, which before lay like a dull and unactive body, becomes a perfect fluid; and ye can no sooner make a hole in it with your finger but it is immediately filled up again and the upper surface of it levelled. Nor can ye bury . . . a piece of cork under it but it presently swims on the top; nor . . . a piece of lead on the top of it but it . . . immediately sinks to the bottom. Nor can ye make a hole in the side of the dish but the sand shall run out of it to a level . . . And all this merely caused by the vehement agitation . . . for by this means each sand [grain] becomes . . . a dancing motion.

Of course, Hooke could hardly have guessed the fantastic shapes of real molecules, but he seems at least to have correctly visualized them as rolling or dancing around each other at close range like shaken grains of sand when, as we now know, the gently balanced forces of repulsion and attraction produce the fluidity we call the liquid state. And it has long been almost equally evident that the gaseous state is nothing but a further intensification of molecular motion (collectively considered as higher temperature), in which the repulsing forces overwhelm all the attracting ones, resulting in a vast expansion and thinning of matter for the same reason that a flock of birds roosting cosily in a bush must spread much farther apart when they take off in the rapid motion of flight.

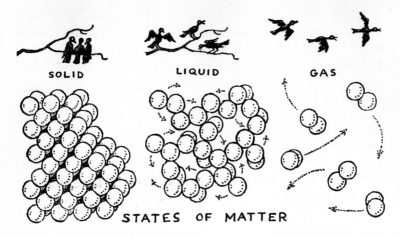

SOLID   LIQUID   GAS

STATES OF MATTER

Another, and more precise, way of explaining gas is to say that the atmosphere is only ⅟₈₀₀ as heavy as water per unit volume. This, of course, is an expression of the amazing general vitality of molecules which, once free of the magnetic sociability of the solid or liquid state, suddenly become as independent as soaring eagles. The nature of their gassy emancipation, indeed, has been measured so precisely that it is now known that the first one thousandth of a degree Fahrenheit above absolute zero would give simple molecules on the average just enough vibration to make them bounce to a level of about seven inches above the ground. Such a temperature has actually been attained on a small scale in a modern laboratory and helps one to realize that the air in a room would literally freeze solid into a kind of powder and fall to the floor if the room could be made cold enough. Yet only a few thousandths of one degree of heat provide enough energy to keep the molecules bouncing off all the walls and ceiling, easily relegating gravity to inconsequence. And from there on up to normal room temperature, the speed and frequency of impact and recoil mount steadily, the molecules maintaining their unsociable gaseousness despite such a crescendo of excitement that their spritely dance is soon turned into a ferocious battle of billions of blows per molecule per second.

To give a slight idea of the varieties of this motion, particularly under the complexities of higher density, there are now known to be "planar systems" of molecules whose atoms vibrate with translatory (back and forth) movement, torsional (around and around) and breathing (inward and outward) motions among others. And also there are stationary and rotating "pyramidal systems" and "cubic, cylindrical, spherical and polygonal systems" of "cyclic and dihedral" molecules with "one-way or two-way principal axes" to guide their "turn groups" and "mirror turn groups" of spinning parts.

As if it weren't hard enough mentally to swallow such goings-on, the mere multiplicity of gas molecules participating in any natural mixture is staggering, and each kind moves at a different speed, inversely proportionate to its weight (since all those in contact must possess the same average energy), just as would interacting billiard balls if made out of hollow celluloid, cork, wood, aluminum, iron, silver, lead, gold . . . In such a melee of mixed and moving spheres, one could let something like pingpong balls represent the extremely light hydrogen molecules (H_2), which are actually batted about much faster than anything else: literally a mile per second in normal air. A cork ball, next in speed, might represent a stray methane molecule (CH_4) at ⅔ mile per second; a wooden ball, either nitrogen (N_2) or carbon monoxide (CO) at ³⁄₁₀ m.p.s.; an aluminum ball, oxygen (O_2) at ¼ m.p.s.; perhaps an iron ball, carbon dioxide (CO_2) at ⅕ m.p.s.; a silver ball, chlorine (Cl_2) at ⅙ m.p.s.; a lead ball, bromine (Br_2) at ⅛ m.p.s.; a gold ball, mercury vapor (Hg) at ¹⁄₁₀ m.p.s. and so on.

Something along these lines, only immensely more complicated, must certainly be going on in the endless super-billiard game played by ordinary air molecules, and this is a good part of what makes the wind blow and what stokes your lungs with the oxygen pressure of life or enables a child to suck lemonade through a straw. For, in case you did not know, the drawing in of breath or the pulling of lemonade by suction up a straw is more realistically describable as the *pushing* than the *pulling* of molecules. Gas molecules just do not have any hooks or magnets capable of pulling each other, and suction will no more pull them

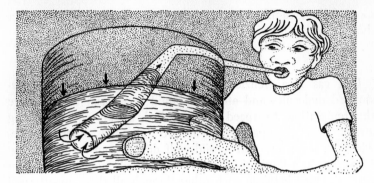

than opening a bird-cage door will pull the bird out. Like a bird, a molecule is powered from within. So, by expanding the hollow of his sealed-off mouth, the sucking child is really only pushing some atmosphere away from his body and letting the increased volume of his mouth harbor so many air molecules from among those flying in and out of the straw that the pressure inside the straw drops far enough below the pressure of the outside air to cause that air to push the lemonade upward from below, thus restoring the balance of nature.

Pressure, as we have said, is closely related to temperature, being essentially just a different aspect of the same molecular motion. Pressure is the collective outward force of moving molecules, while temperature is the motion itself. Thus the difference between hot gas at low pressure and cold gas at high pressure is about like the difference between a room containing a few frightened jay birds that fly to and fro at high speeds and a similar

HIGH TEMPERATURE
LOW PRESSURE

HIGH PRESSURE
LOW TEMPERATURE

room full of calmly roosting hens, pressed so tightly together they can hardly move.

If a gas is a frenzied free-for-all battle of relatively unrestrained molecules and atoms, a liquid is a social dance where the temptation to speed is controlled by an equally strong attraction between partners. The two states thus differ in somewhat the same way that a wild wolf differs from a trained dog. Molecules in a liquid, in fact, are disciplined enough to keep an exact distance between each other through all their unpatterned gyrations. This confines them at definite limits, such as the surface of the ocean or the surface of a dewdrop or at either surface of a bubble.

Yet "liquid discipline" is only a relative term, and a certain number of the more active liquid molecules, not held firmly enough by their attractions, are forever jumping the fence and escaping or, more exactly, evaporating into some gaseous outer wilderness. This naturally happens at any gas-liquid surface where, in the constant interchange of motion, outlying molecules of liquid are always getting knocked across the frontier — inevitably, some so hard they do not find their way back again. That is why a tub of water left in a closed dry room will inevitably raise the air's humidity in the form of more and more H_2O molecules flying about among the nitrogens and oxygens. But the humidity will not go on climbing forever for, as the number of free water molecules increases, ever-larger numbers of them are bound to strike the liquid surface, re-entering it as others leave it until, when

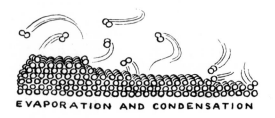

EVAPORATION AND CONDENSATION

the air is fully saturated, the exchange is equal and the level in the tub stands still.

If you have wondered why evaporation has a cooling effect, as is demonstrated in such familiar devices as the common porous water jug of the tropics, it is because the evaporating molecules are inevitably the faster (hotter) ones — their heat gives them take-off priority — and any continuous departure of heat from anything in any state must tend to leave it cooler.

Judging the effect on temperature of a combination of materials in different states is not always easy, however, as may be gleaned from the discovery that adding ice to water in certain cases can raise its temperature many degrees. This is because freezing is a crystallizing process which depends on more than temperature. Very pure, still water can be cooled to as low as 37° F. below zero without freezing, because ice is very reluctant to form unless microscopic impurities of some sort serve as nuclei to start the crystallization. But as soon as you trigger the freezing by touching a sliver of ice or so much as a single speck of dust to such "supercooled" water, the whole mass of the liquid will start crystallizing instantly by chain reaction. This is how an airplane flying through an innocent-looking supercooled cloud may ice up with fatal rapidity. And since freezing necessitates the release of energy (heat) which must somehow be conserved (first law of thermodynamics), the released energy just naturally radiates outward from the growing ice into the surrounding supercooled water, raising its temperature. Thus one finds that 32° F. is not necessarily the temperature at which water freezes. It is rather the temperature of a mixture of water and ice.

Of all liquids on Earth, water is far and away the most common but also, very likely, the most peculiar. Thales of Miletos considered water the basic stuff of which all else is made, including not only steam, snow, ice and clouds but "by absorption" the earth itself, even stones, trees, flesh and bones. Although such an idea is, to say the least, an exaggeration in the light of modern knowledge, water in some form is found nearly everywhere in our world and, as the mother of life and the queen of solvents, it is unique. It is the only substance we are thoroughly familiar with in all the three states of gas, liquid, solid — to say nothing of having a separate name for each. And, almost alone among materials, it is denser as liquid than solid — a fact of vast importance to life on this planet where ice's buoyancy keeps it floating on the surfaces of lakes and streams for the maximum insulation and preservation of aquatic creatures below during the severest periods of winter.

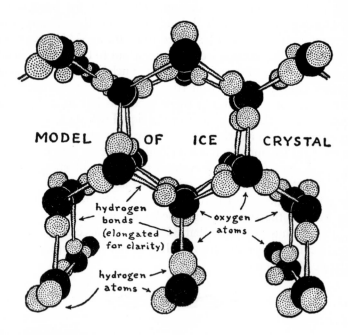

MODEL OF ICE CRYSTAL

hydrogen
bonds
(elongated
for clarity)

oxygen
atoms

hydrogen
atoms

Probably the best approach to an understanding of the complex and dynamic structure of water, indeed, is to look first at its rigid crystal form in snow and ice. Through X-ray analysis and other means, the hexagonal tendencies that build the beautiful snowflake patterns are now fairly well understood. Each H_2O molecule of ice is held at the center of a kind of open tetrahedron (pyramid-shaped 3-D triangle) formed by its four nearest neighbors, one at each corner. The distance from molecule to molecule averages exactly 2.72 angstrom units — an angstrom being one hundred-millionth of a centimeter or (in simpler mathematician's notation) 10^{-10} meters. By a moderately strong attraction called the "hydrogen bond," these molecules are kept in firm relation to each other in the crystal lattice of ice. The hydrogen bond, incidentally, is the direct magnetic yoke between a positive hydrogen nucleus of one molecule and one of the negative outer electrons of another and, as no nucleus but the hydrogen nucleus is exposed enough for such an unvalanced bond, this tie is unique in chemistry and fundamentally different from the closer, stronger interlinking of the three atoms in each H_2O molecule itself. In fact, it is this special hydrogen bond that undoubtedly makes ice stick to ice. Even more significantly, it exerts a steady inward pressure that is responsible for some of water's strange properties and, in ice, gives the lacelike hexagonal trestlework a stress like that of a bridge under a heavy load. When the ice's temperature rises, vibrating and shaking the bridge harder and harder, the load helps to bend, break and finally crumble the whole intermolecular structure at the melting point, which, as is well known, can be lowered many degrees in temperature by putting the ice under extra pressure. Conversely, the melting point can undoubtedly be raised if ice's internal pressure is reduced. For calculations indicate that, if this pressure should be eliminated entirely, as in icy meteorites in space, ice would not melt below 59° F.

As you may have surmised by now, melting quite literally means a stretching as well as a flexing and loosening of the solid, intermolecular bonds. And sure enough, as observed and analyzed with the help of the electron microscope, when ice bursts loose into water its hydrogen bonds stretch out an additional .18 angstroms and its molecules move just that much farther apart. One would expect water in consequence to be lighter than ice, just as lava is lighter than rock, but in water's case it so happens that the freedom of fluidity permits more H_2O molecules to occupy a given volume of space at a separation of 2.9 angstroms than the rigidity of ice permits at 2.72 angstroms. It is as if a battalion of a thousand soldiers completely filled a barrack square while standing stiffly at attention, shoulder to shoulder, elbow touching elbow, but, on "melting" and adjusting themselves into "at ease" positions, they suddenly discover they not only have a few inches between each other but, surprisingly, enough room for a hundred more men in the square. That such an analogy almost literally holds water is indicated by the strongly confirmed evidence that an H_2O molecule *always* has five close neighbors when it is water, while only four when it is ice.

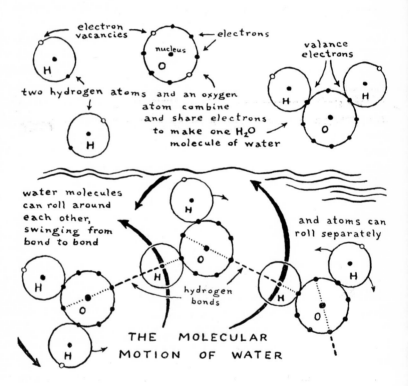

THE MOLECULAR MOTION OF WATER

The hardest thing to visualize or describe about water is the chaotic rolling motion and interchange of its molecules in their liquid excitement. This is a highly complex turbulence not notice-ably suggested by the gentle, macrocosmic rhythm of the barcarole. Although water's hydrogen bonds strictly enforce the law of 2.9-angstrom separation between molecules, the individual hydrogen atoms themselves are bandied about irregularly among the larger oxygens like coins in the marketplace but without ever forgetting their marital proportion of two hydrogens to one oxygen. To accomplish this, the single H electrons must keep popping in and out of the two vacancies in the outer oxygen shells like pistons in an engine even if, unlike pistons, few of them seem to hit the same engine twice. And all the time the hydrogens keep rolling from oxygen to oxygen in their peculiar chain-reaction, zipperlike motion. Of course, it hardly needs mentioning that the angle be-tween the two H atoms in the H_2O molecule cannot remain a definite 105°, as in ice, but becomes variable, adding greatly to water's flexibility. And the excess of energy that gives water so much of its vitality is suggested not only by the explosive com-bustibility of hydrogen in the presence of oxygen — which is what destroyed all the great European airships — but also by water's eager circle of surplus hydrogens crowding around every oxygen atom while, paradoxically, only a few angstroms away three frus-trated oxygens may fight over a single little hydrogen.

Naturally, this means that every atom in water sooner or later has valence intimacy with countless other hydrogens and oxygens, in effect making the whole body of the water, chemically speaking, a single large molecule. By this reasoning a microscopic water droplet floating in a cloud is not just a swarming quintillion of H_2O molecules but one single $H_{2,000,000,000,000,000,000}O_{1,000,000,000,000,000,000}$ molecule. And all the oceans of the earth can be scien-tifically approximated as simply $H_{2 \times 10^{46}} O_{10^{46}}$.

There are a few other reasons why H_2O alone does not fully express the nature of water. Water has turned out to be im-mensely more involved than the ancient mariner dreamed possible

— and is getting to appear more so every year. Probably its most revolutionary complexity turned up in 1934 when Harold Urey discovered "heavy water." He found that the purest water is made of something besides hydrogen and oxygen, something with an atomic weight of two, or double that of hydrogen. This substance, called deuterium, is a second form of hydrogen and is now known as an isotope. To explain isotopes, we must introduce a new elementary particle beside the proton and electron: the neutron. A neutron has essentially the same mass as a proton but it is electrically neutral. It is a basic part of the nuclei of all atoms except ordinary hydrogen and, although it has little chemical effect, the number of neutrons present in any atom determines what isotope or variety of the element it is. The deuterium nucleus contains one proton plus one neutron, around which circulates the usual lone electron as in ordinary hydrogen.

NEUTRONS AND ISOTOPES

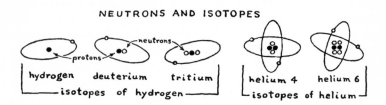

hydrogen　deuterium　tritium

— isotopes of hydrogen —

helium 4　helium 6

— isotopes of helium —

Deuterium or "heavy hydrogen" atoms are comparatively rare, accounting for only one out of about five thousand hydrogens, but these few also can combine with oxygen to form the compound D_2O. A drink of D_2O tastes almost exactly like H_2O but, mysteriously, seeds will not sprout in it and rats, watered with it, die of thirst. And now a third isotope of hydrogen, called tritium, is known, as well as the three isotopes of oxygen: O^{16}, O^{17} and O^{18}; these six variations of the two elements being combinable in eighteen different ways. When the several sorts of water ions (created by out-of-place electrons) are added, pure water is composed of at least 33 substances. And this is without even considering the foreign elements in ordinary water such as sodium, chlorine, carbon, calcium, sulfur, fluorine, potassium, nitrogen, phosphorus, magnesium, aluminum, lithium, boron, rubidium, zinc, iron, copper, lead and many others with their isotopes, ions and unnumbered compounds.

It is probably these alien complexities that are mainly responsible for the terrifying tricks that turbulent water full of bubbles can do. As every engineer knows, such water can, and often does, chew up a ship's propeller. It can punch holes in a water main until it looks like cheese or blast the valves of a giant dam as destructively as a high-explosive bomb.

You wouldn't think offhand that so much havoc could be wrought by nothing but water and bubbles. But the denseness of water makes it remarkably incompressible, and modern 20,000-frames-per-second photography has revealed that the walls of a collapsing bubble smack together with such a shattering impact that, delivered simultaneously by millions of bubbles and repeated trillions of times, it can make bubbles quite measurably eat away the hardest steel. Hidden behind this potent froth lies the mysterious phenomenon called cavitation, the curious hollowing out of water at its weak points. These microscopic flaws, we now know, are the real seeds of bubbles. Countless and ever-moving, they are the unassimilated oases of gas or solids that naturally flow throughout the dynamic homogeneity of the liquid.

How much actual difference they make is shown not only in the virtual elimination of bubbles when water is purified but also in the resulting increase of water's tensile strength. For, unlike gases which cannot pull liquid up a straw, pure water with its continuous bonds of hydrogen has the pulling power of a strong cable. Indeed, it is not only incompressible but virtually unstretchable. This pulling power explains how the tops of 300-foot sequoia trees get their moisture from the ground when transpiration from their leaves generates negative pressure in the sap arteries. The atmosphere does not push the water up, nor could water be pulled nearly so high if it had enough impurities in it to break the rolling continuity of linked hydrogen-oxygen-hydrogen-oxygen-hydrogen atoms. But the magical chains of extremely pure H_2O accomplish the lift easily and, according to laboratory tests by Dr. Lyman J. Briggs, could ideally pull their own weight vertically as high as 9,000 feet (nearly two miles) before snapping. In the words of Dr. Robert T. Knapp of the hydrodynamics laboratory at the California Institute of Technology, "You can hang heavy weights on an open tube of such water without breaking it. How? Just take a [large-sized] tube with both ends open, fill it with this water, and fit leakproof pistons or plungers into each end. Then . . . hang the top piston from the ceiling, and hang five hundred pounds on the bottom piston. The weight will be suspended there as if glued."

Most people feel they know the differences and changes in states of matter pretty well, especially in the familiar case of steam-water-ice, but even here things are not as simple as they seem. At least three distinct types of boiling have been observed and are now known as nuclear (the familiar burbling of separated bubbles in your teakettle), transition (the hotter, louder boiling where slugs of vapor form explosively over the whole heating surface at once), and film boiling (where a still hotter surface is blanketed with a thick, smooth, transparent film from which vapor rises in a steady roar). And there are at least six kinds of freezing, one of which produces an improbable ice of cubic molecular structure and another, under very high pressure, an ice so dense it sinks like glass in water.

There are also the partial freezings that produce so-called liquid crystals which look liquid but are revealed by polarized light to be organized as solid in one or two dimensions, their molecules forming either long brittle chains (as in some proteins) or filmy plates (as in graphite or silica gel) that can still slide or flow about in their unlocked second or third dimensions. And there are the uncrystallized, apparently frozen liquids like hard shoemaker's wax, which can be molded into a serviceable tuning fork but which, if a musician leaves it on his shelf for a few years, will be found to have flowed into a puddle of "honey." Glass is an extremely slow-flowing liquid of this type, tar a faster one, and the very hard, hot, dense, molten material inside the earth a particular case we have just begun to measure directly.

The basic difference between the liquid and solid states, of course, is always crystallization, the liquids having random, un-fixed molecules that can slip or slide past each other even if (as in glass) the frictional forces between them reduce the sliding to "slower than molasses," while the true solids have molecules that are locked into a regular crystal lattice whose forces not only pre-vent sliding but tend to restore any dislocated molecules to the original positions in the pattern.

Water, it must be remembered, is only one particular kind of liquid. Most of the others do not have its peculiar rolling motion of hydrogens and oxygens, but rather a sliding motion like a mass of lively snakes. The oils are good examples of this, for they are composed of a wide variety of such centipedelike molecules as the octane (C_8H_{18}) described earlier, or nonane (C_9H_{20}), decane ($C_{10}H_{22}$), nonadecane ($C_{19}H_{40}$) and much longer ones. You might suppose that these slithering serpentine members would lie fairly flat, belly-to-ground fashion, at least when oil is stretched out into its thinnest films, but surprisingly, due to lateral magnetic polarity, the oil snakes habitually stand on their heads, side by side, something like blades of grass clinging to metal in the manner of weeds on the bottom of an old boat. The evidence is that the hydrogen bonds at the "head" end of each molecule bite into unstable outer electrons of nearly any solid surface like so many leech mouths, while their "tail" ends swing free, per-mitting encroaching material (such as the ends of other oil mole-cules either similarly attached to near-by solids or part of loose intervening films) to slip past them without friction, willy-nilly. Hence derives oil's familiar oiliness as the classic lubricant, the slipperiest of the slippery, that makes machinery workable and eases the wheels and axles of the world.

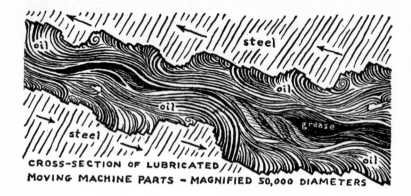

CROSS-SECTION OF LUBRICATED
MOVING MACHINE PARTS — MAGNIFIED 50,000 DIAMETERS

Greases and fats and soaps are all made out of long chain molecules more or less the same as oil — and each kind works in its own surprising way. Soap, for instance ($C_{17}H_{35}COO\text{-}Na$), has a snaky molecule of some seventeen carbon atoms, each with two little hydrogens attached, an extra hydrogen on one end for a tail and a large head of oxygen, carbon and sodium (Na). It so happens that the sodium of the head has an affinity for water and for that reason it reaches out toward the nearest H_2O molecules whenever the soap is wetted as in washing. The hydrogen tail, on the other hand, is repelled by water and tends to avoid it by clinging to anything else it can find around such as molecules of grease or other bits of foreign matter which, in such a context, are considered as dirt. Thus each microscopic speck of dirt is

CROSS-SECTIONAL
VIEW

SOAP AT WORK

progressively caught by the tails of all the soap molecules that reach it until it is surrounded by thousands or millions of them all facing outward, completely covering and insulating it from the water. That is soap's age-old secret, its technique of cleaning. It swallows the dirt as a mermaid swallows oysters and, mermaidlike, its long molecular tresses swirl outward into the water in cascades of microscopic loveliness, creating an exotic world of significance hitherto undreamed in your washtub.

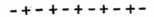

In order to explain water's action as a solvent, it is helpful here to introduce a basic ingredient of the earth's oceans and a real common denominator of blood, sweat and tears: salt. Although salts are of many varieties, which can be defined in general as compounds of acid and basic radicals (made of excess positive and negative ions respectively) whose magnetic interaction gives them their characteristic salty tang, we will consider just simple sodium chloride (NaCl) or table salt. If you can abide a bawdy little illustrative analogy, let NaCl stand for an eager sailor named Nate (Na) who has just come down the gangplank to take in tow an attractive and well-stacked dame called Chloe (Cl). Such a briny combination of male and female elements, one of whom can receive exactly as much as the other can give, closely parallels the union of sodium (Na because the Romans called it natrium), its lone (eleventh) electron protruding outside its second shell, and chlorine (Cl), wanting a single (eighteenth) electron for fulfillment in its third shell. Almost as soon as the two atoms touch each other, inevitably Nate's prodigal electron finds a welcome haven while Chloe's need is precisely filled, and the resulting compound (salt) is strongly held together in a very stable cubic lattice of alternating sodium and chlorine atoms that are true atoms no longer.

Chemists sometimes describe the reaction in this pseudo-romantic valence as the "burning" of sodium in chlorine. Certainly it is violent enough to be considered a kind of combustion, and the powerful magnetic bonds thus created obviously derive from the fact that Nate is not quite all of himself afterward while Chloe has become more than she was and, as the new NaCl molecule, they are the salt of the earth both to each other and to the world — literally not independent atoms any more but just two linked ions: the male sodium ion (Na+), who has become positive by losing his negative extra electron in chlorine, and the female chlorine ion (Cl−), who has become negative by accepting the same negative electron from sodium. Thus the eternal masculine and feminine principles repeat themselves in the atomic realm as positive and negative ions, Nate and Chloe, ever distinct yet ever yearning to be one — even when dissolved in the sea.

This brings up the unique solvency of water, the ancient mystery of the deep, where salt is so thoroughly dissolved it never sinks to the bottom and the problem of economically separating it from the H_2O has become a major object of modern research. Water's extraordinary solvency, indeed, stems from its high "dielectric constant," exceeding that of any other known liquid, which can reduce the attraction between oppositely charged ions in solution to scarcely 1 percent of their original strength. Water molecules do this by ruthlessly swarming over and between the embracing ions in their midst like ants upon their prey, effectively "swallowing" the ions in the manner of soap molecules swallowing dirt. Since electrons shared between the oxygen and hydrogen atoms in water (H_2O) are perceptibly closer to the oxygen atoms, the oxygens have a slight net negative charge while the hydrogens are measurably positive. This is why the oxygen (−) parts of water molecules cluster around each positive ion, such as sodium (Na+), and why the hydrogen (+) parts crowd in upon each negative ion, such as chlorine (Cl−). It is water's own magnetic formula for dissolving ionic matter — by insulating and neutralizing its parts. It is why the oceans have become steadily saltier for billions of years and must go on getting saltier — even as the Great Salt Lake and the Dead Sea.

The simple, cubic, lattice structure of solid salt is a good introduction to the formation of crystals, which are the only completely rigid solids. Dry salt (NaCl), in which all lattice angles

are right angles (90°) and where each sodium ion is surrounded by six equidistant chlorine ions (north, south, east, west, up, down) and vice versa, is like the basic, cubic girder outline of a steel office building — the simplest possible repeating pattern of form. And it is not held together just by magnetic force, like a nail that can cling at any angle to a bar magnet or swing from a single point, but is in effect riveted and cross-linked at several points with each neighboring member. Its strength is shown by its high melting point, below which even the most violent thermal vibrations of the molecular girders are not enough to break the rivets.

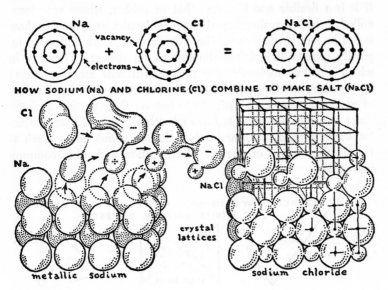

HOW SODIUM (Na) AND CHLORINE (Cl) COMBINE TO MAKE SALT (NaCl)

And yet the simple regularity of the salt crystal is formed automatically, by nature's way of least resistance, either when sodium "burns" in chlorine or when salt water evaporates, leaving solid salt behind. In either case, the sodium and chlorine ions just naturally group themselves alternately like boys and girls at a party where every boy wants a girl on either side and every girl wants to sit between two boys — only the "sex instinct" of salt ions is so much stronger that it is virtually impossible for two similar ions to touch each other at all, with the result that they form a completely regular three-dimensional pattern of plus-minus-plus-minus-plus ions, the salt lattice, simplest of crystals.

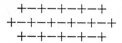

Just as other crystals are more complex than that of table salt, however, so are most molecules more irregular and complicated in form and nature. Yet all have some sort of definite shape, even if it is a flexible one like, say, that of rubber, whose very long, coiled, swiveling-spring-shaped chain molecules easily explain how it can be stretched to many times its natural length and yet completely recover its original dimensions on release. The way in which any two molecules (or their constituent atoms or ions) fit together, whether snugly, rigidly, loosely or flexibly, depends, of course, not only on their shape but on their motion and the exact way they are presented to each other. Quite different structures may indeed be formed out of the same molecules — such as the different kinds of quartz, sulfur, carbon and other common materials.

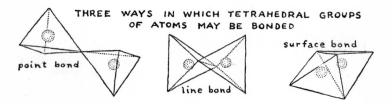

THREE WAYS IN WHICH TETRAHEDRAL GROUPS OF ATOMS MAY BE BONDED

point bond

line bond

surface bond

All this becomes increasingly understandable as you look deeper into molecular shapes, which, as they become more complex, tend to produce more lacelike or spongelike forms with many long narrow struts and stays like a cantilever bridge or like any sort of elaborate scaffolding. The emptiness of such trestlework accounts for the low density of the very complicated organic molecules, few of which are much heavier than water. The simplicity of the little two-atom molecules, on the other hand, produces denser stuff such as rubies or iron pyrites and the simplest-of-all single-atom units of pure elements make the even denser iron, silver, lead or gold, where the struts are no more than knobs, permitting the bridgework to pack down into something resembling a neat stack of bricks.

If the lattice patterns of such crystals are even more countless than wallpaper designs or musical themes, it is not because they are any less bound to repeat themselves in their three-dimensional way. For in doing just that, they make themselves the third stage or size order above the atoms and molecules of which all solid matter is constructed: an order now usually known as the crystal unit, which seldom has a definite place of beginning or ending but, like wallpaper, has a fixed magnitude to its repeating pattern no matter where you begin measuring it. By way of example, there are *atoms* called silicon and oxygen, and a *molecule* of silicon dioxide made of one silicon atom joined in a particular way to two oxygens. And now we discover there is also a *crystal unit* named quartz, which consists of three molecules of silicon dioxide arranged in a certain spiral or screw form. Like the flowers on a papered wall, you can mark a piece of quartz anywhere (at any molecule) and the pattern will repeat after every unit distance (the length of three silicon dioxide molecules) as far as the crystal extends. Each such unit has all the basic properties of quartz. In fact, it *is* quartz. It is the smallest possible piece of quartz. For nothing less has ever been demonstrated to be quartz. A single molecule of silicon dioxide quite definitely is not quartz. Even two such molecules, however aligned, cannot be quartz because quartz is actually a spiral lattice, and it takes three molecules to create its essential screw pattern.

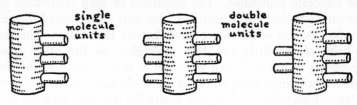

BASIC MOLECULAR PATTERNS IN CRYSTALS

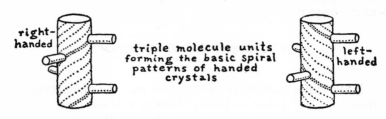

This truth is so important and characteristic of matter that it is worth the effort of visualization. Each molecule can be considered as a peg sticking out of a piece of broomstick. If the unit of pattern is one molecule, then every peg must exactly copy the peg next to it, all sticking out the same side of the broomstick in an even row. If the unit is two molecules, the pegs can stick out two sides of the stick, perhaps alternately. And it is only when the unit reaches three that they can occupy three sides of the stick, making possible the forming of a kind of rudimentary spiral staircase which has the option of turning either to right or left, clockwise or counterclockwise, as it goes down the broomstick. Something like this in essence is accepted as the explanation of the two kinds of quartz, often called right- and left-handed, whose crystal faces, observed in sequence, spiral off to right or left and correspond to quartz's well-known power of rotating the plane of polarization of light in either direction.

Such handedness (right or left), of course, is possible only to a perfect crystal whose lattice forms a single and continuous system. The growth of such a regular lattice, as crystallographers have long known, must start from a single nucleus, such as a microscopic dust particle or some other irregularity or happenstance that somehow brings the first molecules together into the key relationship. From here on, succeeding molecules will naturally follow the pattern already established as the line of least resistance, layer after layer of them continuously attaching themselves to the growing crystal in the correct order, settling out of formless gas or liquid into regimented solid, like the spool-shaped snow crystal that literally begins with an invisible dust mote in the sky. Obviously, only a very slow and peaceful accumulation will give the lattice flawless regularity — a circumstance nature in the raw can seldom provide — which accounts for the rarity of large naturally perfect crystals like the Hope diamond. So most crystalline solids turn out to be conglomerations of many small, if not microscopic, individual lattices that sprang from separate nuclear seeds, like large snowflakes which are the agglutinations of hundreds or thousands of tiny hexagonal crystals that collided by chance during their hours or weeks of development in the sky.

This is not to say that the joining of any kind of molecules into a crystal lattice cannot be studied from an ideal or abstract view, and the mathematicians have actually been ahead of the physicists and chemists in working out many of the laws of crystallography. Long before Euclid, some geometer asked himself, can I pave a floor with regular-shaped tiles of any number of sides? The answer, of course, quickly proved to be no. Only three kinds of regular tiles will fit to cover the whole area: the triangle, the square and the hexagon. This seemed quite obviously a divine restriction. Centuries later, Plato was thrilled by the revelation

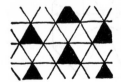
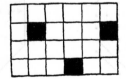
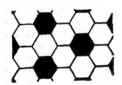

that a comparable decree limited the number of regular convex solids to five — the same five that Kepler would one day use to test his planetary spheres.

Although this did not have an obvious bearing on natural things of the earth as then understood, a time was to come after nearly two thousand years when a Danish bishop called Steno began to experiment scientifically with the "regular solids" of crystals, a research which culminated in 1782 when the Abbé René Just Haüy, a French crystallographer, discovered that the curious regular angles of any known crystal could be mathematically explained by the simple assumption that the crystal was composed of many very small identical regular "bricks." Haüy's Law of Rational Indices was not soon accepted, but it marked the first actual measurement of atoms or molecules and, perhaps more importantly, gave the first concrete understanding of space quantization as applied to the microscopic world — an answer to the ancient Greeks who had pondered the ultimate nature of matter and more than a hint that the same music of the spheres which separates the rings of Saturn also regulates the orbits of entities so tiny they have never been directly observed.

Haüy's Law was another way of saying that the lattice spacings of atoms permit certain particular crystal symmetries — and no others. A square made up of evenly spaced dots, for instance, cannot be turned into a regular octagon (figure of eight equal sides) no matter how you slice it, because that would mean dividing each side of the square into three parts in the proportion of $1:\sqrt{2}:1$ — which is impossible with integral dots because $\sqrt{2}$ is not an integer.

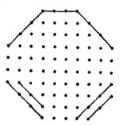
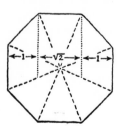

You probably did not learn this sort of thing in school, of course, because it is not included in Euclid's geometry of *lines*. Crystals instead follow the earlier geometry of Pythagoras, a geometry of *points*, from which evolved the modern Theory of Discontinuous Groups, which has already discovered much more than physics has been able to use. One of its simplest theorems, for example, proves that "the symmetry elements of crystals can be grouped in 32 different ways, and no others."

The crystallographers have long since then sorted every known crystal, according to its outer shape, into one of these 32 classes. But the mathematicians did not pause at the outer crystal and, imagining the atoms and molecules inside might also have characteristic shapes, they had proved by the end of the nineteenth century that "there are just 230 different ways of distributing identical objects of arbitrary shape regularly in space," a triumph of abstract theoretical logic that unexpectedly took on great practical importance in 1912 when x-ray analysis of the interior of crystals first made possible their actual sorting into the 230 space groups already divined.

Just as the Periodic Table of elements was found to follow a kind of insistent, sagacious harmony, the natural arrangement of atoms thus proved to be tuned to a deep but fathomable music of its own — if one more peremptory yet perhaps also one more beautiful than any contemplated by Pythagoras.

Such modern melodies of the spheres may, I think, be most simply introduced as the keys to something formal and familiar like those historic piles of spherical shot heaped up beside the century-old cannon of war memorials. For those neat pyramids of cannonballs represent exactly how the atoms are packed in the lattices of gold, silver, copper, aluminum and other elemental crystals. If you study such a pile carefully, you will find that any ball in the interior of it touches exactly twelve other balls: six around its equator at the same level and three around each temperate zone, above and below. There is obviously no closer way to pack spheres, but there are two forms of this twelve-point packing. After the second layer of cannonballs has been placed upon the first with each ball nesting in a hollow between three below it, the third layer can be so started that none of its balls will be directly above any of the lower balls (as in the piles of ancient shot) or so that every ball is exactly above one of the first-layer balls. These two basic alternatives are possible because there is room for a ball only in every second hollow of each layer and, in the choosing of which set of hollows to use, it is the third layer (like the third molecule in quartz) whose position in relation to the other two makes the crucial difference.

It so happens that the first of these packing alternatives tends to make a large lattice of spheres form a cube, and probably for this reason grains or flakes of gold, silver, copper or aluminum are normally cubic or squared off in 90° angles as seen under the

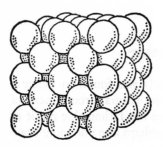

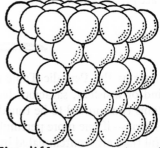

The atomic packing of gold tends toward a cubic form.

The different packing of magnesium tends toward a hexagonal spool.

THE PACKING OF SPHERES

Looking vertically down on a pile of cannon balls, as here, we see two hollows, A and B, in either of which we may place a ball to start a third layer. Choice A leads to the cubic lattice of gold (above), choice B to the hexagonal lattice of magnesium.

microscope. The second packing, on the other hand, tends to produce a hexagonal spool of 60° angles as in the crystals of magnesium, which, for some still unknown reason, always employ this alternative.

Entirely different and looser ways of packing spheres or atoms, of course, may also produce cubic, octagonal, hexagonal and other forms, such as the simple salt cubes already described where each ion touches six others, the more complex iron and steel crystals where each atom meets eight neighbors and quadrilateral and octagonal forms abound, or the lovely hexagonal ice crystals where every molecule touches only four mates. Plainly, four is the minimum number of touch points in solid packing, for no lattice could keep from collapsing (melting) if all its component spheres supported one another in only three places. Yet this minimal tetrahedral packing need not be weak, as is evidenced by the diamond, hardest of natural substances, which is nothing but a four-point lattice of carbon atoms at angles of 109° 28' from each other.

Moreover, there is plenty of mystery behind the simple beauty of a diamond, one soon discovers, for its strictly equidistant, tetrahedral structure is definitely less stable at ordinary temperatures than another somewhat similar but looser three-point packing of carbon, the nonequidistant one that forms graphite. How two such different materials as a diamond and a pencil "lead" can be made of the same latticed carbon atoms just by switching from four-point to three-point packing is difficult to see, especially as the layers of both materials show virtually identical

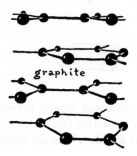

graphite

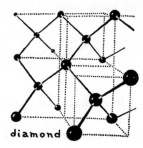

diamond

hexagonal honeycomb patterns when viewed broadside in the electron microscope. But the explanation obviously lies somewhere in the angular relationships among the carbons, which crowd closer together for diamond (density 3.51) and stretch farther apart for graphite (density 2.25). This shift is revealed by x-rays to act entirely in one direction (perpendicular to the honeycombed layers), thus inevitably separating the lattice planes of the graphite far enough to weaken seriously the atomic ties or any other causes for friction between their smooth surfaces which, once turned loose to slide easily over one another, give this solid lubricant its characteristic plumbaginous slipperiness.

It was only in February 1955, by the way, that the actual transformation of graphite into the prince of gems was proved possible for the first time when four researchers of General Electric Company finally solved this long-baffling problem in synthesis — a job that turned out to be much harder than shifting a layer of cannonballs into its alternate set of hollows, though not so different in principle. The pressure at which diamond becomes more stable than graphite had been calculated to be about twenty thousand times greater than that of sea-level atmosphere at room temperature. Yet prolonged pressures even as high as 425,000 atmospheres proved unable to budge graphite "over the hump" from its relatively unstable posture until it was heated (at a somewhat reduced pressure) to nearly 4,000° F., a point where its thermodynamic state must have approximated that in the natural diamond wombs deep under the earth, for suddenly the carbon layers snapped together into the 109° 28′ diamond configuration — at one flash turning a pencil "lead" into a jewel a third smaller but worth many hundred times more!

There is inevitably an element of guesswork in any pioneering experiment in crystallography, because no actual crystal lattice can be perfect or complete in this irregular world. There are bound to be holes in it somewhere or long rifts or faults where one layer shears against another, the dislocated surfaces attracting or repelling each other according to whether the areas of compression (+) in one match up with areas of tension (−) in the other or whether areas of similar "sign" clash in opposition. Such dislocations or grain boundaries are inevitably under relative stress on the average and are therefore known to crystallographers as regions of energy. Because of uneven resistance to their progress, they tend to follow spiral courses in the lattice while, collectively, their reactions upon one another cause them to align in curious invisible waves that creep forward something like dunes on the desert.

Although a single large crystal is seriously weakened and normally breaks only where there is a slipping of molecules along one plane, most crystals are compounds of many tiny semi-independent lattice systems for the same reason that marbles poured casually upon a tray will arrange themselves in tight groupings at various odd angles to one another. This is why wrought metal is tougher than cast metal, for hammering it and working it increases the number of dislocations and regions under stress — and stress means hardness or strength.

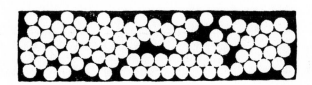

Yet there are kinds of stress, and each has its limits in each kind of lattice. The elasticity of spring steel in a safety pin obviously depends on the magnetic bonds that give its atoms their capacity to recover their original stable positions after being stretched or strained within definite limits. If forced beyond the so-called "yield point," steel will start to "creep." Elasticity will begin to be replaced by plasticity or ductility and, perhaps farther on, a fracture, depending on the exact combination of stress and material. You might not guess that a rock could be so bouncy, but by 1957 researchers had succeeded in fashioning a spring out of quartz, finer than a human hair and coiled to about an inch long, that can be stretched to arm's length, its elasticity so perfect it "never" develops fatigue. Such a spring has since been used in a gravity meter so sensitive no term is known for what it can measure.

In many compounds, elasticity is affected also by the tendency of minority atoms to coalesce like ice crystals in the sky, forming snowflakelike centers of foreign structure that, as they grow with the passing years, eventually constitute the collective weakness known as age hardening. And several kinds of evidence show that even in the densest solids atoms are far from absolutely fixed. Though most of them may be anchored most of the time, their "chains" permit them to vibrate about a mean position, while some are always shuffling from mooring to mooring, others more freely drifting or even flowing merrily along like a brook or a breeze. Under stress, minority atoms have repeatedly been observed to "float" or "sink" toward the tension or compression levels of a lattice, depending on whether they were bigger or smaller than their fellows, and in the case of quenching red-hot metal may often produce a fallout amounting to a kind of atomic hailstorm.

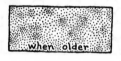

Just as perfume diffuses almost instantaneously through air and dye almost as fast through water, so do solids diffuse in their subtle way through solids. The process is surprisingly rapid when two heated metals are clamped tightly together, such as two cylinders (of gold and lead) which interfused almost completely within a few days in the famous experiment in 1896 in England conducted by Sir William Roberts-Austen, Assayer of the Mint. Even a gas will deeply pervade a solid; thus do the carbons out of methane readily creep into the lattice hollows in very hot iron to make case-hardened steel.

Solid diffusion is mechanically like putting a few black marbles into a box almost full of white ones, then shaking it. Even if the box is quite tightly packed, the slightest bit of play will enable some marbles to alternate their positions and the black marbles will move about and distribute themselves among the white at a diffusion rate related to the tempo of shaking which, atomically speaking, is the temperature. The tiny atoms of hydrogen thus leak through the densest materials with particular ease, making it practically impossible to purify anything else in their presence.

O·O·O·O·O·O·O·O
O·O·O·O·O·O·O·O·O
O·O·O·O·O·O·O·O·O

Purity in earthly matter is of necessity a relative term, for even so-called pure gold, the buried coin of the realm, is about .4 percent copper and other "impurities." Only recently has science discovered how to insulate and refine an element to the degree of eliminating all but one alien atom per billion, as in the case of a new metallic silicon that has doubled the heat resistance of missile transistors and as "the purest product ever made by man" (for $980 a pound) is helping to open up a new age of metals — the latest in the long sequence of metallic ages that began about 4000 B.C. with the discovery of copper, probably on the upper Nile. From bronze, which shortly afterward appeared as an alloy (90 percent copper, 10 percent tin) much harder than copper, through iron and steel, which have dominated the metals ever since the early days of swords and made possible the Industrial Revolution, the modern light-metals age of aluminum, magnesium and titanium developed into the present advent of specialized metals like zirconium, hafnium and beryllium (of great importance in atomic piles for their effect on neutrons), uranium, plutonium and thorium (as fuels), molybdenum (in jet engines), lithium, lightest of solids (as a lubricant) germanium (in transistors), gallium and so on — each individually and in combination being explored actively and continuously for new uses. A good three quarters of the elements of the Periodic Table, technically speaking, are metals — the solid underpinnings of material civilization — although many of them are too soft for usefulness while unmixed and so must be judiciously alloyed with others before they can serve humanity.

The hardness and strength of alloys as compared with elemental metals obviously derive from their compound structure: the zinc atoms lodged in the copper lattice that make it brass, the precise combination of chromium, cobalt and tungsten that creates the very hard, noncorrosive stellite, the innumerable and mysterious harmonic crystal intervals in the various resonant alloy combinations that put the ring into bells. The hardness in each case comes from the pressure of foreign matter warping or crimping the smooth lattice. It is as if one had dumped sand into an engine journal. The sliding planes have been jammed. This effect is perhaps shown most clearly by its absence in the surprisingly pliable copper-nickel alloy long used for encasing bullets, a metal mixture later revealed by x-rays to be soft because the nickel atoms added to the copper happen to match the copper atoms so closely in size that they just slip into vacancies in the copper lattice without appreciable strain.

The famous medieval swords made in India and sold to the western world from Damascus are a fine example of special alloy qualities. For one of the marks of genuine "Damascus steel" was the characteristic wavy whorl pattern which, under a modern microscope, turns out, like the Milky Way in a telescope, to be composed of curving bands of millions of independent specks. These have now been analyzed as cementite crystals, tiny clusters of molecules made up of three atoms of iron combined with one of carbon, which is the form excess carbon takes after the treated hot iron has absorbed all the loose carbon atoms it can hold in its lattice hollows.

By a long process of heating, cooling and hammering, during which the cementite crystals had their needlelike points rounded off, the swordsmith would work the steel into a state of remarkable

TEMPERED CEMENTITE STEEL
MAGNIFIED 1000 TIMES

strength combined with great elasticity, the edge receiving its keen-
ness in large part from the very hard, invisible cementite particles
that acted as teeth in an extremely fine saw. Such, no doubt, is
the secret of the noble blades used in the famous trial of skill
between Richard the Lion-Hearted and Saladin, described by Sir
Walter Scott, in which the crusader, taking his sword in both
hands like an axe, came down with a terrific blow upon an outstretched mace, cleaving the heavy iron in twain. Whereupon the
defender of Islam threw a gossamer veil into the air and neatly
sliced it by drawing his scimitar across it until the two halves
fluttered separately to the ground. Veritably it was as much a con-
test between great qualities in the steel as between great men.

Grinding metal with a stone, of course, is just a slower way of
cutting into an ordered lattice, this time with the hard crystals of
silicon or quartz, whose sharp edges actually rake and hoe sizable
masses of molecules away. But polishing, surprisingly enough, is
a completely different thing, as it depends not on any sort of digging but on rubbing the metal of the surface until it is warm and
soft enough to flow into its own pits and furrows, often literally
drawing a pliant skin of material over the deeper crevices yet without quite destroying even the outer crystalline lattices.

The fact that heat and electricity flow so easily through most
metals is evidently due to the comparatively loose outer-shell electrons in these elements. While lattices in general may be held
together by their wild-oat electrons acting as a kind of mortar, like
the four shared carbon electrons of the diamond molecule, the
conductive metals in particular have such lax valance electrons
that their atoms can roll, swivel and slide over one another to
an extraordinary degree, giving the pure state of each of these
substances its characteristic ductility as well as providing innumerable easy channels for the transmission of thermal and electromagnetic energy.

Just as heat is nothing but average molecular and atomic motion (including the motion of electrons), electricity turns out to be primarily a stream of valance (outer) electrons, which may have been induced by a generator or a battery to circulate around and around a loop-shaped wire. Obviously, the generator no more creates the electrons than an engine driving a leather belt manufactures leather. It is just because each copper atom happens to have its first three shells completely filled with two, eight and eighteen electrons respectively, while that single footloose twenty-ninth electron is itching in its outer shell with practically nothing to hold it, that copper (element 29) is such a good conductor of electricity. The relationship of heat to electricity is shown by the increase in electrical resistance as a metal gets hotter until, near the melting point, atomic motion becomes so great that electricity can hardly be conducted through it at all. Conversely, electrical resistance decreases with cooling until suddenly (in the case of many substances) it ends slightly above absolute zero in the phenomenon known as superconductivity — which permits a current, once started by a generator, to keep on running (or coasting) for days after the generator has been removed.

A FLOWING ELECTRIC CURRENT OF ELECTRONS AMONG ATOMS

The strange world of absolute zero, having now been virtually attained, is teaching us a good deal not only about electricity and magnetism but about several others of the deeper significances of matter, as we will see in the next chapter. Meantime, I need only mention that most solids, logically enough, take on an increasing brittleness (the opposite of moltenness) as they grow cold: a steel hammer may break into pieces if used in 50° F.-below-zero weather, while rubber at — 310° F. (the temperature of liquid air) will shatter like glass, and petals crumble to the touch — yet lead, as it goes way down in temperature, becomes oddly elastic and resonant, mercury can be tied in knots and helium (superfluid at —456°) creeps out of a cup in defiance of gravity (see pages 356–57).

♌ ♀ ♌ ♂ ♄ ☿ ☽ ♆ ♃

There seems no end to the discoveries and uses of the natural materials of Earth, even though many elements have to be almost endlessly tested and tried before they achieve practical value. Sulfur, for instance, is not only expensive but extremely hard to find, coming mostly from salt domes a thousand feet underground. One could perhaps live a lifetime completely unaware of sulfur. Yet without sulfur there would be no giant industries and very possibly not enough bread or beef to feed us, for sulfuric acid, called the king of chemicals, plays some part in the manufacture of nearly everything we ever touch "from cotton diapers to bronze caskets." Land is fertilized with its aid. Oil is "cleaned" by it. Steel is "pickled" in it. Literally more than two hundreds pounds of it are consumed in the United States per year for every man, woman and child.

Have you heard of the group of fourteen elements (numbers 58 through 71) called the lanthanons or first series of rare earths? Not fitting very well into the general harmony of the Periodic Table, they form an odd little appendix in the sixth octave — yet together these metallic substances compose about .012 percent of the earth's crust and have unique magnetic properties, besides producing misch metal used in cigarette-lighter flints and as an additive in steel, while their chlorides aid the production of chrome, aluminum, silk, fertilizer and dentifrices. Most common of them, cerium (element 58) has made its mark, in oxide form, as a polish for optical glass.

Glass, incidentally, is a fused mixture of sand, alkali and lime, from which research has already developed such varied products as woolly insulation, woven fabrics, sponge-glass building blocks that look like limestone but weigh a twentieth as much and make excellent floats for life rafts, a glass "grease" that lubricates white-hot extrusion steel and a new plate glass you can drive nails through.

The Assyrians evidently were the originators of chain mail as protection against swords and spears, and chain mail has a modern parallel in fiber metallurgy, which, by using techniques borrowed from the paper industry, has now created the light, porous but strong "matted-metal" felt that bonds the linings of jet engines, reinforces jolt-proof ceramics and is easy to shape into the most complex forms.

The ancient Chinese, for their part, reputedly discovered that quilted cotton is nearly as good as chain mail at stopping sword thrusts, to say nothing of being more comfortable betweentimes — and this in turn finds its modern counterpart in the army's "bullet-proof" nylon jacket that proved its value in Korea by halving the numbers of casualties. "More efficient ballistically than any available metal," the nylon in the fused layers of this eight-pound garment will "resist a .45 bullet fired pointblank" and "virtually all grenade fragments from an explosion three feet away."

Nylon, by the way, is just one of the great and bewildering variety of "giant-molecule" synthetics that now seem to be almost exploding from the researchers' test tubes — products that include fibers, films, foams, glues, rubbers and plastics of all kinds — and which are all artificially put together out of the long chain type of molecule found naturally in oil, coal, wood, rubber or anything that is alive or has ever been alive. Without going into the organic basis of these so-called high polymers here, I must point out that study of them has at last given man his clearest concept of what causes the characteristic properties of matter and has made possible the nailable glass, bulletproof nylon, squeezable bottles, unbreakable records, waterproof sheeting, unshrinkable cloth and so on that so embellish modern civilization.

Indeed, perhaps most important of all the lessons of the giant molecules is that the degree of freedom in molecular motion is what mainly determines whether something is glassy, woody, leathery, rubbery, clayey, gluey, greasy, soupy, watery. For it is an oversimplification to say such states are just a matter of temperature, even though heat produces fluidity and the average piece of plastic will change from the glassy to the rubbery state in rising 80 degrees on the Fahrenheit scale. Nor can one say that states are dependent merely on the length of the molecular chains, even though the lengthening of chains does increase solidity — the boiling point of petroleum products, for instance, is known to rise 1 percent for every 2 percent increase in chain length. It is rather more a question of how tightly bound, how closely branched and cross-linked are the chains — in effect, how sticky or tangled the molecular spaghetti.

VARIOUS STATES OF LONG-CHAIN-MOLECULE (POLYMER) PLASTICS

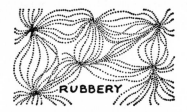
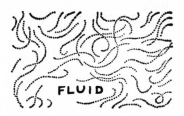

When a cool, brittle plastic is warmed and softened, its frozen molecules, which were only quivering, begin to squirm. The spaghetti comes alive. At first only short segments of it move. Perhaps a stretch of four or five atoms rolls slightly. Then a string of two dozen atoms arches its spine. What was glassy is turning leathery. And still the spaghetti is listless and not fully aroused. But as longer and longer segments start twitching and rippling in manifestation of heat, the "leather" inevitably softens. How much toughness it retains naturally depends on how tightly knotted or how frequently cross-linked are its chains. If the chains are aligned preponderantly in one direction, of course the material will have greater tensile strength in that direction. In any case, it is not long before hundreds of atoms are free to swing in unison like skip-ropes between the link points, while intermittently coiling and recoiling within the limits of their bonds. By this time, the stuff has become definitely rubbery, its elasticity depending partly on the amplitude of free coils between linkages, which, by un-coiling, permit it to stretch, and partly on the energy of its random writhing, which, by tirelessly opposing the stretching, ensures its eventual complete recovery. The molecular action in rubber can thus be compared to two girls, one at each end of a whirling skip-rope, who have a hard time pulling apart against the centrif-ugal force of the rope — analogous to stretching the rubber. The farther apart they go, of course, the more strongly the whirling energy in the rope resists them, until ultimately it draws them back together to their original distance — letting the rubber return to rest in its natural dimensions. Such a struggle between oppos-ing forces well explains why a rubber band heats up when it is stretched or, similarly, why a gas heats up when it is compressed, both materials being subjected to stresses resisted by the relentless energy of normal molecular motion.

EXTENSIBILITY OF THE RUBBER MOLECULE

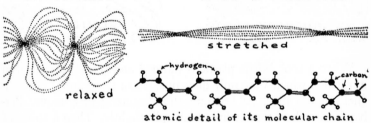

stretched

relaxed

atomic detail of its molecular chain

If its temperature keeps on going up, most rubbery materials must eventually yield their shape, turn gooey, and begin to ooze like honey as the link points in the spaghetti come apart, the skip-rope softens and breaks and whole molecules start sliding past one another. Stickiness is here revealed as the collective effect of friction opposing the independent motion of entire chains, or as magnetic snarls in the tangle that is writhing and struggling to be free. Plastic engineers control such viscosity mainly by regulating the chain length or degree of polymerization, cracking the molecules into shorter pieces for greater fluidity or building them longer for toughness and rigidity. A plastic's tendency to flow or creep can even be entirely stopped (up to surprisingly high temperatures) if the somewhat shifty centers of entanglement are reinforced or replaced by chemical cross-links from chain to chain.

In fact, this is exactly what Charles Goodyear accidentally discovered in the winter of 1839, when, according to one story, the bouncy little inventor got mad at the snickers of onlookers in the general store at Woburn, Massachusetts, and threw his experimental handful of sticky "gum elastic" mixed with sulfur upon the hot potbellied stove. A few moments later, recovering his composure enough to scrape it off, he was amazed to see that, "instead of melting like molasses, it had charred like leather." Quite unwittingly, he had created the first weatherproof rubber — cross-linked by vulcanization.

Yet sulfur is not the only boon to rubber. When the tire industry grew up, it was discovered that the addition of a handful of pulverized carbon black can make a 5,000-mile tire good for 40,000 miles. Although at first this was not clearly attributable to the fact that a single pound of these grimy granules of charcoal possesses more than an acre of total surface, most of which will adhere to the rubber molecules, today the surfaces of solids in general (and powders in particular) have come to be recognized as fairly bursting with energy — energy that is expendable in any form from gripping a turnpike to fueling a fire — a truth not easy to deny in the face of the all-too-frequent explosions of dusty grain elevators and ill-ventilated flour mills.

And so, we orbit onward into the mysterious fields of energy that the physical sciences, for all their experiments with ferocious boron fuels and the terrifying hydrogen plasmas (stolen from the sun), have hardly begun to explore — on into fields that await our deeper understanding of the atom, of its nucleus and, if that be possible, even of the mystic abstractions that seem to be matter's essence.

10. the netherrealm of the atom

AS I LOOK UP out of the deep sky, I find it almost as easy
to see atoms as stars — especially now with my mind's eye coming
into fuller focus. For sometimes the electrons seem to stream
past me like missiles out of the abyss. I cannot think of it as
night, there being no night here. Instead, I try to remember that
this black surround with the lights that streak across it is part of
my native orbit, part of my world which has just begun to explore
itself. And I reflect that these electron missiles are probably everywhere — moving even through the darkness of my own body —
and that, as with any vehicles in the gloom, there is no knowing
who or what or how many influences may be guiding them.

Nor can I seriously think of evading such ubiquitous and will-
ful mysteries. On the contrary, they consume me. Explore them
I must, while they are ingredients of myself, the grain in my
world. I feel my consciousness plunging willy-nilly into their
deepest depths, heeding no travail, to test their very core.

The microscope is a helpful tool, of course, but one cannot lean on it over-far. For the microscope really only divides the mystery without, in itself, solving it. Better: the ample regimen of experimenting, tooled with ordered thought, particularly abstract logic. And it needs be focused on the question area. Can energy now be treated as a substance? Or is this begrained ether within the atom a secret outcrop of some wider, subtler growth? Where next will I sink my spade, where cast my hoe?

While grubbing steadfastly at the roots of things, indeed, I find so many bugs and stones I must use a sieve for grading the soil. And I need a fresh bearing now and again — a perspective of older days to keep my brain in orbit.

What did Empedocles of Agrigentum in Sicily think the world is made of? And what keeps it from falling apart?

"The earth is a kind of meal," he said in 450 B.C., "cemented together with water."

Did any of the ancient philosophers suspect there are signs of the zodiac also in the atomic world and changing billions of times a second? It seems extremely unlikely, since there was no generally known number higher than ten thousand nor any such thing as a clock or a standardized time interval shorter than a full day and night. But in any case, it is now virtually impossible to assay the dreams of science in the day of Archimedes, when a philosopher was regarded a magician if he could lift a half-ton stone with the help of four ropes arranged in a block and tackle. Even the simple lever required deep study by no less a man than the great Aristotle, who wrote in his *Mechanics*: "As the weight moved is to the weight moving it, so, inversely, is the length of the arm bearing the weight to the length of the arm nearer to the power."

But Aristotle kept on asking fundamental questions. What is density? Is there a center of gravity? And little by little, haltingly and often incorrectly, he formulated what historians now consider one of the earliest mathematical laws of dynamics: that the velocity of a moving object is directly proportional to the "force from behind" it and inversely proportional to the resisting effect of the medium it moves through. Some of his groping passages, written on goatskin in the middle of the fourth century B.C. are remarkably close to Newton's first and third laws of motion (see page 316):

> Bodies which are at rest remain so owing to their resistance.
> When one is running fast, it is hard to divert the whole body from its impetus in one direction to some other movement.
> The force of whatever initiates motion must be made equal to the force of that which remains at rest. For . . . as there is a necessary proportion between opposite motions, so there is between absences of motion. . . . As the pusher pushes, so is the pushed pushed, and with equal force.

The thinking behind such formulas appears the more extraordinary from the fact that it had virtually no benefit of experiment or careful measurement in either time or space, and it was, along with that of Democritos, perhaps man's very first serious attempt to define the basic laws of dynamics. Manifestly, the ancient philosophers were so intent on knowing WHY that they seldom asked HOW or HOW MUCH. The latter questions seemed to them unimportant, unworthy — the kind of thing that slaves and artisans would worry about. And so, lacking the support of accurate observation, their work on the whole was lamentably lame.

By the sixteenth century A.D., however, qualitative science had begun to shift toward quantitative science. Friar Roger Bacon's cry of "Experiment, experiment!" had been heard. Tycho Brahe became a great prophet of precision, and his successor Kepler, who had learned the lesson well, summarized it for the modern world: "To measure is to know."

At the same time the new-fledged spirit of experimentation was developing the technique of postulation, of trial and error as tools of learning — a method exemplified by the reaction of the English astronomer Thomas Blundeville, who, reading De Revolutionibus, remarked; "Copernicus . . . affirmeth that the earth turneth about and the sun standeth still . . . by help of which false supposition he hath made truer demonstrations of the motions and revolutions of the celestial spheres than ever were made before."

Galileo, meanwhile, was taking his place as the first great experimenter and sire of modern physics. He intuitively understood that HOW is a tough enough question for this stubborn world. "Nature nothing careth," as he put it, "whether her abstruse reasons and methods of operating be or be not exposed to the capacity of men."

GALILEO GALILEI

So he stalked nature with great patience, observing such simple things as a lamp swinging slowly back and forth in the cathedral of Pisa. He timed its cycles with his own pulse — he was seventeen then — until he was convinced of its absolute regularity, a realization that resulted seventy-seven years later in the building of the first pendulum clock. His meticulous experiments with the mechanics of fluids enabled him to invent the first thermometer (a glass bulb and tube filled with air and water). And his study of refraction produced the first astronomical telescope (see page 426), through which he measured the mountains of the moon, as well as his compound microscope (five feet long) through which flies appeared "like lambs, covered all over with hair, and with very pointed nails by means of which they can walk on glass while hanging feet upwards."

Less dramatic but more profound was Galileo's comprehension

of the concept of acceleration, which he defined as a change of velocity either in magnitude or direction. This was an abstract idea that no one seems to have thought much about before. And in using it to test the still accepted Aristotelian precept that a moving object requires a force to maintain it, Galileo easily demonstrated that it is not motion but rather acceleration which cannot occur without an external force. Deliberately rejecting common

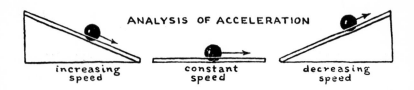

ANALYSIS OF ACCELERATION

increasing speed   constant speed   decreasing speed

sense as a prejudiced witness, he let nature herself speak in the form of a "hard, smooth and very round bronze ball" rolling down a "very straight" ideal groove lined with polished parchment, and then rolling up another groove, clocking each roll "hundreds of times" with "a thin jet of water collected in a small glass." Thus on the humble basis of fact he showed that, while downward motion (helped by gravity force) makes speed increase and upward motion (hindered by gravity force) makes speed decrease, there is always a "boundary case" in between the two where speed ideally remains constant (without any appreciable force) — and that, by reducing friction, this boundary case can be made to approach a horizontal level where gravity has no effect.

Similarly testing the speeds of various weights dropped from various heights, he also drafted a law of falling bodies: "that the distances traversed, during equal intervals of time, by an object falling from rest, stand to one another in the same ratio as the odd numbers beginning with unity." And his beautiful analysis of a cannonball's trajectory into horizontal and vertical components of motion and acceleration was one day to be of enormous help to Isaac Newton in solving the riddle of gravity.

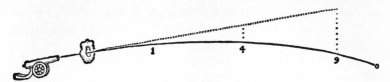

As Galileo had been born in 1564, the year Michelangelo died, so he died in 1642, the year Newton was born. Thus was the baton of scientific insight passed mysteriously from the blind, seventy-eight-year-old prisoner of the Papal Inquisition to a premature baby "tiny enough to put into a quart mug" whom no one expected to live. His father died three months before he was born and his mother soon remarried, so little Isaac was packed off to grandma's, which turned out to be an isolated farm near Grantham in the English midlands where there were no other children and little excitement save for the Cromwellian raiders who occasionally looted the "royalist" corn and animals.

Poring over medieval books on alchemy or mathematics while he was supposed to be tending sheep, the lonely boy grew up showing little promise as a farmer. But he learned to think for himself. It is told that one stormy day he wanted to find out how hard the wind was blowing. Having no weather instruments, he hit upon a unique method of his own: he jumped as far as he could against the gale and then jumped with it, carefully measuring the difference in distances, attributable to the wind during the time he was in the air, which readily gave him the wind's velocity.

At Cambridge, within three years of taking up geometry he had mastered the range of mathematics from Pythagoras to Isaac Barrow (his own teacher) so thoroughly that he had learned to generalize the so-called "infinitesimal geometry" into a new kind of analysis he called "fluxions," meaning roughly "rates of change" or "velocities." From Galileo's dynamics he naturally thought of a moving point as describing a curve. And, using Descartes' analytic geometry, he confidently placed the curve on a graph between coordinate axes, calling the vertical and horizontal components of the point's velocity the "fluxions" of x and y, denoted as "$\dot{x}$" and "$\dot{y}$." In logical consequence, the "fluxion" of the "fluxion

$\dot{x}$" became "$\ddot{x}$," a change of a change (motion) or an acceleration — and so on. This form of mathematics has since become known as the (differential) calculus.

Newton had to leave Cambridge in the fall of 1665 when the university closed on account of the great plague then raging in London, which eventually accounted for 68,000 deaths. So he went back to live in the dreary little house in Woolthorpe where he was born and there continued his amazing solitary research which included experiments with prisms into the nature of light and, most portentous of all, an effort to coordinate and complete the great investigations of Kepler and Galileo.

ISAAC NEWTON

$$F_{grav} = G \frac{m_1 m_2}{r_{12}^2}$$

Since it had become accepted knowledge that the earth is round with real antipodes where Chinese and Bushmen live upside down and where things fall upward in relation to Europe, there were a number of theories of gravitation already under serious discussion in university circles and in books — but evidently few of these envisioned the pervasive tendencies of falling objects as extending continuously beyond the region of the earth. Aristotle had maintained that the heavenly bodies, being composed of ethereal substance, could have "neither gravity nor levity." Copernicus, on the other hand, had speculated that "gravity is just a natural inclination, bestowed on the parts of bodies by the Creator . . . and we may believe this property present even in the sun, moon and planets." Some earlier philosophers had long since rationalized a law of symmetry as the motivating force of this ubiquitous hunger under which all things crave to attain the center of the universe, but Copernicus' demonstration that the earth may no longer be assumed to be in the central position had recently begun to undermine their argument. Descartes, with characteristic imagination, had visualized the whole heavens as a high-pressure

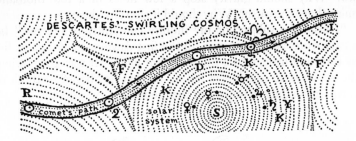

vortex of invisible atoms elevated by their swift circling motion and relentlessly pressing all heavy objects toward the center of the earth. Galileo had circumspectly contented himself with writing that "we do not really understand what principle of virtue moves a stone downward any more than we know what moves it upward when it is separated from the thrower, or what moves the moon round, except possibly that word (which more particularly we have assigned to falling), namely, gravity."

It remained solely for Kepler, most intuitive of all, to make the bold deduction that not only does a falling stone approach the earth, but also the earth approaches the stone. "If two stones," he wrote in his *Astronomia Nova* in 1609, "were removed to some place in the universe, close to each other but outside the sphere of force of any third cognate body, the two stones, like magnetic bodies, would come together at some intermediate place, each approaching the other through a distance proportional to the other's mass [*moles*]." And in his *Tertius Interveniens* (1610): "The planets are magnets and are driven around by the sun with magnetic force." Whereupon he predicted (correctly) that the sun must rotate and pictured its rays as giant arms directing the planets along their appropriate orbits.

But all these theories (and a score of others) seemed somehow weak and unconvincing, if not evasive, to Newton. And what did they add up to mathematically? He instinctively knew there must be a better explanation somewhere. He pondered intently upon the extent and mystical steadfastness of gravity, which, he felt, must be the manifestation of some simple, logical and general law. Why should gravity stop a few miles or a few thousand miles above the earth? Why should it stop anywhere?

"I keep the subject of my inquiry constantly before me," he was to write later, "and wait till the first dawning opens gradually, by little and little, into a full and clear light." It was about when the apples were ripe in the fall of '66 that he "began to think of gravity extending to the orb of the moon."

The ways of minds, of course, are inscrutable, and Newton could not later recall just how it happened (if, indeed, he was ever seriously interested in doing so), but a falling apple could well have been the means. After all, an apple in the air a few feet away appears about the same size as the moon. And both are objects that move naturally in our sight. Was there any reason to suppose the moon is excused from obeying the same law that applies to apples? Has any object ever been proved to be too big or too remote to fall? What about shooting stars, which Newton must have seen and wondered about? They come from far beyond the earth and yet apparently fall even faster than apples.

Is it not quite likely also that Newton had read in the introduction to *Astronomia Nova* Kepler's specific declaration that the earth is attracted by the moon as well as the moon by the earth? And might he not have heard of Kepler's original speculation that the intensity of this yearning is inversely proportional to the square of the distance of separation — though Kepler later emasculated his conjecture by unsquaring the distance, probably in the interest of simplification? Could some such hint have suggested a mathematical formulation of the all-pervasive influence that leaps from star to star?

Whatever put the far-fetched idea into his head, twenty-three-year-old Isaac suddenly saw the moon as something falling and, in his own words, "compared the force requisite to keep the moon in her orb [orbit] with the force of gravity at the surface of the earth, and found them to answer pretty nearly." From Kepler's established harmonic law that "the squares of the years are as the cubes of the orbits" he logically "deduced that the forces which keep the planets in their orbs must be reciprocally as the square of their distances from the centers about which they revolve." Since the moon was well known to be 60 times as far from the earth's center as we are at its surface, the earth's pull thus ought to be 60 squared, or 3,600 times as strong here as out where the moon is. And since things here fall sixteen feet toward the earth's center in the first second, out there things (including the moon) ought to fall only $\frac{1}{3,600}$ as far, about $\frac{1}{20}$ of an inch, in the same time — which tiny bit, to Newton's delight, turned out to be just what was needed to keep the moon (traveling $\frac{5}{8}$ of a mile a second) from flying off at a tangent out of her orbit.

In this manner did Newton derive his great law of the inverse square, which, however, he did not publish for more than twenty years, presumably because of doubt about certain accepted but crudely measured astronomical "facts," or perhaps an apprehension of controversy and probably neglect under the pressure of concentration upon such rival interests as alchemy and the solution of various challenging and cryptic riddles of medieval tradition: the elements of "the philosopher's stone," the elixir of life, the dimensions of Solomon's temple . . . Also, there is evidence that, although he knew intuitively from the beginning that "you could treat a solid sphere as though all its mass was concentrated at the centre," he did not hit on any mathematical proof of it until 1686. The time lag here can explain something of how Newton voyaged through his "strange seas of thought alone." Great ideas came to him first as flashes of vision. Only later could he build logical foundations under them. A perennial bachelor who often forgot to eat or change his clothes and has been called "profoundly neurotic," his deepest instincts were occult — so much so that John Maynard Keynes called him "not the first of the age of reason" but "the last of the magicians."

Yet Newton did not pretend to know the cause of gravity but only its behavior. "I do not deal in conjectures," he once remarked. And the wonderful generalizations of his laws of motion and gravitation, published in his *Philosophiae Naturalis Principia Mathematica* in 1687, won acceptance through their beautiful simplicity as practical mathematics rather than as abstract philosophy. Behold the universality of his dynamic declarations, which are the first and only criteria by which the Copernican doctrine can be tested by observation.

Law of Inertia: A body at rest will remain at rest, or a body in motion will continue in motion in a straight line with constant speed, unless constrained to change that state by the action of an exterior force.

Law of Acceleration: Change of a body's motion is proportional to any force acting upon it, and in the exact direction of that force.

Law of Reaction: Every acting force is always opposed by an equal and opposite reacting force.

And again, his famous Law of Gravitation: Every particle of matter in the universe attracts every other particle with a force proportional to the product of their masses and varying as the inverse square of the distance between their centers.

Of course, the strangest thing about this last law, which was the first to raise mass to a basic concept and the first to encompass the whole material universe with a measurable force amounting to a kind of inorganic love, was not that the sun pulls the earth but that (as Kepler divined) the earth pulls the sun just as hard and that every sparrow, fish, snowflake and molecule influences not alone the whole earth but also the moon, sun and all the stars. Indeed, that the entire universe is full of falling bodies, every mass-point pulling every other mass-point inevitably and forever from the descending mists to the rising tides and even unto the slow precession of the equinoxes.

But Newton was well aware of forces besides gravity in the world and distinctly foreshadowed modern atomic chemistry when he wrote:

And now we might add something concerning a certain most subtle spirit which pervades and lies hid in all gross bodies, by the force and action of which spirit the particles of bodies attract one another at near distances and cohere, if contiguous; . . . and there may be others which reach to so small distances as hitherto escape observation . . . and electric bodies operate to greater distances, as well repelling as attracting the neighboring corpuscles; and light is emitted, reflected, refracted, inflected, and heats bodies; and all sensation is excited and . . . propagated along the solid filaments of the nerves.

Newton must have wondered whether this "subtle spirit" binding matter together could be related to gravitation — whether the atoms can be tied mathematically or harmonically to the stars. But finding a common equation for electrons and galaxies certainly cannot be easy, for many physicists, including Einstein, have since sought just such a unified formula, and there is no clear assurance that anyone has yet come anywhere near success. And now the whole idea of force in the world is being deeply questioned, with the modern view tending toward the elimination of the concept from physics altogether.

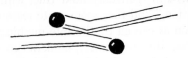

Since the only known place where force can be measured is where something material acts upon some other material, it may be interesting to consider now just what "material contact" really is. Is the familiar "force" of friction what it seems to be and was assumed to be until this century: an actual grinding of particles against particles with nothing in between them?

Of course, we know now that the answer is no. Physical impact is far from what it appears, and the phenomenon grows in complexity as it is studied more closely. When two billiard balls click together, they bounce in the way a comet "bounces" off the solar system, guided in its curving path by mysterious and seemingly remote influences. Or you might visualize the colliding atoms as two nations at war for, although the territories may consist largely of empty fields and woods with a hundred feet of "nothing" between one soldier and the next, still the two armies are firmly held apart.

The first two classic laws of friction were formulated by Leonardo da Vinci, who said that when solids rub against each other, the frictional force is (1) proportional to the load or pressure of one upon the other and (2) independent of the area of contact. These observations still "generally hold true, with no more than ten percent deviation," and they seem quite reasonable under the old view of friction as caused by the intermeshing of protrusions in adjacent surfaces. But surprisingly, modern experiments of high precision have proved that both of Leonardo's laws are wrong and, in fact, that they should be reversed. Even though they seem correct because the contact area is usually roughly proportional to the load, the frictional force has turned out to be really pro-

portional to the area of contact and independent of the load.
Indeed, the intermeshing of protrusions has recently been exposed
as the great delusion of friction, since all the tests show that
smoothing out roughness eases friction only in the coarse stages and
that there is definitely a limit beyond which polishing a surface
*in*creases rather than *de*creases resistance.

This is because friction comes almost entirely from molecular
cohesion rather than from the grinding of humps — which explains why the best bearing metals have proven to be alloys with
various large atoms that make lattices too coarse and irregular to
form neatly interlocking chemical bonds. In fact, it is practically
certain that the real function of teeth in a friction hacksaw is to
carry enough oxygen from the air into the cut to maintain the
microscopic "flames" essential to the proper working of the saw
— and this despite oxygen's being such a good lubricant that it
amply accounts for surfaces sliding more easily in air than in a
vacuum.

Another recent finding is that the increase of friction with the
slowing down of sliding surfaces reaches a maximum while the
surfaces are still moving and, below this very slow speed, friction
decreases again — probably because of creep. As we saw in the
last chapter, all solids, including lattice crystals, creep or slowly
change shape even though the forces acting upon them may be
very slight, the creep speed being proportional both to the frictional resistance (inversely) and to the softness of the material.
The creep of hard steel, for example, is so slow it cannot be observed, while soft lead may creep up to a millionth of a centimeter
a second, a foot per year.

A much faster kind of friction is the sudden impact of two
colliding bodies, which may either bounce apart without damage
or break to some degree depending on their structure. According
to one calculation, if a golf ball had as high a "coefficient of
restitution" (bounciness) as have some precision crystals, it would,
after 440,000 bounces off a crystal pavement in a vacuum, still be
rebounding to half its original height. In the case of less resilient
materials, however, much of the energy upon colliding goes into
plastic deformation. When two cannonballs hit, for instance, an

"ellipse of contact" is created around the momentarily compressed surface where they touch. And to a depth of about a third of the mean diameter of the ellipse below the surface in each ball, the crystal breakdown keeps pace with the ellipse, its outer boundary spreading in the form of twin ellipsoidal fronts inside the ellipse — fronts whose advance cannot be halted until the compression energy (momentarily stored in the crushed molecules) is sufficient to make the balls stop approaching each other and begin to separate.

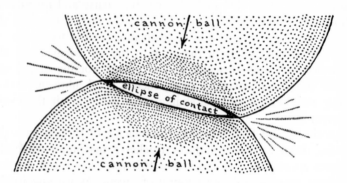

According to the law of entropy (second law of thermodynamics), all these kinds of friction convert energy from a more orderly form (as in a regular lattice) to a less orderly form (as in a broken lattice or the random molecular motion of heat). But the process does not stop with breakage or heat, for it is now known that most chemical reactions either absorb or release energy in the form of light or sound or electricity.

A tiny crystal cube one millimeter on a side, for example, has some 100,000,000,000,000,000,000 energy "levels" occupied by the valence electrons of all its constituent atoms — levels so closely spaced that, for most practical purposes, they form a band or continuum within the crystal. Such a grain of sand can be made to glow, sizzle or emit sparks, perhaps discharging energy in many forms at once — energy which, we shall see presently, is actually always "granulated" or quantized into distinct parcels in much the same way that matter is made up of separate, measurable

atoms, and for the very good reason that it and matter are basically the same thing.

This surprising two-in-oneness of energy and matter, first
clearly demonstrated by Albert Einstein in 1905, explains how
the mass of an atom's nucleus can be less than the sum of the
masses of all its nuclear components, the difference being the
"packing loss" or binding energy that holds the nucleus together.
A strange kind of addition, you think? But such relationships
will become clearer when we have had a chance to look into Einstein's famous equation $E = mc^2$, which says, with beautiful simplicity, that energy (E) equals mass (m) times the square of
celeritas (c), symbol of the velocity of light.

To comprehend this, in turn, we need to get better acquainted
with the atom as it is now known, so we can visualize its many
and peculiar parts and at least build up some sort of mental
picture of what this weird inner frontier of knowledge is like.
There is, of course, hardly a need to point out the difficulties
physicists have had in discovering the atom's so-called elementary
particles, since these "objects" are much too small to be seen by
any known kind of microscope, and they must be deduced only
from the evidence of their tracks and deeds in a bubble chamber,
photographic plate or in one of the great new particle accelerators whose increasing dimensions and importance are making them
the modern architectural counterparts of the pyramids of Egypt
of the Gothic cathedrals of Europe. Such indirect techniques
have been said to make the task of discovery at least as hard
as figuring out the path and caliber of a bullet fired at a flock of
birds just by observing the birds.

Yet at the present writing, no less than 30 elementary particles
have already been discovered and at such a rate that there has
not been enough time yet to complete the tougher job of think-

ing up theories to explain them. As these elementary particles evidently inhabit the atoms of all elements when conditions favor them, they constitute a Table of Particles that amounts to a kind of inner family of elements of the second order within the classical table of elements described in the last chapter. As such they are a big new step toward the ultimate "partless parts" sought by Leucippos in Abdera — if, indeed, there should ever turn out to be anything anywhere small enough to be really indivisible.

A mere quarter-century ago there were only four "known" sub-atomic particles: the electron, proton, neutron and photon. The first three, discussed in the last chapter, are the main building blocks of atoms: positively charged protons and uncharged neutrons in the central nucleus and negative electrons revolving through the vast firmament around it. The photon, on the other hand, is the modern name for the quantum unit of radiation first vaguely postulated by Newton as a "corpuscle of light" three centuries ago but not generally accepted until 1905, when Einstein convincingly demonstrated that it could literally knock electrons from metal surfaces and formulated his Photoelectric Law to establish it as "the building block of the electromagnetic field." More elusive than the electron, as we will learn in Chapter 12, the photon exists only while moving at the velocity of light, 186,282 miles a second. It is a particle that can never be at rest, for its mass and energy are created by its motion in the proportion $E = mc^2$. Don't be dismayed if this strikes you as mysterious, because it is mysterious. It was mysterious to Einstein too, for he knew enough, in this dawning era of knowledge, to ask only HOW of the world. Honoring the unknown as a kind of sacred manifestation, he once said, "The most beautiful and most profound emotion we can experience is the sensation of the mystical."

As the years went on, physicists, experimenting humbly with the four primary particles, found that they needed new concepts to satisfy their equations — that something other than mass, density, electric charge and velocity must distinguish one particle from another. What was this difference? Could it be described or explained?

In testing various ideas, it turned out that the concept of spin untangled several mathematical snarls. For the evidence is that all these particles spin on their axes like planets and asteroids and, if they are electrically charged, the spin makes them tiny magnets. This can hardly be explained except to say it is part of a natural electromagnetic law under which electric generators and motors operate all over the earth. But the spin fits in with quantum theory as an integral and measurable trait of each particle, the electron, proton and neutron being considered to have a spin of ½ while the faster spin of the photon is 1.

How actual the spin of these particles is is hard to say, but there is no doubt that they behave as if they are really spinning. They are certainly doing something that has rhythm to it. And those that are magnets are responsive to the magnetic fields they happen to be in, abiding by the quantum restrictions that permit a particle with spin ½ only two positions: its axis pointing either with or against the field. A particle having spin 1, on the other hand, enjoys a choice of three positions: its axis with, against or perpendicular to the field.

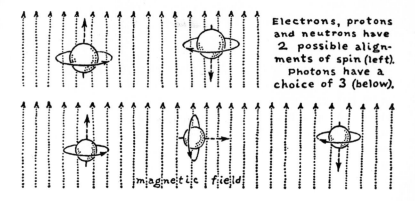

Electrons, protons and neutrons have 2 possible alignments of spin (left). Photons have a choice of 3 (below).

Another new and helpful concept is known as the exclusion principle. This famous law, formulated by Wolfgang Pauli of Austria, applies to all particles with spin ½ and says in mathematical language that inside the atom, just as outside, no two objects can fill the same space simultaneously or, more specifically, that only one particle of a kind can occupy a given quantum "state." Thus only one electron at a time can be spinning in a particular direction and revolving in a specific orbit around a given nucleus — which goes a long way toward explaining why there can be no more than a fixed number of electrons in each shell of an atom, and this in turn (as we have seen) is a key to the harmony of the Periodic Table.

Of course, it would be only natural at this point to ask why particles spin and why electrons obey an exclusion law. But we must try to be patient and not revert to the primitiveness of the ancient Greeks even if the atom world now seems to make little sense. For there are still plenty of HOWs that need answering first and, as Galileo discovered, the HOWs not only get answered much more easily but their answers are apt to throw more light on the WHYs than the WHYs' own answers do — if indeed the WHYs get answered at all.

And so we come to the next peculiarity that was noticed about particle behavior: the fact that these entities do not live independently but react upon each other just as definitely as a pair of gamecocks or lovebirds. The first such coupling to be recognized and analyzed was one between the electron and the photon. The electron was found to pulse in an electromagnetic field, unaccountably but continuously emitting and absorbing photons, and this amazing reaction turned out to be the basic means by which field and electron exert force upon each other — a vital, physical relationship that soon established itself as the cornerstone of quantum electrodynamics and, incidentally, produced the first apparent violation of the law of conservation of energy.

By violation I mean the photon's capricious appearance and disappearance. For how can a photon containing energy be spontaneously emitted or absorbed by a stable electron without suddenly altering the total of energy in the system? This was the baffling question to which quantum theory answered that "the photon is emitted and reabsorbed so fast that the gain in energy cannot be detected, even in principle." As a result, the phenomenon has come to be called a "virtual process" to distinguish it from an actual one. But the phrase "virtual process" is not meant to imply an unreal process, for the fact that the photon's energy is not detectable in this case does not prove it is nonexistent. It only testifies that it does not affect the conservation of energy, on the ground that "quantum laws deal only with observable quantities."

By such down-to-earth reasoning is the first law of thermodynamics neatly spared its exception. Yet the elusive photon exists as something empirically tangible — and this can readily be tested by the addition of enough energy from outside (accelerating the electron, for instance) to convert the photon from a virtual to an actual particle.

If the four basic particles as thus presented seemed to come close to explaining the atom in 1930, the scientific world would soon realize that they had not come close enough. One of the best-known though paradoxical fruits of the quantum theory was that fundamental particles not only behave like particles, they also behave in some ways like waves. And the solution to the electron's wave equation yielded a puzzling negative frequency as well as a positive one, in much the same way that $\sqrt{4}$ equals -2 as well as 2. But since frequency is proportional to energy in quantum mechanics, this in turn suggested the idea of negative energy — whatever that might be. Should such an absurdity be taken seriously or was it just something extraneous like a shadow, a forgotten dream or the lingering grin of the Cheshire cat? Could there really be an antipode of energy?

Physicists did not agree at first as to how to handle "negative energy," but presently one of the best and youngest among them, Dirac of England, found a mathematical way of proving that this weird concept has a "physical significance" — that if an ordinary, negatively charged electron could lose its normal energy and pass into a state of negative energy, it must reverse its charge and become a positively charged electron — which would be something like a hole or bubble in a sea of electrons. Not only that, implied Dirac's theory, but "if a positive electron collided with a negative electron, they would annihilate each other and their mass would be converted into photons with an equivalent amount of energy. Conversely, if enough energy could be concentrated in a small volume, as in a high-speed collision between two particles, a positive and a negative electron could be created."

Although this fantastic implication was not uttered as a valid prophecy, it could as well have been. For it was fulfilled with promptitude and precision when Carl D. Anderson of the California Institute of Technology discovered in 1932 an actual positive electron, soon to be named the positron. Not only did it have the mass of an electron and exactly one unit of positive electric charge but, when an electron and positron were induced to meet, they annihilated each other. Yet still they could be (and literally were) re-created by certain "energetic collisions."

Does it not seem preposterous than a mathematical equation, a purely abstract relationship not based on experience, should thus show us what is going on inside the atom? But it has happened again and again in physics, chemistry and equivalently in many other branches of science. The method actually works, and one cannot avoid realizing that it must express a profound truth about the nature of our world. Bertrand Russell has gone so far as to define matter as merely "what satisfies the equations of physics." And more and more, we see, as we delve deeper into the nature of things, that the abstract relationships of elementary entities are what really constitutes matter — that the particular harmony of each combination is the true essence of what it is made of. In fact this idea, far from new, was strongly implied by Pythagoras and developed quite remarkably in Plato's famous intuition that the four Greek elements (fire, earth, air and water) were essentially four abstract shapings of empty space into pure geometric form: the tetrahedron being the basic atomic shape of fire, the cube of earth, the octohedron of air and the icosahedron of water.

Anyhow, the abstraction of material symmetry that developed out of Dirac's theory came to fruit not only in the positron, which is now considered the antiparticle of the electron (which it cancels), but also in the general concept of antiparticles that can cancel or counter all particles. Thus new equations for the proton and neutron soon brought to theoretical light the antiproton (of reverse charge) and the antineutron (magnetically reversed), which were actually produced and detected twenty-odd years later in 1955 and 1956 with the help of the giant Bevatron at the University of California, which was built especially for the purpose. And even the photon now has its antiparticle, mathematically speaking, though here "the two solutions to the equation can be interpreted in the same way and the photon and antiphoton are indistinguishable" — or, as one physicist put it, "the photon is its own antiparticle."

If anyone seriously thought that antiparticles (theoretically combinable into what is termed antimatter) could be the final word in subdivisions of the atom, however, he did not think so for long. For even the theory of the antiparticle left little room for doubt that encounters between particles and antiparticles would sometimes produce brief exchanges of material analogous to a lightning stroke between a positive cloud and a negative mountain. I am not referring now to anything like a head-on collision between a proton and an antiproton, which would completely destroy both, but to a near miss, when they shave close enough to affect each other drastically but incompletely. Here theory indicates that the antiproton would flip a quantum of negative charge to the proton, leaving both particles electrically neutral: the proton would become a neutron and the antiproton an antineutron, but the pair of them would still be symmetrical and therefore able to annihilate each other if they ever collided. The obvious point in this instance, however, is the quantum of electrical charge flipped from the antiproton. Could this brief shot of energy (if it really happened) be considered another elementary particle?

The Japanese physicist Hideki Yukawa thought so and called it the meson. He also calculated that it must be emitted and absorbed again all in $\frac{1}{100,000,000}$ of a second and, since it lived in the very heavy nucleus of an atom (the mysterious central habitat of protons and neutrons) it must be quite heavy itself (between 200 and 300 times as massive as an electron, he figured) and might well contain the powerful energy that holds the nucleus together — something that had remained completely unexplained up to that time. It took researchers about twelve more years to find Yukawa's particle, but when it showed up at last in 1947, weighing some 260 electron masses and in three forms (positive, negative and neutral), it fully confirmed his brilliant intuition. It is now called the pi meson or pion and is considered to be the unit of a virtually continuous emission and absorption from the nuclear core, serving collectively as a kind of potent, mystic ligature binding the nucleus together.

Yet another discrepancy appears whenever a neutron for any reason has been knocked out of its natural place in the nucleus, for the normally stable neutron seems to have a streak of delinquency in it, becoming hopelessly unstable as soon as it gets out of sight of home. In fact, about eighteen minutes after its departure from the nucleus on the average, it spontaneously ejects an electron and turns into a proton. Such sorcery, of course, makes sense only if these "particles" are all basically made of the same primordial stuff which can somehow "flow" from one to another. Yet the proton and electron added together are some 1.5 electron masses lighter than was their mother neutron so, according to the law of conservation of energy, 1.5 electron masses or its equivalent in energy (780,000 electron volts) must have escaped somehow in the decay and birth.

Where could it have gone? The Italian physicist Enrico Fermi, with the help of Pauli, suggested that some almost undetectable unknown particle must also have been emitted like a ghost's placenta when the neutron broke up, and that it took off with the missing energy. He gave the shy little whatever-it-might-be the appropriate name of neutrino, but for some twenty years this hypothetical will-o'-the-wisp looked to many theorists like just a bookkeeper's symbol for a slight discrepancy in the accounts. All agreed that it was the epitome of elusiveness, with zero charge and virtually zero magnetic moment, to say nothing of being as swift and tiny and intangible as a photon, only vastly more unstoppable and completely invisible. Study of radioactivity in the sun, however, eventually showed that neutrinos must be produced so abundantly there that "some 100,000,000,000 of them pass through each square centimeter of the earth's surface per second" and so subtly that all but a freak few continue on straight through the molten interior of our planet and out the other side like a bullet through a cloud without hitting a single electron or any other particle on the way. To make them even more incredible, physicist George Gamow has declared that "a beam of *neutrinos* would go without much difficulty through the thickness of several light-years of lead!"

When a long series of tests culminated in actual detection of neutrinos in the famous Los Alamos experiment of 1956, physicists sighed with conscious relief that finally this "last of the theoretical parts of the atom" had been proven a reality. Could anything have more perfectly fulfilled Lao Tzu's ancient intuition: "The softest of stuff in the world penetrates quickly the hardest; insubstantial, it enters where no room is"? The neutrino even completed the so-called "dozen-particle theory of matter" in which all of the particles and antiparticles so far described were logically sorted into four groups: (1) the heavy particles (proton, neutron, antiproton, antineutron); (2) the short-lived middleweight mesons (positive, negative and neutral pions); (3) the light particles (electron, positron, neutrino and antineutrino); (4) the photon. It was a neat arrangement with the groups nicely interconnected by the three basic reactions already mentioned: the Yukawa process connecting heavy particles with mesons, the Fermi process connecting heavy particles with light particles (neutrino, etc.) and the Dirac process connecting light particles (electrons) with pho-

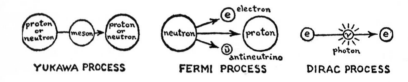

YUKAWA PROCESS   FERMI PROCESS   DIRAC PROCESS

tons. With the known general laws of physics, such as the conservation of energy, of momentum and of electric charge, physicists now had a kind of atomic algebra for writing equations and solving problems about particles — a method which might seem to an outsider like just shuffling symbols around but which actually could, and usually did, yield a reasonably exact prediction of what would happen in a new experiment, how long it would take and so on. The fact that both atomic bombs and atomic generators became realities on little more than the "dozen-particle theory" suggests how much can be accomplished with such a simplified concept of matter.

And then came the mu meson or muon! There was no theoretical justification at all for this surprise morsel of mystery (discovered by Anderson as early as 1937), which turned out to be one of the decay products of the charged pion — which, if you remember, lives only about a hundred-millionth of a second and theoretically should decay into a positron and a neutrino. Yet this unwanted baby on the doorstep of science was but the first gentle hint that the age of atomic innocence had ended on Earth, for around 1950 a whole procession of new ephemeral particles appeared — all utterly unexpected and unexplainable by previous theory. Strange V-shaped patterns were noticed on lead plates struck by "cosmic rays" inside cloud chambers, mysterious splittings whose careful analysis established the existence of what are

now known as K mesons or kayons and also the very baffling lambda particle, which is even heavier than the neutron. Then came the still more massive and stranger sigma particles, both charged and neutral, and the negative and neutral xi's, heaviest of all.

These last three types — all heavier than protons or neutrons — are collectively called hyperons in token of their massiveness. And their strange presence in the world is not made any less mysterious by the fact that they are born to live and die in the over-all time span of less than a billionth of a second, quite a different thing from the stable protons and neutrons — collectively called nucleons — which are the main, central building blocks of matter.

Of course, it is pretty generally admitted among physicists that there are now already far too many particles within the atom. Indeed, the present era of atomic knowledge is reminiscent of the long Ptolemaic age in astronomy when the confusion of

TABLE OF ELEMENTARY PARTICLES

Weight class	Mass in units of 9.1085 × 10⁻²⁸ grams	Particle symbols — matter	Particle symbols — antimatter	Name	Generic name
No weight	0 0	$\nu°$ γ	$\bar\nu°$	photon neutrino, antineutrino	LEPTONS
Light weight	1	e^-	e^+	electron, positron	
Middle weight	206.9	μ^-	μ^+	muons	MESONS
	264.5 273.3	π^- $\pi°$	π^+	pions	
	966	κ^+ $\kappa°$	$\kappa°$ κ^-	kayons	
	1,835 1,837	p^+ $n°$	p^- $n°$	proton, antiproton neutron, antineutron	NUCLEONS
Heavy weight	2,181	$\Lambda°$	$\Lambda°$	lambda	HYPERONS
	2,327	Σ^+ $\Sigma°$ Σ^-	Σ^+ $\Sigma°$ Σ^-	sigma	
	2,583	$\Xi°$ Ξ^-	Ξ^+ $\Xi°$	xi	

"obviously needed" planetary spheres, cycles and epicycles blinded astronomers to the simple but unobvious truth of sun-centered motion. Many physicists are therefore trying to boil the 30 present particles back down to a dozen or less — but it is not easy in the face of the tangible tracks actually made by these errant objects on photographic plates and in bubble chambers with accumulating evidence of their individual masses, spins, charges and other characteristics. At the very least they must be something more than figments of mathematics. Even a geiger counter can readily record some kinds of single particles, and anyone may literally see the so-called alpha particles (helium nuclei) by looking at the luminous numerals of a watch in the dark with a magnifying glass — the light being composed of tiny sparklets that correspond to sunshine on the ocean, each speck of luminescence separately shot out by a radioactive atom which, in doing so, transforms itself into a different kind of atom. And lately, not content with merely observing particles, physicists have actually begun to create or transmute them artificially in the great accelerators — even to manufacture whole atoms and fairly large molecules out of carefully combined parts.

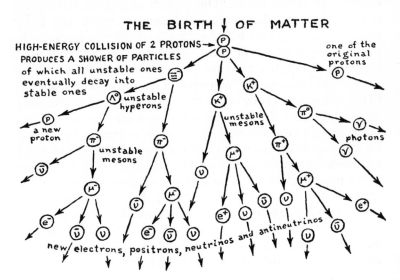

THE BIRTH OF MATTER

The frontier of understanding in the atom is meanwhile advancing inexorably deeper and deeper into the nucleus, which not only contains much more than 99 percent of all matter but is so small that the whole of it occupies only a thousandth of a millionth of a millionth of the "vast emptiness" enclosed by the outer electrons. This, of course, makes the density of the nucleus a thousand million million (10^{15}) times that of ordinary materials. Yet the evidence shows that the nucleus is itself far from solid, containing room for free motion and having a still heavier core at its center made of stuff so dense that a normal-sized pill of it would weigh two million tons.

Whether that core in turn may be more or less "fluid" again, with a still smaller and denser kernel somewhere within it — and how far such a sequence might continue — are questions still apparently far beyond our means of investigation. Even the density of the nuclear core is somewhat speculative, but the nucleus as a whole is becoming well established under the mounting data of modern nuclear research.

Perhaps the most accurate picture of the nucleus is the "liquid drop model" devised by Niels Bohr and John Wheeler after the discovery of nuclear fission. This concept emphasizes the fluidity of this region of moiling protons and neutrons, which seem to be somehow lubricated yet held together by the flux of mesons continuously bursting out of them, streaming back and forth and being sucked in again. Obviously, a nucleus is quite different from the vacuous "solar system" of a whole atom and is more analogous to the concentrated body of our sun. Its comparative crowdedness can be judged by the fact that a hydrogen nucleus has a radius nearly equal to the diameter of its single proton, so that if the nucleus were as big as a tennis ball, the proton would be like a golf ball inside it. On the same scale, the nuclei of the heavier atoms in the upper half of the Periodic Table of elements would range from the size of a basketball to double that volume, each with from 100 to 275 golf-ball protons and neutrons buzzing within.

In shape, the nucleus naturally tends toward a sphere, and research indicates it has a kind of fuzzy "skin" with density fading away on the outside — a mysterious and nebulous aura perhaps knit together by something on the order of surface tension which, however, for a reason unknown, never seems to make it stiff. And since it stays always flexible, the nucleus does not have much constancy in its round shape. Instead, like a falling raindrop, it evidently oscillates from egg to bun forms and may sometimes (like the earth) be pear-shaped. In various ways it quivers, sending rapid but measurable waves around and around its surface, waves which in turn affect (or participate in) the tumbling motions and complex orbits of the particles inside it. For all we know, the so-called particles (protons, neutrons, mesons . . .) inside it all merge together like drops of milk in a spoon. Or are they really more like puffs of smoke in a bag — or thoughts in a mind?

THEORETICAL MODELS OF ATOMIC NUCLEI AND THEIR PARTS

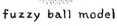

hydrogen   helium   lithium   beryllium   boron   carbon

a few schematic representations

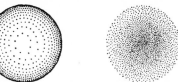

early shell models   fuzzy ball model

experimental
model of a
proton

liquid drop
model

symmetric
uranium nucleus
of 92 protons

An even more troublesome thing about the nucleus, though, is the nature of the force that binds it together — that holds the

positively charged protons in their close brotherly embrace despite
the familiar electromagnetic law that poles of similar charge must
repel each other and with increasing strength as they draw closer
together. Nuclear physicists have long since concluded that the
nuclear binding force must be as distinct from electromagnetic
force as electromagnetic force is distinct from gravitation. Although all three are undoubtedly related and perhaps are just three
aspects of the same influence, each has its own properties.
Electromagnetic force, for example, is stronger than gravity within
its own range but, unlike gravity whose pull increases with nearness, its symmetrical positive and negative forces tend to cancel
each other to create the balanced neutral atom of ordinary matter.
But the nuclear force, a lot more powerful than either of the others
in its unimaginably tiny precincts, evidently feels no polarity and
is centrally cumulative like a kind of supermicroscopic gravity of
the second order, increasing with nearness at a much faster rate
than the inverse square of the distance up to an extremely close
range, when it not only begins to decrease but ultimately reverses
its direction and becomes repulsive.

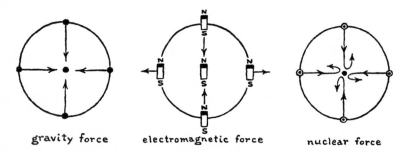

gravity force   electromagnetic force   nuclear force

Although it is not yet known what inverse power of the distance this cryptic nuclear force increases at, certainly the strength
of attraction between nucleons has shown itself to be uninflu-
enced by whether they are charged protons or uncharged neutrons.
Yet beyond such garnered scraps of knowledge, the crowded
complexity of the nucleus — seemingly more like a bunch of cats
fighting in a sack than an organized dance of entities — has made

it very difficult for nuclear physicists to make head or tail out of the influences involved. For while a planet's interaction with the sun can easily be treated as a simple two-body problem since other gravitating bodies are much too far away most of the time to have an appreciable effect, the tight-milling nucleons in any atom heavier than hydrogen inevitably pull one another with nearly equal but shifting strength in several varying directions at once.

All such problems notwithstanding, the nuclear researchers are probing their way forward through the night, shooting streams of electrons and neutrons into abstract darkness like volleys of ping-pong balls, some percentage of which must bounce off an unseen stone at significant angles, trying to analyze nucleons as complexes of interrelated two-body reactions, measuring what proportion of its time the average meson spends "inside" other "particles" — ever seeking better ways of penetrating the incredible smallness of the atom, a smallness most of us find only too easy to forget. By that I mean it is not enough to realize that ten million atoms arranged in one straight line would barely reach across the head of a pin. For each of these atoms must be enlarged to the size of a house to bring its nucleus up to pinhead dimensions, which at the same time would make the ten million house-sized atoms extend to the moon. Thus one would have to imagine a real pinhead at least as big as the whole earth to make an atom's nucleus just visible on the same scale — and this nucleus is the speck that science weighs with an accuracy of one part in a million and whose "skin" and component particles are now being measured separately and are found to have deducible thicknesses and densities and all sorts of characteristics that are turning out to be what J. B. S. Haldane once called "not only queerer than we suppose but queerer than we can suppose."

To look into this strange netherrealm of the atom in a slightly different way, let us now go back into the early 1920's and see how it all appeared to Niels Bohr, then the leading atomic physicist. You remember from the last chapter that the famous Bohr theory of the atom, published in 1913, pictured the sunlike nucleus as surrounded by planetlike electrons revolving in strictly defined shells around it. Bohr, who worked for years in Ernest Rutherford's laboratory in Manchester, had developed this idea from Rutherford's discovery that the atom possessed a nucleus and from J. J. Thomson's earlier beanpot concept of the atom as a swirling flow of electrons like beans, each element of the Periodic Table being composed solely of atoms with a particular number of electron beans.

But Bohr went much further than either Rutherford or Thomson and tied his atom neatly to the new quantum theory by showing that not only did all three of Kepler's laws for planets hold in the case of the electron revolving around the nucleus of hydrogen, but another law — a curious quantum law which was not noticeable among bodies as big as planets yet was truly fundamental — also applied. This was the law that electrons can move only in certain orbits and in no others. It is a harmonic law akin to the rule that restricts Saturn's rings to precise dimensions and to the abstract principle under which there are just 32 symmetry groupings of crystals and exactly 230 distributions of identical objects in space (see page 291).

The Bohr atom was thus elaborated into seven shells, roughly analogous to the seven notes of the scale or the seven planets of antiquity, the inmost shell having room for exactly two electrons, the second eight, the third eighteen, and so on, according to the curious rule of doubled squares described in the last chapter. But there turned out to be a lot more harmonic order than that, for these shells are themselves sized according to a strangely simple rule of single squares. Thus the first shell of the hydrogen atom is one angstrom unit (1Å) in diameter, the second is 4Å, the third 9Å, the fourth 16Å, etc., which is mathematically reducible to the series 1^2, 2^2, 3^2, 4^2 . . . Å.

If you should wonder how a hydrogen atom with only one

electron can have so many shells, it is because any electron may jump from one shell to another and will do so (on the average) as soon as it has the required energy. Moreover when a shell is not occupied, it is still there in abstract truth, as is shown by the fact that an electron can always find it. For the electron never orbits between shells: it always jumps the whole way or not at all. That is how the law of quantum mechanics has been found to work within the atom.

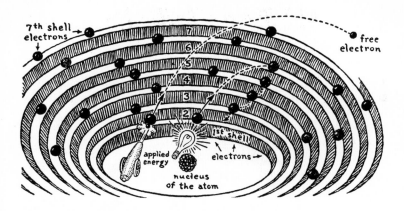

Until we look closer at what the electron is made of in the next chapter, it is perhaps enough to say now that the atomic shell structure is something like a set of invisible terraces built of nothing but abstract law. If enough light, heat or some other form of energy is applied to an atom, its electrons cannot help but jump to a "higher" terrace — farther away from the nucleus. One quantum of energy received makes one electron jump one terrace farther up, and if the electron receives enough energy to go beyond the seventh terrace, then it is completely free and the atom has become ionized (missing an electron). Likewise, an electron may jump down the same series of shells or terraces, giving back to the world its quanta of energy in discrete photons of radiation — evidently strictly fulfilling the law of conservation of energy without neglecting its quantum method of doing so. It is a strange performance, this — hard to get used to after our years of extravagant, if not always carefree, irregularity in the macroscopic life — but it is entirely law-abiding and plain as plumbing once you catch on to it.

Each terrace, according to one analogy, contains a room or apartment in which electrons may dwell in pairs of opposite spin like married couples. The lowest and smallest terrace (inner shell) is the most exclusive and popular, but its room holds only one couple: two electrons who, of course, must be of different "sexes" (spins), according to Pauli's exclusion principle: that no two particles of a kind can occupy the same quantum state. If

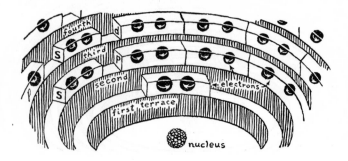

there happens to be only one electron in this "bridal chamber" (as in the case of a single hydrogen atom) that one will inevitably be lonesome and any footloose electron in the neighborhood who can contrive to fill the vacancy will eagerly do so. The second terrace shell has an apartment of four rooms, one room being slightly smaller than the other three. This room will hold an electron couple with "zero angular momentum" and the other three will take couples of "one unit of angular momentum," the smaller room being technically subshell s (for sharp, a spectroscopic term) and the three larger ones constituting subshell p (for principal).

And so is constructed the Bohr atom, shell by shell, subshell by subshell. The third shell, if you remember, has room for eighteen electrons — distributed among three subshells: s holding its usual 2 electrons, p holding its 6 electrons, and subshell d (for diffuse) holding 10 electrons "of angular momentum two." The fourth shell now adds a fourth subshell *f* (for *fundamental*) with room for 14 electrons ("ang. mom. 3"), making its total 32. Thus the physicist has a neat way of designating the exact arrangement of electrons in any part of an atom: $3d^{10}$ refers to the third shell's subshell *d* containing 10 electrons; $6p^5$ means the sixth shell's subshell *p* with 5 electrons. The designation $6p^5$ also indicates that this shell is part of element 85, astatine (At), since that is the only element with a subshell *p* of 5 electrons in its sixth shell. And as all subshells *p* have room for six electrons, $6p^5$ clearly further reveals that astatine must be chemically receptive to any element such as hydrogen, lithium, boron or sodium with a single fancy-free electron in its outer subshell.

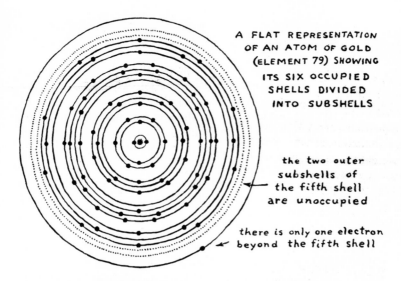

A FLAT REPRESENTATION OF AN ATOM OF GOLD (ELEMENT 79) SHOWING ITS SIX OCCUPIED SHELLS DIVIDED INTO SUBSHELLS

the two outer subshells of the fifth shell are unoccupied

there is only one electron beyond the fifth shell

Inevitably, all this must strike an innocent pedestrian as pretty complicated, but Bohr's model has nevertheless proved enormously clarifying to chemists and in many ways fruitful. Fact is, God's world, as seen by science, is not turning out to be the essence of simplicity — certainly not in the usual sense of that term. On the contrary, complexity seems to be one of its surest ingredients if not a basic criterion of its value — for the same reason that complexity is an accepted indication of quality in a watch. Bohr faced this realization squarely, and his extraordinary vision of the atom did not arrive simply or blossom without a deep struggle. His friends describe him as having hammered out his beautiful electron shells partly in speculative conversations with many a skeptical fellow theorist in England, Germany and at the Institute of Theoretical Physics in Copenhagen during World War I and in the early twenties — pacing intently around and around his table like a symbol of one of his own electrons, arguing profoundly, distractedly lighting his pipe again and again while absent-mindedly strewing the matches like photons behind him.

Among Bohr's first concrete results was the exact determination of electron velocities in each atomic shell, which, being quantized, came out much more perfectly than had the harmonics of the planets under Bode's Law. In the first four shells of the hydrogen atom, for example, Bohr found the electron moved at 2,160 kilometers per second, 1,080 k.p.s., 720 and 540 k.p.s. respectively — almost incredible speeds, yet related in the exact abstract proportion of 12:6:4:3 and following the inverse-square law as precisely as Mercury, Venus, Earth and Mars who, though spaced in a more carefree manner, also orbit progressively slower as they are farther removed from the sun.

But why was there this subtle difference between the way of the stiffly regimented atom, in which only certain orbits exist and the way of the relaxed, carefree solar system, in which any orbit is possible? This curious but fundamental disparity in an otherwise harmonious world seemed unaccountable and was very disturbing to physicists of the day. It figuratively shook what they had assumed to be bedrock under their principles — and it shook it in tiny, regular, quantum jerks.

What could this mean? How could one unified vehicle be a track-bound trolley car one minute and a free-wheeling bus the next? How could the quantum world of electrons operate on one principle and the classical world of stars (full of electrons) operate on another? Was there any dividing line between the two? Did they overlap, or did each fade into a mysterious no-man's-land of unknown dimensions somewhere in the middle?

Bohr boldly led the way out of the woods by showing mathematically that, although the quantum theory is never exactly equivalent to the classical, there is always a correspondence between them that grows more and more exact as dimensions increase and the incredible vibrations of the microcosm relax into the lower frequencies of our familiar macroworld. This correspondence principle, in fact, became very important in the relentless efforts of physicists to understand what matter really is.

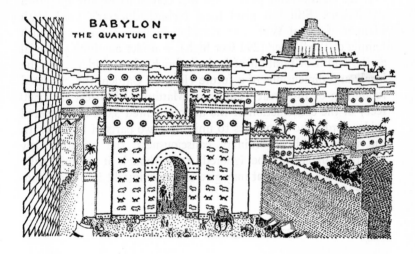

BABYLON
THE QUANTUM CITY

For a good analogy of the principle, imagine ancient Babylon in the seventh century B.C. with its straight brick-paved avenues and vaulted sewers extending over several square miles of land. And let's assume that the bricks are all identical and laid in one continuous system throughout, exactly fitted end to end and side to side, and that the same bricks form the foundations of all the houses from the Ishtar Gate to the famous Tower of Babel.

Then any mason building a house in Babylon will naturally lay his first course of bricks neatly upon those already there in an exact relation, according to the sacred Marduk Building Code which none dares defy. Thus every block of buildings will be incorporated into the same system, spaced in integral multiples of the Babel brick — leaving, say, exactly 22 bricks across a street from wall to wall, or 69, but never 46½ or 33⅝ or 81.44327+. You could call this a quantum law, the brick being the quantum unit or minim than which there is nothing smaller.

But of course, brick dimensions need concern only the brick makers and masons who actually handle them, and even these handlers probably have no awareness of their bricks' over-all implications. For every landowner feels free to build his house wherever he chooses and people are not conscious of any quantum restrictions. Still less need King Nebuchadnezzar's Lord High Planner of Royal Works, overlooking Babylon from the seventh temple of the Tower (290 feet high), consider anything so trivial as the width or position of a single brick when working out the locale and dimensions of a future Hanging Garden, the projected rebuilding of the great Temple of Marduk (1,500 feet by 1,800 feet) or the construction of the unprecedented 3,000-foot covered bridge across the Euphrates to unite the two parts of the city. In the macroworld of ordinary consciousness, the quantum law can thus practically be ignored, even though it is universally obeyed — a paradox that may give us a new insight into the meaning of liberty.

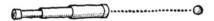

While Niels Bohr plumbed the atom in Europe, others were sounding it from various angles in other continents and running up against the same abstruse quantum limitations — even in the realm of electromagnetism. As early as 1909, Robert Andrews Millikan in America successfully measured the charge of an individual electron in one of the most elegant of the great classic experiments. This involved watching a laboratory cloud of microscopic oil droplets through a special optical instrument as the droplets floated in air illumined by a beam of light. Shining like asteroids in sunshine, hundreds of these tiny orbs were made to drift between two exactly horizontal metal plates so equipped that Millikan could regulate the rate of falling or rising of any visible droplet by means of a set of very sensitive controls that changed the electric potential of the plates to whatever positive or negative charge was required. Naturally, the oil droplets had been subjected to friction when sprayed by atomizer beforehand, and this had rubbed extra electrons upon most of them, giving them a negative charge. So the attraction of the positively charged upper plate and the repulsion of the negative lower plate tended to counteract the slight downward influence of gravity, a circumstance that en-

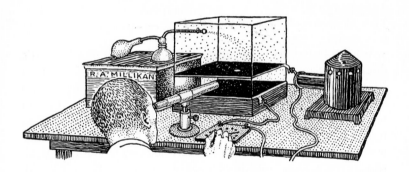

abled Millikan to balance any convenient droplet in suspension between the plates and to hold it stationary long enough to record the strength of the electric field around it — a measured quantity which, combined with the droplet's observed rate of fall when both plates were electrically neutral, made possible a calculation of the droplet's exact charge. This droplet charge, in turn, always came out as an integral multiple of a certain fixed minim charge, called "e" because it is the charge of an electron — which finally confirmed Faraday's famous intuition that any atomic charge must be a multiple of some basic electromagnetic quantum (see page 251).

So electricity had been revealed to be made of something like Babylonian bricks, too. And in the process the electron had been awarded a new dimension. Calling an electrical charge a dimension, of course, may be taking liberty with a plinth of our material universe, for electromagnetism seems to be one of those ubiquitous underlying abstractions that can be defined only in terms of its behavior. Like heat, it is a statistical function of motion. But where heat is random motion or the collective effect of the speeds of countless atoms or molecules, electricity is nonrandom or polarized motion, the collective effect of the velocities of many electrons flowing in a particular direction. And if heat can propagate itself through an intangible radiation made of photons moving at the speed of light, so has electricity a corresponding aspect of propagation by electromagnetic radiation, likewise made of photons.

We shall go deeper into photons in Chapter 12, but here let's dwell briefly on electromagnetic behavior in general. Electricity is named after *elektron*, Greek for amber, a substance known at least as early as 600 B.C. to "attract mustard seeds" and sometimes emit sparks after being rubbed with wool. And magnetism is named for the Greek coastal district of Magnesia on the northwestern arm of the Aegean Sea where lodestone was found, which Thales said "must have a soul because it moves iron." Although the Chinese seem to have known a similar magnetic iron oxide (Fe_3O_4) even earlier (some say in 2700 B.C.), calling it "the stone that loves" and fashioning floating compasses of it that steadfastly pointed toward the lodestar, no one seems to have proved any definite connection between electricity and magnetism until the last century, when an Italian jurist named Grandomenico Romagnosi accidentally discovered in 1802 that an electric current flowing through a wire will deflect a magnetic needle in its vicinity.

This discovery, duplicated and properly announced by Hans Christian Oërsted, the Danish scientist, in 1820, set many scientists to experimenting in the now combined field of electromagnetism.

And progress accelerated, soon culminating in the discovery by Joseph Henry in America in 1830 and Michael Faraday in England in 1831 that a moving magnet, in turn, will induce an electric current to flow in a wire.

This great revelation of inductance, soon developed by Faraday and later James Clerk Maxwell of Scotland into the strange new theory of the "field," was, of course, the key to the dynamo, which led directly to the large-scale generation of electricity that is now considered indispensable to modern civilization. But, beyond its obviously practical side, the integration of electricity and magnetism sounded the knell of the 200-year-old mechanistic theory of matter as an association of mass-points by exposing the incongruity of any kind of material point as a physical reality and replacing it with the pervasive concept of continuous fields of energy — a switch that the unborn Albert Einstein would one day applaud as "the most profound and fruitful one that has come to physics since Newton."

And what did Faraday and Maxwell mean by "the field"? Clearly, they meant a mathematically definable region extending through space and containing measurable influences: the gravitational field of the sun, the magnetic field of a magnet and so on. In this way they neatly got around the old Newtonian puzzle of what transmits "action at a distance" by eliminating the distance — so that instead of reaching out unaccountably and instantaneously across a void of nothing, action simply propagated itself at a finite speed (that of light) and permeated space with the familiar inverse-square intensity in all directions. Electromagnetic forces were admittedly more complicated than those of gravity but that was natural, for they were evidently more fundamental and probably included gravitation as "a special case."

Meantime, the many ingenious experiments by Faraday, Henry and others had clearly demonstrated the working differences between electricity and magnetism, including the particularly striking contrast in their field orientations. Lines of electric force, for example, form a field that is everywhere *perpendicular* to the surfaces of conductors (wires, tubes, etc.), while lines of magnetic force compose a contrary field that is always *parallel* to magnetic

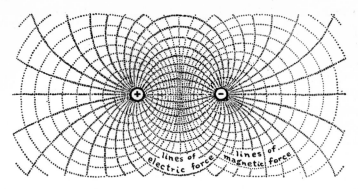

surfaces. And these two sets of force lines are respectively analogous, in familiar gravitational terms, to the lines down which falling objects drop *perpendicular* to a surface (as of the earth) and contrariwise to the path lines of moons or satellites orbiting *parallel* to the same surface. Such rather mysterious yet graceful correlations illuminating the warp and woof of the electromagnetic tapestry were eventually compiled, along with all other experimental data, into laws governing basic electrical and magnetic behavior which the mathematical genius of Maxwell found a way to express in four beautiful relations — which have served as the cornerstone of electromagnetic theory ever since.

Because of Maxwell's untimely death at the age of forty-eight in 1879, before the electron was discovered, he could hardly even have guessed what was going on inside an electric conductor or a magnet. But that did not really matter much, since atomic particles are virtually beyond visualizing anyway. And besides, Maxwell's equations proved so conclusive he could accurately predict almost any electromagnetic behavior with them and often did — including such abstruse things as radio waves, which, in his day, were considered — if they were considered at all — as mere metaphysical fantasy.

By the time the electron was discovered to be the natural unit of electrical charge and current, the electric industry was growing up fast, gaining experience and new insight daily. Its confident engineers accepted in their stride the new knowledge that the so-called positive charge possessed by glass after being rubbed with silk really meant it had lost electrons, while the antipodean negative charge found on hard rubber brushed with fur indicated a corresponding gain in electrons. The theoretical physicists had already extended the early analogy between electromagnetism and gravity to the idea that currents in wires tend to persist for the same basic reason that the motions of large masses tend to persist under Newton's law of inertia. For do not electrons, after all, have mass and therefore momentum when in motion — a momentum that turns out to be strongest when the wire carrying the current is wound in a coil of many turns, creating the maximum magnetic flux? And from here, what could be more natural than to compare the flow of current through such a coil to the easy sliding of a material body upon a slippery surface — and the electrical resistance of the coil to the gentle friction between body and surface which steadily resists its motion?

If a mathematical structure built up from a sequence of such analogies has helped engineers to harness intangible electricity into modern electronics, a somewhat similar technique at the same time advanced the even more mysterious lore of magnetism to its own remarkable present state. Perhaps the greatest clue to the inner nature of magnetism so far uncovered is the so-called gyromagnetic ratio between the magnetic force and the spin of elementary particles. For the stability of this relationship is strong evidence that the "desire" of the whirling top to keep its axis upright is in essence none other than the "love" of "the stone that loves" — that the gyroscopic and magnetic compasses of modern navigation both work, basically, on the same principle — indeed, that the almost emotional yearning exhibited upon these disparate macroscopic and microscopic scales may even be a component of the primal stirring of life itself.

In any event, every spinning electron is now accepted by physics as "a tiny permanent magnet": its strength designated as one magneton. Even protons and the uncharged neutron have definite "magnetic moments" attributable to spinning, as has the rotating nucleus as a whole. But the entire atom may or may not add up to a magnet, depending on how many of its magnetic parts (electrons, etc.) neutralize one another. This is because electrons, protons and neutrons tend to go in pairs, spinning in opposite directions like the propellers of a twin-motored airplane geared to cancel each other's torque. The atom as a whole will be a magnet only while there is an imbalance of spins, which must happen when the number of electrons or other particles is odd or when most members of some particle group spin one way instead of pairing off in counterrotating symmetry. The iron atom, for instance, is bound to be magnetic because its third electron shell has an incomplete subshell d with five electrons spinning in one direction and only one electron the other way, producing a net magnetism of four magnetons.

From this you may wonder why every piece of iron is not a powerful magnet. It is only because magnetic atoms in their turn tend to neutralize each other through being knocked about in random directions by their natural thermal energy. In fact, no material can become magnetic until some force stronger than thermal agitation aligns a majority of its magnetic atoms in one direction. This force could be a bolt of lightning striking ferrous oxide on Mount Olympus, instantaneously turning whole cliffs of the ore into magnetite or lodestone. Or it could be just the natural sorting process of crystallization organizing atoms as they cool down and stack themselves into a lattice. In the latter case at least, there is little doubt that random atomic and molecular motion (ordinary heat) is the mortal enemy of magnetism, for all magnetic materials lose their magnetism when heated to the point where the forces of thermal disorder begin to overpower magnetic discipline. In iron this critical temperature is 1,420° F.

But obviously coldness alone is not enough to make metal magnetic. This is because the single unified crystals of magnetization, called magnetic domains, are usually very small (numbering a few million or billion atoms), and their magnetic axes of polarity ordinarily have a choice of at least two directions (six in the case of iron), paired parallel but opposite each other in conformance with neighboring polarities, which results in most of them being neutralized almost as completely as paired electrons. Thus not only must a piece of metal, to be a magnet, be made of magnetic atoms like multiengined planes with more propellers spinning one way than the other, and these arranged in magnetic domains like huge aircraft carriers with most of their thousands of planes heading, say, forward, but the domains in turn must be given a preponderant orientation as if vast fleets of the carriers were ordered to steer most of the time southeastward, seldom northward or westward.

The domain phase of magnetization has been actually seen under the microscope in the past decade, by smearing magnetic metal with fine iron-oxide powder in colloidal suspension to outline the domains as they bodily shift their axes step by step under magnetic field pressure — often accompanied by faint audible clicking sounds known as the Barkhausen effect. Perceptible transition regions called walls separate the domains by a few millionths of an inch and, during the process of magnetization, advance fairly steadily in waves, showing a kind of zipper action compounded of millions of atoms and molecules successively swinging into line. Thus do the individual domains grow wherever their constituent crystal axes are most nearly parallel to the field, converting new lattice members, rank by rank, row on row, in surging tides at the expense of less favorably oriented domains next to them — measurably changing the dimensions of hard chunks of iron, cobalt, nickel, gadolinium or other magnetic alloys as their straining lattices snap and contort in response to the mystic "love" force of gyrating magnetism.

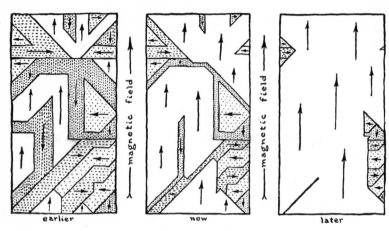

GROWTH OF MAGNETIC DOMAINS
IN METAL PLACED IN A STRONG MAGNETIC FIELD

If this new-discovered wonder of nature has not been made crystal-clear by this presentation, it is not surprising. For magnetism is still on the frontier of knowledge, and plenty of deep mystery remains. Yet the researchers and engineers have already made astonishing progress in their current struggle to develop stronger magnetic fields. They measure these in gauss, a unit of strength named for Karl Friedrich Gauss, the great German mathematician, the potency of which can be judged by the fact that the earth's magnetic field is about a third of one gauss at New York City. The strongest permanent magnet yet made has a field of about 10,000 gauss, while an electromagnet, consisting of a coil of wire around a metal core that amplifies the field generated by the current in the coil, can approach 60,000 gauss. Although this seems to be the limit of the magnetic capacity of metals, the most powerful modern magnets operate without cores in air

or a vacuum and have attained to several million gauss, a concentration of energy able to melt steel like butter or explode it
with the violence of TNT, producing a pressure of approximately
a thousand tons per square inch.

Today's theorists think of a magnetic field as something like a
gas, which can be intensified by compression, by crowding its lines
of force. And the fact that its density and energy increase as
the square of the field strength gives enormous potentiality to this
form of power — a power whose curious natural manifesta-
tions have ranged from turning the ammonia molecule (NH_3)
inside out to unaccountably reversing the polarity of giant stars in
the course of a few days.

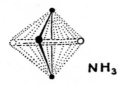

NH_3

And don't forget that, as we saw was true of heat, magnetism in
large perspective is a *relative* property whose magnitude depends
ultimately on the frame or viewpoint it is measured from. Which
is a way of saying that, because an airplane lands "hotter" on the
deck of a carrier moving in the opposite direction, so must a great
fleet of coordinated carriers loaded with buzzing planes (representing a magnetic field) be stronger to an observer moving or
spinning *against* rather than *with* their prevailing direction.
This can be considered as but basic groundwork for grasping
relativity — which we will come to in Chapter 13 — and clearly
suggests one of its aspects in the beautiful lines of force that define
the electromagnetic field, flowing abstractly on and on without
beginning or ending anywhere or where.

If electromagnetism is but one form of energy in the world —
and thunderous evidence from the nuclear front denies it is the
greatest one — we might do well to consider now the strange
genie lurking among protons and neutrons whose muscle is

stronger than his weight by the incredible amount of the speed of light multiplied by itself!

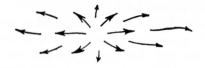

Appropriately, it was none other than Einstein who explained that the only reason men had not noticed the nuclear monster before our century was that this being kept his real life strictly to himself like an overcautious miser who had never been known to spend or give away a penny. Nevertheless, one of the miser's moneybags eventually began to split, showing a tiny hole from which a keen Polish researcher named Marie Curie and her French husband Pierre managed to extract a peculiar glowing substance. This they refined, after two years of strenuous work, into something worth a thousand times more than gold: a new element they named radium for its amazing radioactivity — and which made Marie the most famous woman scientist in history.

In such fashion did the dawning twentieth century reveal the awful potency of the atom's center, whose binding force there easily counteracts the electromagnetic repulsion of proton for proton, + for +, but whose steep decline in power with radial distance rapidly diminishes its grip on the bustling outer fringes of the bloated nuclei of the heavier elements. This is the secret of radioactivity, the disintegration or fission of heavy matter and the tendency that explains the instability of every atom heavier than lead (element 82)in the sixth octave of the Periodic Table, particularly seething radium (88), exuberant uranium (92) and all the transuranic synthetic elements. Some of these turgid substances spontaneously transmute into lighter elements in so few minutes that it is almost impossible to find out what they are — or were — made of. And of course, present atomic power is little more than a controlled exploitation of uranium's natural instability, based on the discovery in Germany in 1939 that blasting an atom of the uranium isotope U^{238} (92 protons, 146

neutrons) with a fast neutron or two was enough to break it apart
into an atom of barium (56 protons, 81 neutrons) and an atom
of krypton (36 protons, 46 neutrons), plus the splash of a few
neutrons left over and, most significant of all, about 200 mev
(million electron volts) of energy in the form of light, heat and
radiation. At the same time, if the cast-off neutrons could immediately be made to strike more uranium, a chain reaction
would be produced. This was the principle of the famous Hiro-
shima A-bomb.

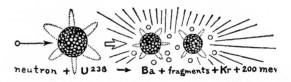

neutron + U^{238} → Ba + fragments + Kr + 200 mev

Although fission is thus an efficient power releaser from big
atoms that lose mass and energy whenever they split apart, the
opposite is true of small atoms which, being stable, must absorb
a great deal of energy before they will crack, spending none in
the process. Small atoms instead shed mass-energy ("the packing
loss") when forced to fuse together against electromagnetic repulsion. It is a fusion requiring a lot of initial energy from outside, because protons with identical (positive) charges must be
hurled extremely close to each other before the nuclear binding
force will grab and lock them, but it pays handsomely in the
end and is the key to the mighty H-bomb, in which two deuterium
(H^2) atoms are knocked and welded into a single helium (He^4)
atom plus 24 mev of radiant energy. In comparing this with the
output of uranium fission, it is apparent that fission produces more
energy per nucleus, yet, on the more practical "pound for pound"
basis, fusion exceeds fission by "about seven times," not to mention using a "fuel" that is vastly more abundant and inexpensive.

There are many ways of setting up both fission and fusion, of
course, and undoubtedly some of each will be important sources
of power in the future, along with direct energy from the sun,
cosmic "rays" and surely other developments now still undreamed.
Whatever comes, it can hardly be more revolutionary than the

domestication by fission and fusion of the atom's nucleus, which is certainly our profoundest technological accomplishment up to now. For the atom has just given man an impressive hint of how he may eventually escape the solar sovereignty and become something more than a mere son of the sun — how ultimately, perhaps even in a literal physical sense, he may graduate into a citizen of the universe.

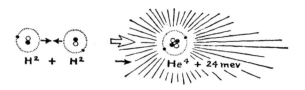

Still another fundamental way of looking into the weird netherworld of the atom is through the gateway to absolute zero. Here men have already reached to within much less than a hundred thousandth of a degree of what is defined as the complete absence of heat. One of the most successful techniques for approaching this unearthly purity of negation has been to line up the nuclei of very cold copper atoms in a magnetic field, then remove the field, letting the nuclei revert back to a random arrangement. The energy expended in this reversion leaves the nuclei weaker and quieter, which is the same thing as cooler. Theoretically, after many repetitions of the process, they should attain absolute zero when their disorder (entropy) is complete, but their own slight nuclear magnetism in real life does not quite permit this totality of relaxation.

Certain metals, however, cooled even to within a few whole degrees of absolute zero, have revealed the phenomenon of superconductivity (described on page 300), when "all" electrical resistance vanishes and surplus electrons flow onward through atom after atom as freely as the moon flows through "empty" space. This seems to be related to the equally fantastic superfluidity of liquid helium at 4° above absolute zero, a component of which flows in the form of "whole atoms completely without friction," slipping along as a film a few millionths of an inch thick that tends to cling to solid surfaces yet moves at a foot per second, even siphoning itself spontaneously out of cups. Physicists theorize that such a superfluid can exist only after the last traces of heat have somehow "separated" themselves from it to vibrate independently "relative to the superfluid background" of absolute zero. If this turns out to be more than an abstract interpretation, it seems to indicate not only that absolute zero is attainable on Earth but that friction is a function or attribute of atomic motion (heat) and that, in the astronomical perspective, it may be something peculiar to certain kinds of vibrant atomic worlds like ours, while other more elemental, perhaps more innocent and generalized, matter moves and spins somewhere somewhen with as little restraint as the headlong flight of the galaxies.

There is little doubt, you see, that heat is a more restricted property than we usually remember, for already physicists are working to discover the laws that govern "a temperature range" that reaches downward from absolute zero — where the motions that still exist must soon be given a separate collective name. These motions seem to consist primarily of the spinning of nuclei, which continues after all motion of whole atoms, and perhaps even of electrons, has died away. This subabsolute state, of course, is very hard to explore, but we already know that some spins have more energy than others and that spins (in their magnetic essence) react upon one another, with the result that high-energy spin can spread through matter in much the same way heat does. Even low-energy spin or the lack of spin seems to spread like a "wave of cold" where the energy of spinning has dissipated, permitting a substance to go on losing energy below absolute zero.

Whatever the nature of this nadir world beyond the ordinary laws of thermodynamics, its recent discovery is sure testimony of the fantastic potential of nature in every direction. From out of the sun, for example, and from out of the stars, probably even from beyond the Milky Way, come the assorted particles called cosmic "rays" that are so dense in the high atmosphere that black mice exposed in a balloon 20 miles high have turned white in a few hours. Although many of these particles are known to be the nuclei of heavy elements, including gold, lead and (appropriately) the rare earths, a few have been measured to have the almost impossible energy of many quintillion electron volts — of which one eminent physicist remarked, "To accelerate a flea to an equivalent speed would require all the energy released by a million hydrogen bombs."

How many the lessons to be learned from outer space! And how endless the prospects from within, where curious momentary elements completely separate from the Periodic Table keep revealing themselves: positronium, the fleeting partnership of an electron and a positron with no nucleus at all; superdense mu-mesic hydrogen where a negative muon takes the place of the hydrogen electron; and the flash-lived kayon+ electron− or pion+ electron− "atom" — glimpses of grist for the dream mills of some latter-day Leucippos.

A Chinese poem written by Lao Tzu more than two thousand five hundred years ago says that the best knots are tied without rope. This hoary wisdom may be interpreted as meaning that relationships are more real than things. It is a conclusion we can reasonably have come to in this chapter on the physical depths of the atom, for, plumb as we will the nuclear core, we cannot fathom matter entirely as matter. A factor of unpredictability amounting to a subtle willfulness begins to appear in that impalpable postulate, the electron, even while its behavior explains gross properties (such as tension and electric charge) to mathematical perfection.

Come to think of it, what do we mean by perfection anyhow? Is perfection more abstract than the song man sings in this paradoxical world of known form but unknown content? Could total perfection be already here unbeknownst — its immeasurable virtue throbbing in the atom, its axes but willingly spinning out their little quanta of warmth and love, the very compend of goodness?

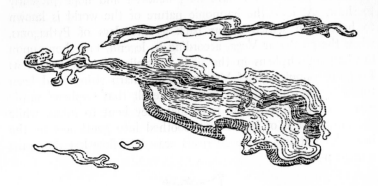

11. of waves and music

WE HAVE A SMALL CABINET marked SPACE LIBRARY
in this station and, as anyone might have guessed, its four dozen
books include a Bible. Although I am not much given to
reading Scripture, I was idly thumbing through it after my
last watch when what should my eye light upon but the
ancient Mosaic commandment: "Thou shalt not seethe a kid
in his mother's milk."

At first blink, this hardly seems to apply to us here. Nor,
I might add, does it strike one as a reasonable restriction even
for terrestrial nomads or goatherds who traditionally stew their
meat in milk and who may have few nannies with any to
spare. Yet there are certain mysterious discords in life — even
in space life — that instinctively repel us, and one must admit
that boiling any creature in a symbol of maternal love must
inevitably be among them.

On the other hand, the sympathetic frequencies and deep harmonies in this universe, which can be intuitively felt but hardly explained, may well be a source of more than matter or life or mind — as I have long believed and hope presently to show. At least the harmonic nature of the world is known to have been sensed as far back as the days of Pythagoras, when the great star Vega, according to legend, first shone upon the harp of Orpheus in the little constellation now known as Lyra. In popular belief Vega's celestial harp strings had been tuned by the Sun himself with the result that Orpheus' music was so enchanting to the trees that they bent to listen, while the most savage of beasts were soothed into gentleness by the bewitching strains and even rivers ceased to flow lest they miss a single note.

As for Pythagoras, the manifest perfection of the intervals of the spheres (see page 67) was to him but one aspect of an omniscient harmony — for had he not observed and defined the exact musical-scale intervals on a harp string and had he not recognized fundamentally similar abstract relationships throughout all creation — even to the essence of matter itself? According to the books I've read, the Ionic lyre had been perfected early in the seventh century B.C. by old Terpandros of Lesbos, "father of Greek music," who increased its strings to seven and "canonized the heptachord." No one knows for how many tens of thousands of years before that men blew on reeds or twanged strings to make music, but by Pythagoras' day every competent phorminxist or citharist must have known that shortening or fretting a string changed its note, and no doubt many had learned by improvisation how to play octaves, fifths, fourths, thirds or other pleasing intervals. This was both natural and expectable, for children and birds often sing in fifths and fourths and a simple horn (such as the bugle) will produce many such exact intervals just by being blown with differing intensities.

But Pythagoras seems to have applied the philosopher's WHY to all this and to have noticed that the extremely sympathetic relationship we call an octave comes from exactly doubling or halving the string length, that is, in a 1:2 proportion, while the harmonious fifth has a 2:3 ratio and the fourth 3:4. He or his followers may even have explored the 4:5 interval of the third or still less obvious consonances.

In any case, the evidence is that these discoveries led to deep contemplation of the abstract ratio of numbers and geometric figures and particularly to a new mathematical relation: the harmonic mean. The harmonic mean expresses a pitch ratio be-

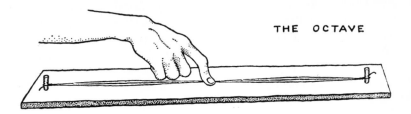

THE OCTAVE

tween neighboring musical notes that is a good deal more subtle than the arithmetic mean, which merely averages them, or than the geometric mean, which equally tempers their proportions. Thus if we take, for example, the numbers 6 and 12, their harmonic mean is 8 (which exceeds 6 by one third of 6 and is exceeded by 12 by one third of 12), their arithmetic mean is 9 (which differs from both 6 and 12 by the same number, 3) and their geometric mean is approximately 8.486 (such that $6 : 8.486 = 8.486 : 12$).

It was the fortune of the harmonic mean that it came to appear to the Pythagoreans as one of the most divine endowments of nature, not only in music and the heavens but in flowers and hills, in moving animals and waves of the sea. Even the abstract cube was held sacred because its eight corners form the harmonic mean between its six faces and its twelve edges. And the other known means and proportions and harmonies all had their special significances as symbols of the integral order in the universe — a concept that was almost wholly intuitive, since no one in those days knew how to analyze a flower or measure a moving wave or count the wingbeats of a sparrow or the musical vibrations of a lyre, nor was there such a thing as a second or a minute to time them by.

It is, of course, hardly possible now to recover the vague nebulosity of that primordial world in which neither maps nor calendars agreed with each other or were considered important and when it was almost unthinkable to make a major decision without consulting an oracle in some spooky cavern or offering a sacrifice upon the altar of Apollo. There were no laws of nature — only tendencies. Stones tended toward earth. Smoke tended toward heaven. Anything could happen and often did. So if musical tones could be expressed in numbers, why could not any shape or sense or quality? Some of the Pythagoreans regarded the number 4 as the essence of justice, perhaps as we think of square (4-sided) dealing, while number 7 signified the "right time." And they theorized about the harmonic relation of heat and cold, of wetness and dryness, light and darkness, maleness and femaleness . . . indeed about all balances and symmetries they could imagine.

That is what the members of the brotherhood probably meant by their doctrine that "all things are numbers" and that every structural form is, in essence, a piece of "frozen music." Explaining it long afterwards, Aristotle wrote that "the elements of numbers are the elements of things and therefore things are numbers." Of course, in Pythagoras' lifetime this was only an unwritten concept, for those were the days before writing was used for anything much except royal monuments, religious inscriptions, legal records, maybe a few business tallies. They were the days of the great lyric poets — Pindar, Simonides, Bacchylides — when prosody and melody were a single art and the ode a public celebration. Most teaching then consisted of stories of the great deeds of heroes and gods in far places and times long gone, which came from the lips of bards, rhapsodists and minstrels. Priests, in turn, relied heavily on the emotional effect of chants and ritual dances, for it was obvious that music could control the human heart, raise the courage to fighting pitch, quench the fires of anger, even cool erotic yearning. Specifically, the *Iliad* tells how the heroes of the Trojan War kept their wives faithful at home by leaving them to the care of the right musicians. And it was accepted among Ionian physicians that an oboe played in the Phrygian mode was a sure cure for sciatica, particularly when aimed at the affected part. All in all, it was an appropriate era in which to name music the common denominator of the universe. There were even occasions when a choice of melody directly affected the outcome of an important battle, and I can find little reason to doubt that one particular change of tune, attributed to Pythagoras himself, actually sealed the doom of Sybaris, then the greatest city in Europe. It is a significant tale.

Sybaris, you may recall, was the famous home of the Sybarites in the arch of the foot of Italy, renowned for its extravagance and luxury. Founded in 720 B.C. under a liberal charter that allowed "any person of Hellenic speech" to become its citizen and backed by the merchant princes of great Miletos in Asia Minor, whose last king was Croesus, it had grown so rapidly that in a little over a century (according to the historian Timaios), it attained a population of 300,000 free persons, while its city walls (in Strabo's account) were more than five miles around. Even if caution should lead one to halve the first of these figures, Sybaris was still a city without peer in Europe: not only the largest but by all odds the richest, and "overflowing with finely woven woolen materials, painted Ionian and Corinthian earthenware, Oriental jewelry and silver plate, unguents, medicines, spices, glass and carved ivory," all towed to its warehouses up the short canal from the sea. And there also, it is said, were unloaded "cargoes of Egyptian cats," an exotic novelty to Greeks, who had formerly made pets only of dogs and ferrets.

So plush and decadent did the Sybarites eventually become that it is claimed their patricians "never walked" but, even to go two houses down the street, "took a chariot." They were the first Europeans to have steam baths and elaborate plumbing and had earlier invented the chamber pot as a between-course accommodation to be passed around at great banquets. For an indication of how seriously they took their eating, Herodotus describes a certain "Smindyrides of Sybaris who went to a wedding at Sicyon with his private fleet which included a thousand cooks, fishermen and huntsmen." And Sybarite hedonism at its culmination relaxed sexual inhibitions to such a degree that "their women had complete liberty to do as they pleased and lay alongside the men at their licentious parties, waited on by naked youths and girls." From this, one hardly need ask why there was no known class of Sybarite courtesans. Chorus girls and models there were aplenty, however, and mannequin parades were often a feature of the more formal feasts where the quality of the gowns exhibited may be judged from Aristotle's report that a particular one containing no gold or silver thread was sold for twenty talents (about $15,000).

Outdoor processions were more imposing still. The dashing Sybarite cavalry, "five thousand strong and recruited of young men from the best families," often rode through the city wearing saffron robes over their breastplates. Their proudest stunt was the coordinated prancing of the magnificent matched horses which had been painstakingly trained to dance to the music of flutes, an accomplishment so marvelous, so unsurpassed that no one saw any flaw in its perfection. No one, that is, except Pythagoras, who held sway over his humble, barefoot devotees upon a beautiful cape near the neighboring city of Croton.

Pythagoras' observation might never have become known to the world but for the fact that when Croton at last grew big enough to rival Sybaris toward the end of the sixth century, serious differences arose between them, culminating in war in 511 B.C. Aristotle described the principal engagement of this strife as a charge by the entire Sybarite cavalry upon the smaller Crotonite army. Few of the Sybarites seemed to doubt that they would overwhelm their enemies in the first rush, but the Crotonites were better prepared than they knew. For Crotonite scouts, on Pythagoras' advice, had learned the music of the Sybarite cavalry band. Furthermore, Milon, the Crotonite general, already a legendary hero for having been six times the champion wrestler in the Olympic games and six times in the Pythian ones, was dressed in a lion skin and brandished a great club like Hercules. He inspired supreme confidence in his troops and well-distributed musicians, who calmly awaited the advancing enemy. And just before the clash, Milon gave a sign to his flutists who piped up such a tune that all the Sybarite horses started dancing and prancing, permitting the Crotonite spearmen to close in with deadly effect. Within a few minutes the whole Sybarite army was in flight, fiercely pursued by the Crotonites, who swarmed over the bridges into the city and flooded and destroyed it — so completely that it soon vanished and was forgotten, forgotten so thoroughly, in fact, that modern archeologists, who well know its general location, have scarcely yet found a trace of it.

To what degree this classic victory of the flute may be literally true is at present impossible to tell. But certainly it is close to the tradition of Pindar, who grew up when Pythagoras was an old man and was wont to limn the victories of the spirit in lilting Hellenic phrases — as in his Pythian ode: "Short is the space of time in which the happiness of mortal men groweth up . . . Creatures of a day, what is any one? What is he not? Man is just a dream of a shadow; but when a gleam of sunshine cometh as a gift of heaven a radiant light resteth on men."

Without a doubt, music has long held charms for the human ear, but not until men learned how to count the vibrations of a harp string and compare them with those of reed pipes (as Aristotle and Aristoxenos tried to do) could they begin to understand the true nature of pitch or harmony or melody or even realize that sound is wave motion. But men did eventually analyze pressure and vibrations enough to discover sound waves and, along with sound, they studied waves in general, which turned out to be important not only for comprehending music but, surprisingly, for grasping the very fundamentals of matter itself. This development would probably have astonished Pythagoras — yet it ties in so beautifully with his visionary harmonic order of creation that the most advanced of modern physicists are becoming in effect Pythagoreans again, and it looks as if his celestial music will long be heard in the laboratories of basic research.

The idea of a wave, of course, is very ancient, for not only the sea but all sizable bodies of liquid, and some of solid, reveal surface waves. Fields of grain form obvious waves in the

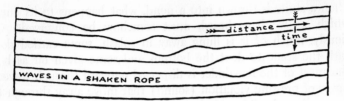

WAVES IN A SHAKEN ROPE

wind, and waves of curvature can be made to flow along a rope
— even waves of quavering flesh upon a portly thigh. Yet there
is much more to a wave than at first appears. Its depths contain
vast mysteries that are still unplumbed by the greatest philosophers
and among which must be included no doubt a key to the
ubiquitous melodies of life.

What is a wave made of? A child gazing at the ocean would
be most likely to assume it to be made of the ocean — in other
words: salt water. This impression would be almost unavoidable
if the wave were viewed from so far away that its details of motion were lost. But of course, a closer look soon reveals that
the ocean wave does not carry water along with it any more
than a wave of wheat transports the wheat. The wave but
momentarily shapes and uses the water it passes, being itself
composed of something less palpable, less constant, more abstract.
For if a wave that marches forward a thousand feet can be said to
be still the same wave (an arguable point), the water in it
cannot possibly be defined as the same water. Like the spindrift
and bubbles, the H_2O molecules inevitably drop behind. Furthermore, if you follow any ocean wave as a single identity, you will
discover that it fades away entirely in a very short time — to be
replaced by another or other waves. In some cases this replacement may appear as a dividing into two waves, like an amoeba
giving birth, yet it always occurs somehow sooner or later, being
a basic manifestation of the nonmaterial essence of the wave.

So of what, then, is this discarnate monster made? Is a wave
really part of the objective world? Yes — it is made of energy
— energy in as pure and palpable a form as we can expect to
know it anywhere: pure energy in motion, perhaps the best
example of ethereal might in the corporeal universe! To illustrate:

when a stone is thrown into a pond, what happens to its energy which, as we have heard, must somehow be conserved? Obviously, much of it is flung away in splash, some carried down with the stone to dent the bottom and some given off as heat. But most of the remainder is dispersed outward through waves — waves of pressure vibration (sound) that move away through the water, air and solid earth faster than the eye can see them, while some also goes into the familiar slow surface waves that live where air and liquid meet, spreading out in the beautiful rings that are too well known to need description.

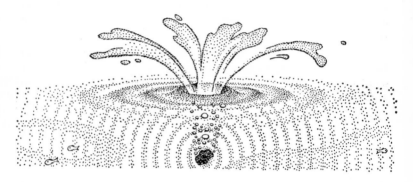

These latter, being among the most observable and best-known carriers of energy, are a subject we cannot afford to overlook in our study of reality. They are the essence of the common ocean waves whose own energy, however, comes mainly from the wind.

The three important dimensions of a wave are (1) amplitude or height from trough to crest; (2) length or distance between one crest and the next in their line of motion; (3) frequency or the number of them passing a given point in a given time which, multiplied by the length, gives the speed.

One would think that virtually everything knowable about ocean waves would have been discovered by the sailors of the earth during their thousands of years of experience upon the sea — but waves are immensely and deceptively complex. Their shapes, for instance, which tend to gravitate from the wind-tossed trochoidal 〰 toward the gentler sinusoidal 〰, vary so much in the complicated interplay of forces at sea that hardly any rule applies. Neither wave height nor size are necessarily proportional to wind velocity, which may change abruptly while the waves coast steadfastly on in remarkable verification of the conservation principle. Furthermore, the wind pulls the waves as well as pushing them in the same way it tows sails by lee suction or lifts wings by the vacuum above them. And the wind is a "two-edged sword" that can propel and level a wave in one action, raising up peaks of water often just to thrash them into spray. That is why the record-sized waves, around 110 feet high, rarely seen and almost impossible to measure from a heaving ship, generally appear during brief lulls (as in a hurricane's eye) when the wind is not there to topple them. Such giants also undoubtedly pack the combined energy of all the lesser waves that blended to form them, a phenomenon corresponding to what is termed in acoustics the looping of sympathetic vibration.

In their attempt to understand the waves, mariners naturally have collected a few rules of thumb, such as "a wave's height in feet equals half the wind speed in miles an hour," according to which a 50-mile gale should create 25-foot waves. Yet this is far from always true, because a wave's height increases also with the length of time the wind has been blowing and with the fetch or distance over which the wave has been building up, so that a 50-mile squall on a small lake may yield only five- or ten-foot waves, while an equally strong gale in mid-ocean has been known to produce heights of 35, perhaps 40, feet. The comparatively recent fetch law states, for example, that the fetch is always proportional to the square of amplitude (other factors remaining the same). Thus a doubling of wave height implies a quadrupling of fetch if nothing else changes. In an actual case, of course, all the factors are constantly changing and are so numerous that predicting the shape or dimensions of sea waves is about as tricky as forecasting weather — and for a similar reason.

More basic to wave nature than its relationship to the wind is a certain interdimensional mechanism within the wave itself.

Have you ever considered the strange evolution of steep, white-capped combers into long, gentle swells? Sea waves as a collective phenomenon eventually pass beyond a storm area, and their height diminishes while their length and speed increase, the conserved energy apparently dispersing itself until each wave has flattened gradually into a swell. Deceptively mild in height and more or less disguised with overlying waves or ripples, the mature swell is nevertheless long, broad and fast, for it still possesses (in spreading form) most of the total power that went into its creation. This basic fact, which will be news to some sailors, can be expressed more specifically by saying that as the frequency decreases or period (time elapsed in one swell's passing) increases, the latter being the reciprocal of the former, the speed correspondingly increases and the wave (swell) length increases faster still. Or in terse, quantitative terms: a wave's velocity is directly proportional to its period, and its length varies as the square of either. A general law for all surface-water waves larger than a small ripple, this can be checked at sea through one of its practical formulas: a wave's speed in knots (nautical miles per hour) equals three times its period in seconds, and its length in feet is 5⅛ times the square of the period. Thus if a patch of foam takes 11.4 seconds on the average to move from one watery summit to the next, the swells should be running at 34 knots and measure 666 feet apart.

The obvious exception to this hydrodynamic rule is where the water becomes shallow, as near a beach, for shallowness is naturally a drag on wave motion, since it imposes a limit on its subsurface components. Under any deep-water wave, all the individual molecules of liquid have been found to move in circular orbits like planets, swinging up and forward with the crests, down and backward with the troughs. While the radii of these orbits decrease rapidly with depth so that, half-a-wave-length down, the motion is only ⅟₂₃ of what it is at the surface, still the movement extends in some slight degree all the way to the bottom of the "incompressible" sea, enabling any wave to "feel" its approach to the shore. The "feeling," of course, comes through the molecular orbits, which, having no room for a vertical component at the ocean floor, must reconcile themselves even at the surface with varying elliptical shapes that revolve flatter and flatter with depth until they are nothing but back-and-forth shuttle motions on the bottom. It is this orbital drag of diminish-

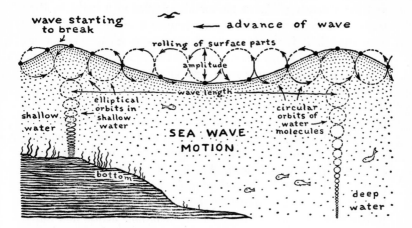

ing space, in fact, that breaks (and brakes) the arriving wave at the beach by holding back its roots — the wave velocity varying, according to Lagrange's law, as the square root of the sea depth — until its crest leans too far forward, curls and thins, finally toppling as surf when the depth no longer exceeds the wave height. And some similar thing undoubtedly happens to sound waves inside musical instruments — indeed, to any kind of waves anywhere that are constrained by the pinch of space.

If the vertical cramping of shallowness thus imperiously cuts down the amplitude of a wave, the horizontal convergence of shore lines has almost as dramatic an effect through the waves' collective reflections, particularly when the shore is steep enough to rebound the waves without much loss in amplitude. Such

SEICHE REFLECTIONS IN A HARBOR

reflected waves, often called seiches by scientists, may slosh back and forth across a lake or harbor like ripples in a bathtub, their largo reverberations producing as definite a pitch as viol strings even though it is much too slow for human ears. Transposing familiar musical terms downward about fifteen octaves, one might speak of a small soprano pond that vibrates every 28 seconds or of San Francisco Bay's deep bass seiche rate of 43 minutes. And if one could record the sounds of such reflections and play them phonographically ten thousand times faster than in nature, they undoubtedly would make recognizable musical tones, perhaps revealing to a trained ear some new significances in the waterways of a nation. It was, indeed, the vast, if subtle, patterns of the swells and their seiche reflections around the islands and atolls of the South Seas that provided one of the most important of navigational systems for the ancient migrations across that lonely third of our world — a kind of tuning in upon the ocean's harmony that has scarcely begun to be understood.

Great as these wind swells can grow on the Pacific, however — and some are known to be half a mile long after a 7,000-mile fetch — they are as nothing compared to the occasional earthquake swells or tsunamis (often misleadingly called tidal waves) which have been estimated up to six hundred miles in length. These seldom-seen phenomena are really a kind of heart beat of the aging earth, for they are created by the periodic jerks or shifts of its crust, perhaps sometimes by volcanic outbursts or rock avalanches deep under the sea. One such seismic sea wave struck the Bay of Bengal without warning on October 7, 1737, and within a few minutes had swept over hundreds of coastal villages and towns, wrecking nearly 20,000 boats and killing some 300,000 people in what was probably the most destructive deluge since the time of Noah.

You may remember the more usual tsunami that hit Hawaii on April 1, 1946, five hours after an earthquake had domed up the sea near Unimak Island in the Aleutians 2,300 miles to the north. As the resulting swells were 90 miles from crest to crest, they were far too big to be noticed at sea, and ships rose gradually over them totally unaware of the deadly power racing southward at some 450 miles an hour to lash its fury upon drowsy Hilo with a series of waves more than twenty feet high and several minutes apart that smashed houses, bridges and railways, accounting, all told, for $25,000,000 in property damage and 159 lives.

At first thought, the approach of a swell 90 miles long and only a few feet high might seem too gradual for such violence — and it is true that tsunamis really are comparatively gentle upon a steep shore. But where they meet a broad coastal shelf or a long, shallow inlet, the sea's depth becoming much less than half the waves' length, Lagrange's law inevitably has a drastic effect on their shape. Their advancing lower slopes are retarded, while their crests continue full speed, overtaking and overreaching from behind, and so the steepening wave front may eventually curl upward and forward into a towering wall to break and crash upon a beach town with catastrophic force. This is presumably the reason why the 1946 tsunami attained its greatest heights at flat Pololu Valley, the third and fourth waves reaching an estimated 55 feet above normal sea level, while the eerie ebbs between them withdrew almost as much below. And the famous Krakatoa swells of 1883 were credited with heights well above a hundred feet, combined with a length that grew to hundreds of miles and a speed no less than that of sound in air which, when augmented by air blast, produced in some parts of the Pacific a particularly strong impression by arriving at the same time as the distant thunder of exploding Krakatoa itself.

The ghostlike tendency of waves or swells to fade away individually while being replaced by others is, of course, what induced scientists to start dealing with them collectively. Hence the designation of the "group wave." An example of a group wave might be the band of breakers moving in upon a beach where, although single waves keep entering and leaving it, the group as a whole remains nearly the same in size, position and average wave velocity.

Another kind of group wave is the rather prim pattern that forms around a moving ship in calm waters, an enclosing series of billows of almost crystalline rigidity that I used to think must be as much a function of the H_2O molecule as is the hexagonal design of snow. I thought so because I had read that the bow wave has always been measured to slant outward at an angle of 19°28′ from a ship's keel line, regardless of the vessel's speed or size. But when I discovered that the bow wave maintains that exact same 19°28′, not only when the vessel is moving through deep water but also when it is traveling in comparable bodies of oil, glycerin, mercury or any other liquid on earth, I realized that the angle cannot be attributable to water alone but rather must be a function of the gravitational force of the whole earth, as the now well-established bow-wave equation ($Vw = \sqrt{g\lambda/2\pi}$) shows. From which one may deduce that space travelers in future centuries, if they find themselves voyaging on the methane or ammonia seas of some planet they don't remember the name of, may simply measure their bow-wave angle and look up the name in a pocket planetary guide (every planet having its own mass and proportionate angle), thus identifying it uniquely as a world.

Another curious characteristic of the bow wave, no matter in what material world it may be, is that, taken in the singular, it becomes concave forward due to acceleration, yet, as its faint

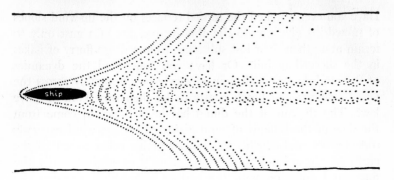

ends keep speeding up and individually fading out, the steady grouping of their maximum phase proceeds in the plural at the same speed as the ship. Likewise do stern waves accelerate in concave-backward form without apparent heed to their equally stable group confederation whose individual members come and go like metabolizing cells through a body.

But the life of every wave is relative not only to any group of which it is a part but also to the angle of its motion. Hence, if it is waning in its march perpendicular to its own axis, it may at the same time be waxing if followed parallel to the same axis — which explains how a slightly oblique comber can break and plunge to its death at your feet on a beach while its continuation in another dimension (sideways) may roll on and on down the length of the coast as successive parts of it reach land in a kind of itinerant lateral immortality.

What is true of ocean waves is, of course, generally true of waves upon other surfaces and in other mediums, such as the unseen submarine undulations where fresh river water meets the sea or the river-bottom ripples of sand which commonly parade up or downstream at speeds as high as an inch a second depending on the complex interplay of current and granular dimensions.

Have you ever watched the serried terraces on the up-wind slopes of snowdrifts give way to the abrasive pressure of a gust only to regain more than their lost substance from a dense flurry of flakes in the succeeding lull? Or have you considered the dynamics of the sand dunes which flow so slowly but inexorably across the world's deserts and beach coasts under their own kind of wave law? The rhythm of the dunes has been found to come from the flow of the billions of sand grains which the wind naturally sorts by size and weight, the coarser grains being tossed to the crests by the main jets (blowing slightly spiralwise) while the finer sand floats off with the gentler side eddies, forming the familiar crescent-shaped dunes known as barchans in Africa and Asia or as medaños in Peru. Along the Nile south of Cairo, small barchans march 30 feet apart at an average pace of about a foot a day, as similar in interrelationship as swells at sea or cloud ranks in a mackerel sky, though lacking the momentum that probably gives liquid waves their acceleration. The dunes' height, limited by the wind, remains one eighteenth their wave length,

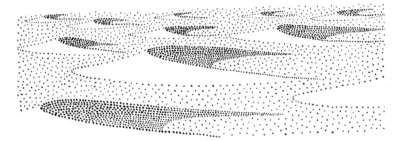

while they are laced all over like sea billows with tiny moving ripples of height one fourteenth their length — the whole a wondrous creeping organism sculped and driven in nearly every detail by the action of air upon flying grains of sand, a corporeal entity whose balance, feedback control and metabolism may be one of nature's most persuasive demonstrations of a prime ingredient of life.

If one were really to analyze the action of any of the kinds of waves mentioned, one would have to separate the complex movements of sand, water, snow, wheat or other substance into

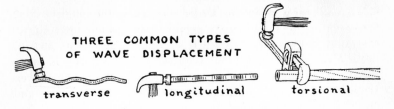

THREE COMMON TYPES
OF WAVE DISPLACEMENT

transverse   longitudinal   torsional

their simpler components known to physics as *transverse, longitudinal* and *torsional* displacements. The crosswise waving of a flag in the wind is largely a *transverse* displacement of cloth, the pulse of steam compression sent lengthwise through a locomotive cylinder by a piston moving in the same direction displaces the vapor *longitudinally*, a twist of a screw driver handle imparts a wave of *torsional* displacement to the screw at the other end. There is no end, however, to combinations of such motions among waves of many other sorts, from magma rhythms in the earth's core that move radially outward in expanding spheres of compression to others that oscillate bodies from stars to raindrops prolate-oblate-prolatewise (alternating football-doorknob-football shapes) and even to the eerie electromagnetic melodies of the human brain.

Going beyond the physical altogether, it might be appropriate here to mention even such an abstraction as the "group velocity" of waves, a mathematical concept used in theorizing

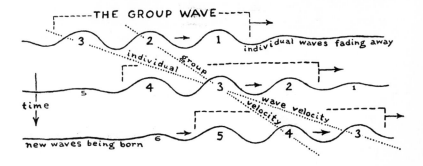

about elementary particles. To visualize this, you could imagine ocean swells of a particular wave length, period and velocity occurring progressively outward from a storm area at a constant rate. This rate is their group velocity. Group velocity is therefore something more remote from tangibility than waves or even than the velocity of waves, for it is the velocity of a velocity and one that must continuously advance from waves to waves. Yet in deep water, surprisingly, the group velocity has been found to remain constantly equal to half the wave velocity, a discovery as simple and beautiful in its way (if you follow me) as the so-called Pythagorean theorem. And, in the case of electromagnetic waves in a plasma, the group velocity equals the square of the speed of light divided by the individual wave (or phase) velocity — which likewise has a meaning that (to a mathematician) seems to sing.

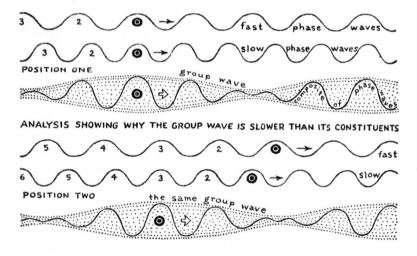

I could go on about waves of waves of waves, of course — and there seems to be no end to the little-known ripples and swells of radiation, gravitation and other influences we are constantly recording up here in space. But the kind of waves easiest to understand harmonically are the longitudinal variety, which include the rapid waves that our ears are almost continuously bringing to our attention as sound. So let us consider the nature of these invisible impulses that mystified the world before modern times — that caused the ancients, according to Leonardo, to wonder whether a bell might be entirely consumed from too much ringing.

Was it not the same Leonardo, incidentally, who sized up sound as a kind of "percussion of the air," whatever that meant? And Newton two hundred years later, who deduced sound's transmission as alternate waves of compression and rarefaction in any material?

Indeed, we now know that sound vibrates all molecules longitudinally: directly toward as well as away from the sound's source. In fact, it is these waves of molecular motion that *are* the sound. And as the natural vibration rate of materials increases with temperature and density, sound as naturally travels faster in warmer or more solid mediums: 4 miles a second along a steel railroad track, 1 mile a second through water and about ⅕ mile per second in the air — depending on how hot it is. Sound is thus only a milder form of the shock waves made by explosion blasts and moves at the same rate. In a still more general sense, it is one of numerous ways in which concentrated energy diffuses itself about the world, as we noted in the case of the stone thrown into the pond.

To be heard and understood, of course, a sound normally needs to have a duration of at least some plural number of waves — waves do not remain in the single state anyway — and such repeated waves add up to a vibration of whatever substance they are in. This vibration, moreover, is on a very different scale from the elementary, submicroscopic molecular vibrations (see page 270); it is a majestic and sophisticated motion by comparison, being a manifestation of a passing energy pattern in the outer macrocosmic world.

A classic example of such a vibration is the twang of a bow string, a sound at least twenty thousand-odd years old on Earth (as evidenced in cave paintings) and very probably ancient enough to have been the beginning of all stringed music. It is again very different from, and newer than, say, the noise of a tree crashing in the forest or of a hoofbeat upon gravel, for it is a regular tone of one frequency or pitch rather than a medley of many irregular, shifting vibrations. In short, it is a single musical note of the simplest kind which, when first heard, must have seemed like purest magic.

Just to be sure its basic nature is clearly understood, may I explain that waving one's finger once in the air will send a slight shock wave of pressure out in all directions at a fifth of a mile a second. But this is neither sound nor music and it makes no sensation in the ear, which cannot detect a single wave. Even shaking the finger back and forth as fast as is humanly possible will not break the silence. But if one could wave it fifty times a second, a faint deep humming note would begin to permeate the air, something like that made by a hummingbird's wings, rising in pitch with any increase in the waving rate.

That, actually, is what pitch is — and all that it is. Pitch is sound-wave frequency. It is to sound what temperature is to molecules or what color is to light (see page 451). Run a stick along a picket fence, slowly at first, then faster and faster, and you will notice the same thing: the accelerating taps of the stick will blend into a rising tattoo that becomes a musical tone. Pour liquid out of a jug and you can hear its gurgling melody descending the tonal scale as the incoming air takes longer and longer to reflect its pressure waves back and forth across the expanding cavity within, thus lowering their frequency — the principle of the bagpipes, trombone, oboe and other wind instruments. And the humming string of the bow or the harp is no different in essence for, waving back and forth, it hits the air each time, sending out regular impulses of pressure that collectively amount to a musical note of steady pitch.

No doubt, the string was particularly inspiring to Pythagoras because it is so easy to observe in action, so simple and amenable to handling and experimenting, and perhaps also because it is so close to the border (if there is one) between the concrete and the abstract. The latter consideration, which Pythagoras seems to have felt intuitively, has since been made much clearer in a modern laboratory. Fixing a needle to a vibrating tuning fork (similar in principle to a string) so that it continuously scratches a wavy line on a long piece of smoked glass passing steadily under it, scientists have caught a permanent graphic record of every motion the fork made — actually a sort of basic phonograph record — revealing the beautiful sine curve of "simple harmonic" sound. Not only is this curve mathematically pure in its simplicity but it has an amazing regularity, repeating itself hundreds of times a second (depending on the pitch), with each wave maintaining an identical length and the same characteristic sine shape even while the amplitude gradually diminishes as the fork's energy runs down.

By such experiments it was discovered that the note called "middle C" on the piano, for example, consists of about 262 complete pressure waves a second, that any sort of regular vibrations at the rate of 262 per second, whether they come from a vacuum cleaner's motor or a bumblebee's wings, will play middle C — confirmation, if any were still needed, that middle C, like every note, is not made of any particular kind of sound but is purely a *rate* of impulses, a *number* — in other words, an *abstraction*.

Pointing up the incorporeal side of harmonic motion still further, the modern general theory of vibrations shows that all materials oscillate in somewhat the same basic way that celestial bodies swing around their orbits: not necessarily describing complete ellipses, however, but commonly alternating their directions in some partial orbit or folded ellipse like a pendulum, or perhaps in the rocking motion of a librating moon. This happens, generally speaking, because every material possesses at least one position in which it can theoretically remain at rest — otherwise it would be a "perpetual-motion machine." And if or when it is in such a position of equilibrium, all the forces influencing each particle of it must (by definition) be exactly balanced. But of course, any little disturbance such as a whisper or a ray of light arriving from outside will move the structure at least a little out of equilibrium into some new and unstable position in which each particle of it will feel a "restoring force" trying to return it to balance again. By the time this force succeeds in getting it back to equilibrium, however, the structure is virtually certain to have picked up such momentum that it will overshoot the position and coast beyond it until another (and opposite) restoring force reverses it once more. Thus is an oscillation set up: the natural harmonic motion called vibration when its path is short but which, on the larger scale, keeps clocks on time, holds stars to their courses and is inextricably involved in the origins of waves and music.

Kepler would have been particularly delighted with the implications of this now well-proved theory, and it seems a pity his enthusiastic letters to Galileo (beginning in 1597) did not elicit more response or some serious collaboration. For Galileo's experiments with oscillating pendulums might have given Kepler just the appreciation of the ellipse he needed to solve the orbit of Mars a long, hard decade sooner. Galileo must have known before 1600 that while a single blow upon a motionless pendulum will start it swinging back and forth over a straight line marked on the ground beneath it, this being the simple harmonic motion of the plucked string, any additional blow or blows at different angles (each also imparting simple harmonic motion) will send it into an ellipse, this being the compound of all the simple wave motions. And if an ellipse could thus be the natural path of a suspended object swinging under complex influences on Earth, why in heaven shouldn't a similar law hold for the paths of the celestial spheres suspended in complex space? Indeed, Kepler might literally have transposed the actual "pitch" of the six known planets to his famous oracular music, for Galileo had firmly established that the pendulum's frequency (pitch) is rigidly dependent upon its length, corresponding in the sky to an orbit's invisible radius.

Understandably, Pythagoras, standing seven times farther back in history, could hardly be presumed to have had more than a vague inkling of the pitch of his wandering stars, yet his observations on the natural intervals of strings were mathematically exact so far as they went — and founded our modern science of harmonics. Without counting vibration frequencies, he could naturally hear pitch and see the nodes that accompanied the elementary overtones. He could see that the pitch is raised to the sympathetic octave or "eighth note" by momentarily holding a finger on the exact mid-point of the string while plucking the center of either half, leaving the whole then vibrating freely in two equal, seesawing parts separated by a node of immobility at the fulcrum. Or raised to the further interval of a twelfth by making the string hum in three equal parts with two nodes.

SIMPLE HARMONICS OF THE PLUCKED STRING

fundamental   octave   twelfth   double octave

Or to two full octaves with four parts and three nodes. Or to any of several other congenial intervals (fifth, fourth, etc.) by shortening the string in simple or aliquot proportions.

This is not to say that Pythagoras knew that when the string is divided in two, by a node or a fret, it naturally vibrates twice as fast — or, divided in three, three times as fast. Nor is there any evidence that he clearly realized the effect of the string's weight or tension on its pitch. Still less could he possibly have understood that the string's outstanding musical quality derives from its free vibration pattern matching its natural harmonics so perfectly (in frequency) that every time its fundamental tone is set going, its harmonics respond as well. More probably, Pythagoras was conscious only of the mysterious relationships between pitch and length of vibrating string segments, and of the mathematical implications of combining two or more notes into a harmonious chord which somehow in the addition — or was it multiplication? — became more beautiful and perhaps more divine.

If it is still hard to accept the obscurity of such musical recesses in the ancient mind, there remains, at least, the sober fact that twenty-one and a half centuries were to pass before the French mathematician Marin Mersenne would at last discover the true basic law of pitch for strings in 1636, stating that the frequency of a string's vibrations varies directly with the square root of its tension but inversely with its length and the square root of its weight. This remarkable three-way summary, formulated just after Kepler's death and during the old age of Galileo, came none too soon for teaching the clavichord pioneers how to avoid having to make their bass strings a hundred times as long as their treble ones: by greatly increasing both the weight of the basses and the tension of the trebles.

Then soon afterward, in the days of Newton and Hooke, while a young man named Johann Sebastian Bach was still experimenting with new keyboards in Thuringia, scientists began to realize that if pitch could be a manifestation of the length of sound waves, loudness or volume of tone must logically be determined by the same waves' amplitude. And also that it would be reasonable to expect that the detail of the wave curve, which could be very complex, might somehow account for its timbre or sound quality.

Of course, it was by no means yet obvious that the hard-to-visualize sound wave was normally a composite thing, blended of many simpler waves crossing, passing and overlapping each other like ripples upon waves upon swells at sea. For the analysis of wave shapes would inevitably be a long and painstaking job requiring the utmost of many dedicated mathematicians — a work that continues to this day with increasingly elaborate equipment but without foreseeable end.

Probably one of the first experiments in compound-wave analysis consisted of hitting one prong end of a vibrating tuning fork with a hammer. This makes a "clang tone" about two and a half octaves above the fundamental note of the fork, because of new and very rapid vibrations that ride upon the fundamental ones like ripples on an ocean wave. But the clang tone alone actually is composed of just as simple a harmonic motion as the fundamental tone, though aligned in a different direction and with a frequency some six and a quarter times higher. It is only the combination of the two simple motions (as shown in the illustration) that becomes complex or double motion. The addition

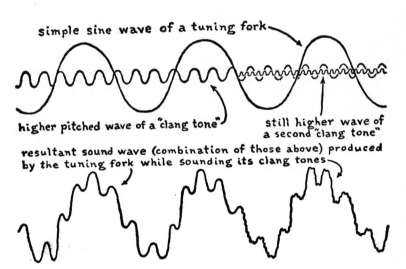

simple sine wave of a tuning fork

higher pitched wave of a "clang tone"

still higher wave of a second "clang tone"

resultant sound wave (combination of those above) produced by the tuning fork while sounding its clang tones

of another clang tone, an octave and a half higher than the first, may then increase the complexity to triple motion — something that happens very commonly. In fact, it is almost impossible to start a tuning fork humming so purely that no admixture of such overtones can be heard.

In the case of a bell — an instrument usually designed for volume and beauty rather than purity — the overtones are actually considered vital to the character of the ring. For it is undeniable that the simple purity of tone sometimes obtainable with a "perfect" tuning fork grows dull in the ear, being in the long run no more of an improvement over a random noise than the architecture of the barracks is an improvement over that of the junk yard. Which goes a good way toward explaining why the world's accepted music has come to be a blend of tones, a deliberate confluence of pitches, volumes and timbres that overlap in every imaginable way.

But what, you may wonder, really happens in a mixture of musical waves? Why are some combinations so delightful, others so excruciating?

Let's take the very simplest mixture possible: two waves with the same frequency and phase, which means two waves that not only endure equally long but always begin and end at the same instants. They may have different amplitudes or shapes but, as their frequency or period is equal, they must certainly be identical in pitch like, say, a gong and a horn both hitting F♯. Furthermore, since they are in the same phase, they must meet at least upon every node and while moving in the same direction, thereby lining up crest over crest, trough under trough. Thus the two waves will reinforce each other, giving their resultant or combination wave an amplitude equal to the sum of both constituent amplitudes. Indeed, so powerful is this compounded volume that it exerts a strong retroactive influence back upon the weaker

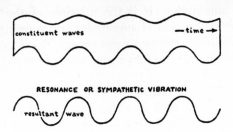

RESONANCE OR SYMPATHETIC VIBRATION

of its constituents and even upon completely external or in-active wave capacities within its range, often rousing them from silent potentiality to loudly energized motion. This is the phenomenon called sympathetic vibration or resonance, and it is what makes an unstruck tuning fork hum in sympathy with another set to vibrating in the same natural key. It also explains the gaps in Saturn's rings (see page 97) and the exaggerated bounciness of certain washboard roads where the natural spring frequency of your car happens to match the wave frequency of the passing undulations.

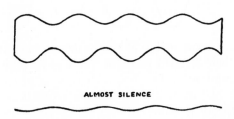

ALMOST SILENCE

The next wave mixture in order of simplicity is two waves of the same frequency (pitch) but opposite phase, similar to the previous combination except that crest will come over trough and trough under crest. This makes the constituent vibrations pull in opposite directions, partially neutralizing each other, since the resultant amplitude is now the difference (not the sum) of their single amplitudes. It is the principle of the silencer, for obviously the subtraction of amplitudes (representing energy and loudness) combines the two wave mountains, if not into complete cancellation, at most into a gentle composite hill of comparative quietude.

But in nature, one can hardly expect two waves of the same pitch to happen to meet in either exactly the same or exactly the opposite phase. Such simplicity would need to be contrived, as it is rather an exception to the normal independence of wave systems. In ordinary random life, the crests of one vibration will come over neither the crests nor the troughs of another vibration but somewhere in between, creating a resultant (see below) that is, however, in the case of equal frequencies, still simple harmonic motion and still obtained by adding or subtracting amplitudes at each point along its length.

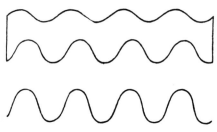

But it is when the pitches of two or more wave systems are different that their blended resultant waves really begin to take on harmonic complexities, for then each compound crest or trough ceases to be like its neighbor, and the constituent crests come sometimes together, sometimes staggered, sometimes nearly opposite. If two waves of equal amplitude, for instance, differ in pitch by only two or three vibrations a second, their phase relationship when they are combined must change constantly (see top of next page), repeating itself likewise two or three times a second, a repetition that puts a kind of throb, called a beat, into the resultant tone. Such beats are really audible group waves, and when they are created by two nearly equal frequencies, they can readily be heard up to a rate of six or seven a

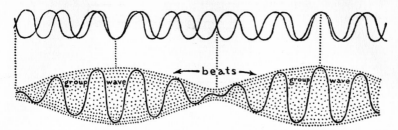

second. Piano tuners commonly listen for them between the paired or trebled strings of supposedly equal pitch. Beyond seven a second, however, the beat frequency merges into sensations of dissonance or consonance, depending on the vibration ratio of the combined notes. The unpleasant clash of two pitches that differ by something between about 5 and 25 percent (in frequency number) is usually considered the main belt of dissonance, beyond which begin the consonant intervals: thirds, fourths, fifths . . . (named for the frequency spans to the third, fourth, fifth . . . notes of the scale), followed by the integral harmonics: the octave, the twelfth, the double octave . . . and so on, with sundry dissonant zones interspersed among them.

It is these consonant intervals that were measured precisely by Pythagoras and that are exceptional among combined notes of different pitch for their simplicty of ratio: the octave or 1:2 ratio being a combination of a low note whose vibrations might be expressed as "bang . . . bang . . . bang . . . bang . . ." and a high note of double the frequency, "bang bang bang bang bang bang bang bang," which, put together, come out —

bang $\frac{\text{bang}}{\text{bang}}$ bang $\frac{\text{bang}}{\text{bang}}$ bang $\frac{\text{bang}}{\text{bang}}$ bang or bang BANG bang BANG bang BANG bang. Played fast enough to make the in-

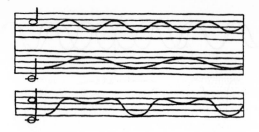

dividual vibrations blend into a continuous tone, it sounds like an octave — as indeed it should. For it *is* an octave.

Actually, a real compound tone is not *quite* so simple as this, for the changing phases subtract as well as add. And in the 2:3 ratio of the interval called a fifth, the combined "ba-ang — ba-ang" (2 syllables) and "bang bang bang" (3 syllables) come out something like "BANGebang ma-bang MANG, BANGebang ma-bang MANG, BANGebang ma-bang MANG . . ." (6 syllables), which, at speed, turns out to be the congenial do-sol (C – G) dyad. Then, adding only a middle note, we have the handsome triad of C major, the do-mi-sol (C – E – G) chord, which, as a composite wave, is already rather too complex to describe — though it is the easy first chord a beginner is taught on the piano.

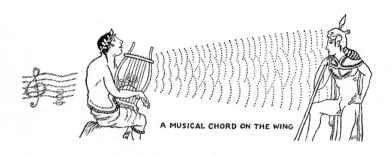

A MUSICAL CHORD ON THE WING

Beyond here, it would seem better to resort to the almost mystic generalizations of Fourier's theorem of harmonic analysis than to try to itemize any more of the vagaries of the musical wave curve, composed of its unending combinations of intervals and accordances, consonances and dissonances, chords and discords. For Jean B. J. Fourier, the French mathematician, discovered early in the nineteenth century that not only can an infinite number of resultant waves be created by mixing these ingredients — just like putting chemicals into test tubes — but, amazingly, any wave curve, no matter how complicated, can be sorted out again into its constituent parts. At first blink, this seems about as feasible as unscrambling eggs, yet there really is an easy technique for analyzing any wave into nothing but simple harmonic curves, and Niels Bohr actually used it in working out his "correspondence principle" (see pages 342–43). I will not take space to pursue the method here, but I must just say that a little of its surprising capacity for revealing the ultimate nature of things can be surmised from the fact that decomposition of waves and curves, like disintegration of bodies, turns out to be possible in any of an infinite number of ways — just as there is no limit to the ways you can wreck a ship or a house or tear up a piece of paper or blow smoke into the sky. And if you are tempted to reject the compositeness of a wave as something mathematical but unreal, just remember that waves themselves, presumably without thinking, combine and sort their own shapes to perfection — passing straight through each other like geometric monsters to emerge completely restored on the other side (see illustration on next page). And this is true of waves ranging all the way from the ponderous surges of galactic momentum to the incredible negative ripples of intramolecular magnetism.

ꓶ < ꓴ N Z — ꓩ ꓵ ꟽ

If natural wave behavior is sometimes hard to swallow, however, the artificial wave combinations tried out by the early pioneers of musical science can be about equally unexpected. The very oldest-known scale in the world evidently progressed downward in pitch instead of up and may be described approximately by the note sequence E – C – B′ –B – A –

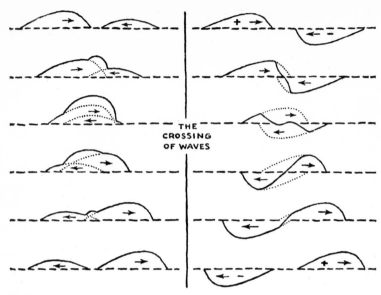

THE
CROSSING
OF WAVES

F – E′ – E, in which B′ and E′ represent tones between sharp ♯ and natural ♮. Curiously, the slowly vibrating bass notes in that dim era were reputedly considered of "high" pitch, while young girls sang in what were called the "low" registers. And on just such weird quarter-tone modes and half-, full- and double-tone ones were hung the earliest plain songs of temple and church, those haunting chants of which some are said to have been handed down uncorrupted from the psalms of David or the Song of Solomon. Of such may have sprung Aristophanes' beautiful chant of the Initiated, his lays of Lysistrata. Of such the wild piping of the Corybantic priest — perhaps even the primeval paeans of Sargon.

Meantime, the Hindus promoted their unbridled scale of 22 alternative notes of variable sequence and the Arabs various modes in quarter tones, while other peoples of the earth tried third-, sixth-, eighth-, twelfth- and even sixteenth-tone music. Yet such difficult tonal parings never could become generally appreciated, and even the relatively simple third tones remained unrecognizable, if not physically painful, to occidental ears.

It was Aristoxenos of Tarentum, the great theorist of music in the late fourth century B.C., who seems to have done the most to develop the Pythagorean intervals of the so-called Lydian mode into a complete diatonic scale. In his one surviving book, *Elements of Harmony*, he defined the pitch difference between the fourth and fifth (intervals) as the unit tone of his scale. Then, needing a subunit, he divided the tone arithmetically into two semitones, and rather arbitrarily placed five semitones in the fourth, seven in the fifth, and twelve in the octave. The fact that these semitones did not fit into their places exactly but only approximately, like planet orbits in their "ideal" spheres, must have disillusioned Aristoxenos, leaving him with what the Greeks called a *leimma* or residue — but it also led him to an interesting (if inconclusive) "calculus by logarithms" that made his work one of the masterpieces of Hellenic thought and established music as a major Greek science alongside arithmetic, geometry and astronomy. Indeed, these four constituted the *quadrivium* of higher classical learning until the end of medieval times.

In A.D. 384, many of the ancient "tones," including Aristoxenos' and some variations by Ptolemy, were reviewed and set in order by Saint Ambrose to be later developed in the Gregorian tradition, and by the Visigoths in Spain and the Byzantines in the East. And gradually, among others, there evolved the five-note melodies known as pentatonic modes, like "Auld Lang Syne" and the Japanese national anthem, both of which were built around the interval of the downward fourth (as from C to G) and can be played entirely on the five black keys of a piano.

And by the eighteenth century, the diatonic scale had pretty well crystallized into its modern form — its notes taking the numerical relationship C 4 – D 4½ – E 5 – F 5⅓ – G 6 – A 5⅔ – B 7½ – C' 8. Thus C and C' make a perfect octave (4:8 =1:2), C and G a perfect fifth (4:6 = 2:3), C and F a perfect fourth (4:5⅓ = 3:4) and so on. And the appealing seventh chord C – E – G – – B♭ – C' was discovered to derive its magic from the simple exactitude of its proportions 4:5:6:7:8! Just why this strangely insistent musical "call" should find its most satisfying harmonic "answer" in a chord exactly a fourth higher, F – A – C' – F', is still not well understood. I think it will undoubtedly be explained eventually by wave symmetry but, in the meantime, the seventh chord seems certainly one of the most beautiful mysteries in nature.

The diatonic scale has thus served its purpose ideally within its own limits, even offering a few perfect intervals and triads in other keys than its own, as the accompanying table shows. Aristoxenos would probably have been impressed by the fact that all its tonal differences in frequency are multiples of the prime number 11. And Pythagoras would surely applaud its plurality of means: E the *arithmetic* mean between C and G, F the *harmonic* mean of C and C', and G the *geometric* mean of C and D'!

Yet, as musicians well know, the diatonic scale failed utterly as a practical all-around tool of music — for the same reason that Kepler's circumscription of the spheres failed as a tool of astronomy. It just would not quite fit! It could do very nicely at certain points or within particular limitations but the mere act of pressing it into place in one region would always and inevitably force it out of line in another. Ill-fitting notes were so common, in fact, in the early clavichords and pianos that they were given the name of "wolves" — they howled so. If a major diatonic scale were constructed starting at D instead of C, it could not possibly match up with all the notes of the C scale since several would be at the wrong pitch intervals. Instead, it would need four new notes for its diatonic perfection. And, to provide for all the twelve musical keys, every octave would have to have 72 notes!

FREQUENCY RELATIONS IN THE MAJOR DIATONIC AND EQUALLY TEMPERED SCALES

Frequency relations	Do	Re	Mi	Fa	Sol	La		Ti	Do'	Re'	Mi'	Fa'
	Middle C	D	E	F	G	A	B♭	B	C'	D'	E'	F'
Octave, key of C	1								2			8
Major triad and octave, key of C	4	(4½)	5	(5⅓)	6	(6⅔)	(7)	(7½)	8	(9)	(10)	
Major triad and octave, key of F	(3)			4		5			6			8
Major triad and octave, key of G		3			4			5		6		
Vibrations, diatonic scale, key of C	264	297	330	352	396	440		495	528	594	660	704
Diatonic vibration differences		33	33	22	44	44		55	33	66	66	44
Diatonic interval ratios		9/8 whole	10/9 whole	16/15 half	9/8 whole	10/9 whole		9/8 whole	16/15 half	9/8 whole	10/9 whole	16/15 half
Equally tempered (geometric) scale, suitable for music in all keys	261.6	293.7	329.6	349.2	392.0	440		493.9	523.3	587.4	659.3	698.4
Tempered interval ratios		$\sqrt[6]{2}$ whole	$\sqrt[6]{2}$ whole	$\sqrt[12]{2}$ half	$\sqrt[6]{2}$ whole	$\sqrt[6]{2}$ whole		$\sqrt[6]{2}$ whole	$\sqrt[12]{2}$ half	$\sqrt[6]{2}$ whole	$\sqrt[6]{2}$ whole	$\sqrt[12]{2}$ half

The mathematical reason for this discrepancy (in case you're interested) is that the perfect fifth contains 7 (supposedly equal) semitones out of an octave of 12 semitones, so that 12 fifths should ideally just fit into 7 octaves. If they did, a fifth (3⁄2) multiplied by itself 12 times should exactly equal an octave (2⁄1) multiplied by itself 7 times. But the twelfth power of 3⁄2 comes out slightly more than the seventh power of 2 approximately by the ratio 519:512 — a sad and shocking little "blot" upon the presumed perfection of the spheres. Shades of Pythagoras — and Aristoxenos' *leimma!*

So to escape the absurdity of a 72-note scale and create a uniformly flexible one in which a piece could be played in any key without noticeable distortion or difference from any other key, compromises had to be made through which the tonal frequencies could be adjusted slightly to make all semitones really equal. In this way, our modern practical scale of "equal temperament" was created, in which twelve proportionately identical semitones exactly span each octave, and A♯ AND B♭ (which differed by a *Pythagorean comma* in the diatonic scale) are one single note, as are all other contiguous sharps and flats. Not just one single note in each scale, either, but one single note all over the world — since A above middle C has been standardized by international agreement at exactly 440 vibrations a second.

Such an even scale had been dreamed about and suggested many times in history, but it was not until the first quarter of the eighteenth century that Bach, while living in the little town of Arnstadt in central Germany, adopted it for its practical advantages and brought it into general acceptance. Not only did he tune his domestic clavichords and harpsichords in this tempered way, making every black key both a sharp and a flat, but he wrote a series of preludes and fugues to demonstrate the virtues of his chosen scale. Called *The Well-tempered Clavier* or

"Equable Keyboard," this famous work of 1722 included pieces
in all twelve major and twelve minor keys and pointed to the
great advantages of unhindered transpositions. While admittedly
a step down from absolute diatonic mathematical perfection (in
which an ideal fifth is 7.019550008654 times the size of an
ideal semitone, which is one twelfth of an octave or $\sqrt[12]{2}$ or
1.05946), the tempered scale smooths out all inequalities into
a uniform imperfection (its fifth exactly seven times its semitone)
so slight that the musician's ear and most piano tuners accept
it with scarce a quaver. Even the different keys, harmonically
standardized though they be, seem to imaginative minds to retain
some of the flavor of the original diatonic individuality and to
strike different emotional chords — D♭ major suggesting dignity
and majesty, F a lighter mood and B♭ minor (to some) a spirit
of licentious abandon.

A usable scale, however, can hardly be more than a tool of
music. What then makes a melody? Is there any reason back of
the rhyme that turns tones into tunes?

This complicated subject was once regarded as so elusive it
was beyond all logic, but modern science, by considering music
in its essence as a form of communication, has learned to apply
mathematics even to the mysterious art of composing. Through
a certain "technique of engineering," in fact, a musically inclined
mathematics teacher at Columbia University named Joseph Schil-
linger early in this century evolved a numerical system that George
Gershwin is said to have used while composing *Porgy and Bess*.
The basic principle is the application of the entropy concept to
melody and beauty. For it is becoming more and more evident
that musical notes have many of the characteristics of elementary
particles and that their patterns of relationship, mysteriously parallel to the structure of the universe, follow the same laws of thermodynamics as crystals, gases or any other measurable substance. A
composer, then, with an eye to physical theory need only make the

entropy (disorder) of his music low enough to give it some recognizable pattern yet at the same time high enough for an element of suspense and individuality, and he may be well on his way toward a judicious compromise between the Scylla of wanton discord and the Charybdis of dull monotony!

The finer points of entropy-oriented composition, of course, have not yet been worked out by the mathematicians, although a series of electronic randomized-pattern "composers" has started grinding out a weird evolution of tunes which, some claim, have already improved to the point of sounding almost as stirring as the dreariest of medieval chants.

The matter of volume of sound has turned out to be easier to understand — its general law: that the energy of a vibration is proportional to the square of the amplitude. And both volume and pitch interrelate with timbre or tone quality, which is a kind of sum-product of all the details through which vibratory energy distributes itself — as, for instance, the stick-slip-stick-slip-stick friction waves of the violin bow upon a string that blends its

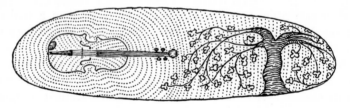

fundamental tone (voiced by resined horsehair on sheepgut) with its harmonics, flowing into the oaken bridge and headlong down the spruce soundpost, spreading thence impetuously across the chamber of the body and through the cells of the surrounding planewood, beech or pine, shaped by interrelated contours, graceful f-holes, invisible nodes, and on outward into the air in all directions at better than 1,000 feet a second, to reverberate anew to the shape of the hall or the natural resonance of surrounding trees and buildings. Thus the strains you hear are literally the living compend of a hundred factors from the hand of the musician to the pitch of the balcony — even to the tensions in your own ear and brain. A trumpet call takes but a tiny fraction of the total noise of pressure from the blower's breath — just those components that can be amplified by the natural vibration of the instrument — and molds them progressively outward with the help of all the molecules they meet, expressing thereby a sort of tuned aspect of the entire local world, including, of course, every other concurrent sound. In the confluence of waves, there may even be tones of inaudibly low or high pitch that react upon each other through resonance or beats to produce clearly audible frequencies. And the relatively pure mid-passage parts of notes from, say, cellos, oboes and organs may be virtually indistinguishable, leaving it to the irregular timbre of their beginnings and endings to tell the listener whether he is in the presence of bowing or blowing.

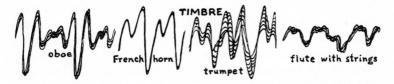

If such fleeting details look meager in print, their sound is actually quite ample in expressing individual character, for there is no known noise or music that cannot be created by the correct superposition of simple harmonic waves — from the cosmic thunder of an H-bomb to a sensitive set of coordinated organ pipes which have been recently taught to say "papa" and "mama."

This general discussion of waves and music may have seemed digressive at times, but I think it was really needed as an introduction to our next delve into the essence of matter. Obviously, most of the macrocosmos tends to form rhythms and cadences which we see everywhere as rows of mountain chains, constellations of stars, banks and ripples of clouds, grids of city streets, processions of trees in the forest, pebbles on the beach, waves at sea, schools of fish under the sea, flights of birds, hair on heads, grain in wood . . . and from here on downward, less and less obviously, more and more mysteriously, into the microcosm, to cells in the body, to fibers of muscle, serried molecules, crystal lattices, networks of atoms, "orbits" of electrons, even to the nebulous maneuverings inside atomic nuclei. Indeed, is there reason to think these redundant waves cease anywhere or anywhen? And if not, why might they not be made of the same potent "substance" with which Lao Tzu "tied" his philosophic knots "without rope"?

We have already noted that a wave is a shape in motion — not normally built of matter (though there are cases, as in surf riding, where matter may be carried by a wave) but rather built of energy — energy that can pass from wave to wave as individual waves are born and die while their group goes on, the energy living and flowing independently of any single form — a fundamental something that is ever more demonstrably the building brick of the world, that mystic abstraction that Job may have first sensed when God demanded of him out of the whirlwind, "Hast thou walked in the search of the depth?" or "Knowest thou . . . who hath put wisdom in the inward parts?"

It would be a help, of course, if man could handle an electron like a billiard ball or view it like the moon, taking its measure in a leisurely way. Even if it were as remote as Jupiter or as strange as Saturn, its music would be a lot easier to comprehend on the macrocosmic scale — as we calculate Jupiter's overtaking of Saturn every twenty years (each time in a different place) as only the overtone to a deep fundamental throb when the passing of these giant worlds works around to a nearly exact repetition once in something over nine hundred years.

But the electron is much more elusive than any planet or palpable object in the macroworld, if in fact it is an "object" at all. As we saw in the last chapter, it is definitely not free to follow any orbit it might happen into, like a celestial body or a sputnik, but must "choose" one of exactly seven concentric shells or energy states that surround its nucleus (see pages 338–339). Nor can two electrons collide like two cannonballs, for they keep a mysteriously inviolate interval between themselves in obedience to Pauli's exclusion principle (see page 324), which has never been known to harbor an exception. Besides, an electron's energy (whatever it really is) has proved to radiate itself outward in the strictly quantized vibrations or waves called photons whose energy has a wonderfully constant relationship to their frequency or pitch. This curious abstract relationship between the "smallest possible" parcels of energy and their frequency (comparable to the magnitude-frequency ratio of pulsing Cepheid stars) was discovered by Max Planck in 1900 and is the key to his famous quantum theory which the world could not believe for several years after he published it, but which has since revolutionized it inside and out.

To use again our analogy of Babylon, it is as if the Lord High Planner of Royal Works had somehow discovered and proved to King Nebuchadnezzar that the size of the Babel brick was absolutely dependent on its color, so literally so that if the king ever wanted to change the tint of his grand palace, he must also (to a very difficult and expensive, if slight, degree) alter the palace's dimensions. One would hardly blame Nebuchadnezzar for contemplating beheading his Lord High Planner before swallowing such a fantastic revelation. Yet Planck handed the scientists of 1900 virtually the same ultimatum, which, under the strong influence of Einstein, they eventually accepted. For by this time, it was common knowledge that color is a kind of pitch or wave frequency, and the energy quanta that form the "bricks" of our whole material world have turned out to be cut most exactly to their own pitch. Planck, appropriately, was an excellent amateur pianist and understood musical theory, which knowledge undoubtedly helped him in working out a precise mathematical figure for the constant relation between frequency and his minim of energy. This increasingly important constant he designated by the letter h — now one of the commonest symbols in physics — a symbol, you will admit, a lot easier to write or read than its fully established equivalent of .000000000000-

000000000000006547 . . . erg seconds. One full erg second, by the way, amounts approximately to the action required to blink your eye once.

If *h* seems an awfully small quantity of something, it is reasonable that it should, for it is the very smallest physical quantity known, namely, one quantum. One quantum of what? Not of energy (since it is a relation between energy and frequency) but of *action*. Physicists use the term action for *energy* (in ergs) × *time* (in seconds) in measuring simple oscillation, or for *momentum* × *distance* in most other uses. Thus a 2-gram ball rolling at a speed of 3 centimeters a second has a momentum of 6 centimeter-gram-seconds. And, in moving a distance of 4 centimeters with that momentum, its action is 24 centimeter-gram-seconds, which would be many septillions of *h*. That is the working meaning of quantized action, and hundreds of the most exacting microcosmic tests have affirmed and reaffirmed the amazing fact that there are no fractions of *h* in the material world — while every year turns up fresh evidence of *h*'s reality as a profound abstraction that can reveal important truth in almost any branch of science.

When I said that *h* signified action rather than energy, I did not mean that energy and other aspects of matter are not also quantized. For this seems to be a thoroughly quantized world in every size range from galaxies to stars to apples to electrons. Furthermore, *h* is a very versatile relation and, multiplied by frequency (usually designated v) in the form hv, it stands for a *quantum of energy* — the smallest possible mote of the basic stuff all matter is presumably made of. In other words hv may be the unsplittable ultimate of the material universe — a kind of abstract primeval atom of energy that embodies, much more truly than our now-familiar chemical atom, the "part" that is "partless" dreamed of by Leucippos and Democritos while strolling the provocative strands of Greece.

It was with thoughts somewhat along these lines that a young French prince got to musing about Einstein's equation $E = mc^2$ in 1922, wondering whether such a declaration of the fixed ratio between mass and energy meant that light has mass as well as energy. He was Louis de Broglie, Prince of Piedmont, a learned historian and part-time physicist. Though not quite the kind of man most people would have expected to inaugurate a new revolution in fundamental science, which was already staggering under the impact of Planck and Einstein, to say nothing of Rutherford, Bohr and others, he nevertheless realized the serious discrepancies in Bohr's theory of the atom with its patched-up correspondence principle and mystic quantum jumps of an electron from one classical orbit to another without really passing through the intervening space. How could even an electron-sized Jupiter become a corresponding Saturn without following some sort of comet's path from one planetary precinct to the other? Must one not choose between Newton's clockwork universe and the strange abstract world of Planck and Einstein without trying to blend them into one theory?

De Broglie thought so. And, even though his idea of a massive photon of light (based on $E = mc^2$) turned out to be pretty wide of the mark, it led him to a discovery of the first magnitude. He was familiar with the evidence that light has wave motion (which we will look into in the next chapter) and from there he reasoned: if light also has mass, which would make it some sort of aspect of matter, why doesn't all matter have wave motion? Why indeed may not matter consist entirely of waves?

This may seem a logical question today, but more than a quarter-century ago the concept of waving matter was utterly fantastic and de Broglie knew he could never get anywhere with it unless he somehow brought it down to solid earth with the aid of respectable mathematics. So he began to rummage around in mathematical notation, which, appropriately, is related to musical notation. He noted that Einstein's $E = mc^2$ and Planck's $E = hv$ could be put together as $mc^2 = hv$, which is easily transposed to $v = \dfrac{mc^2}{h}$, which is just an abbreviated way of saying that frequency (v) is the equal of mass (m) times the square of the speed of light (c^2) divided by h. If the v for frequency naturally reminded de Broglie of Pythagoras' vibrating string, it also gave him a sense of being on the right track — for is not the humming harp a prime example of waving matter?

But what exactly did v refer to mathematically? It meant frequency, yes — but the frequency of what? De Broglie was reasonably sure it must be the frequency of some aspect of matter, since both Planck's and Einstein's equations had had to do with matter and matter's mysterious counterpart, energy. And, as he visualized the vibrant electron looping or whooping around the nucleus, quite manifestly the most active working part of the atom, he naturally picked the electron as the likeliest object of v rhythm.

Burrowing deeper into his mathematical reserves, he then worked out something of the form and functioning of the electron's frequency. As it must be a wave frequency rather than a particle frequency, it was induced to emerge not as an orbiting monad's rhythmic revolutions but as a kind of centralized throbbing. And the actual mathematical equations turned out to be interpretable in three ways: either as (1) a concentrated heartbeat; (2) an explosive spherical pulsation; or (3) both. De Broglie assumed the last alternative: that an atom not only had a kind of localized heart of stable matter but also broadcast an expanding pulsation "forever in step with it and extending all over the universe" something like the now-known rise and fall of the whole ocean under each advancing wave. And since his atom itself was materially representable as a localized group wave that potentially could move up to the speed of light, he concluded that the individual, constituent phase waves (of which the group

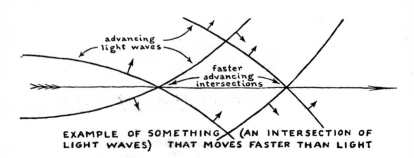

advancing light waves

faster advancing intersections

EXAMPLE OF SOMETHING (AN INTERSECTION OF LIGHT WAVES) THAT MOVES FASTER THAN LIGHT

wave must be composed) might move still faster (inevitably in some nonmaterial way) at velocities ranging from the speed of light upward to infinity!

Naturally, all this was too much for any but the most untrammeled minds in the scientific world, yet, by what seemed almost a divine fluke, within a year and a half of publication of his theory, it was amazingly verified by experimental proof. Neither de Broglie himself nor anyone else seems to have known how to conduct such an experiment, but a researcher in the Bell Telephone Laboratories in New York named C. J. Davisson, with L. H. Germer, his assistant, had an accident in April 1925 while bouncing a stream of electrons off a piece of nickel in a high vacuum. A flask of liquid air exploded near by, wrecking the apparatus and spoiling the nickel surface so that it had to be heated a long time before the vacuum test could be resumed. Not realizing that this particular heat treatment would fuse the myriad microscopic nickel lattices into a few much larger crystals, Davisson and Germer were amazed at the diffraction patterns made by their next blast of electrons — patterns which immediately suggested, and soon proved to have been produced by, the very matter waves deduced by de Broglie.

The Davisson-Germer experiment became a classic and led to a Nobel prize for Davisson as well as de Broglie, for it not only fully confirmed de Broglie's theory of the wave nature of electrons but even verified the extremely short electron-wave length he predicted, which is so much shorter than that of light that, after a bare decade of development, it could provide man with a two-hundredfold further enlargement of microscopic vision through the marvelous new electron microscope.

Such a radical turn of events seemed to many scientists only to perpetuate the growing paradox of particle and wave, because the wavelike photon had so recently developed into a particle while now the most solidly established of particles, the electron, had turned out to be a wave. It was a profoundly baffling paradox too, with waves and particles so opposite in nature (at least to the macrocosmic view) that an attempt to label them collectively as "wavicles" hardly seemed to get to the root of the question.

Yet a Viennese physicist named Erwin Schroedinger at Zurich University saw a wonderful interrelation between a wave's (lateral) front and its "rays" (paths) of outward advance that seemed to clarify the whole enigma. Considering these two dimensions (approximately at right angles to each other) as the warp and woof of matter, he showed how the wave front would reflect or bend around obstacles in typical wave fashion while an advancing segment of the same wave, like a foaming whitecap at sea, could be regarded as the trajectory of a moving particle. In his own words, "if you cut a small piece out of a wave, approximately 10 or 20 wavelengths along the direction of propagation and about as much across, such a 'wave packet' would actually move along a ray with exactly the same velocity and change of velocity as we might expect from a particle of this particular kind at this particular place, taking into account any force fields acting on the particle."

Schroedinger naturally realized that he must somehow tie the pattern of his wave-particles into the shape of the atom, expressing the relation mathematically. For this purpose he chose the model of a small tub of water with its complex of reflecting and interlacing waves, which he described as an "analogue" of electron waves in an atom-sized basin. "The normal frequencies of the wave group washing around the atomic nucleus," he explained, "are universally found to be exactly equal to Bohr's atomic 'energy levels' divided by Planck's constant h. Thus the ingenious yet somewhat artificial assumptions of Bohr's model of the atom, as well as of the older quantum theory in general, are superseded by the far more natural idea of de Broglie's wave phenomenon. The wave phenomenon forms the 'body' proper of the atom. It takes the place of the individual pointlike electrons which in Bohr's model are supposed to swarm around the nucleus."

The Schroedinger equation, in fact, endowed matter with a natural and simple beauty by revealing quanta essentially as waves of resonance, which, being basically Pythagorean in their relationships, had to have integral dimensions in order to exist. Like the moon tides that ring the earth in exactly two complete waves, the crests being on the sides toward and away from the moon, the troughs at the quarters, the electron's quantized crests and troughs always come out even around the atom. This gives the atom the harmonic resonance and integrity of a plucked string with fixed ends. For although the electron's course does not seem to have an end, one could think of it as having two ends fused together in a circle, like the rim of a bell, which thereby achieves its own resonance as it vibrates in a strictly integral number of waves. This is vital in holding the atom (or bell) together. If a bell did not thus oscillate in a cardinal multiple of whole sections, it would have to be broken or at least cracked — which would destroy its ring, removing its very reason of being.

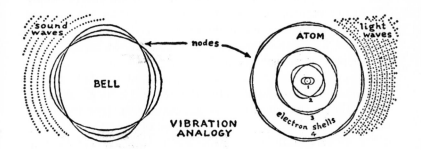

Another way of explaining quanta by Schroedinger's wave mechanics would be to say that each quantum is a discrete segment of vibration bounded by nodes. Such nodes need not be as simple as point nodes in a harp string, which are points of nearly

MODES OF VIBRATION SHOWING NODAL LINES
of a drum membrane (above), a brass plate (below) — the
nodes varying according to where the surface is touched

  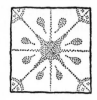

zero motion, for more often, they are line nodes, like the lines of "zero motion" in a vibrating drum membrane or metal plate, which may come in any of several modes or patterns (see illustration), each with its characteristic quantized frequency depending on exactly where and how the drum was struck or the plate held. Even more often, nodes must be surface nodes, amounting to two-dimensional areas of relative motionlessness among vibrating solids — and doubtless volume nodes of three and more dimensions ...

It is hardly possible to visualize all these strange functions even in the macrocosm, while their patterns in atoms, particularly large atoms, are almost hopelessly inscrutable. In the easiest atom of all, the hydrogen atom, Schroedinger analyzed several types of standing waves that could develop. The simplest are what he called the S states, with purely radial wave forms pulsing outward concentrically — either as the 1S state with its single spherical "loop," the 2S state with two loops, one outside the other, separated by a nodal surface about two angstroms from the center, or the 3S state of three loops divided by two nodal surfaces at two and seven angstroms out, and so forth — all these with an additional outer nodal surface at infinity. If you wonder exactly what is waving when such waves come into being — what medium they are in — you probably feel much as Schroedinger did when he midwifed them, for it seems he could only imagine their unknown medium as a mysterious "essence" of mathematical space, which he simply designated by the appropriate Greek letter psi, ψ.

Next in order come his P states, in which the "northern" and "southern" hemispheres of the atom are in opposite phase bounded by a nodal surface intersecting the equator. The 2P state has two wave loops, one in each hemisphere, while the 3P state has an added spherical node dividing each loop into two segments, the 4P has two such spherical nodes, the 5P three such nodes, and so on.

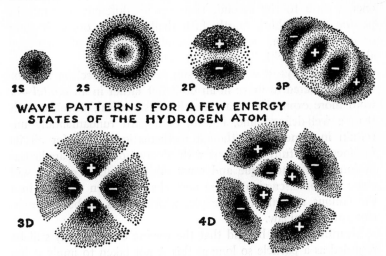

WAVE PATTERNS FOR A FEW ENERGY STATES OF THE HYDROGEN ATOM

Then there are the D states, with two nodal surfaces sectoring the atom like a quartered apple in any of various ways, including a state in which it is sliced nodally through the tropics of Cancer and Capricorn with waves phased alternately $+ - +$ and $- + -$ in the resulting polar and equatorial zones, each state combinable with still other increasingly complex states featuring various numbers of added spherical nodes, 4D, 5D, 6D, etc.

These waves of matter that can thus form the atom are of a kind that stand fixed in one spot like the waves around a big rock in a river or a lenticular cloud in the lee of a mountain. Their various numbers of nodes 1, 2, 3 . . . represent the possible

energy states of the atom with corresponding quantum numbers
1, 2, 3 . . . , so that if you want to know the energy (quantum)
state of an atom all you need do is discover what type of standing
waves it has. This can now be done quite easily in a laboratory.
The quantum conditions come naturally from the fact that, as
with Saturn's rings, only certain wave lengths and frequencies
are possible — that the electron, which pulses some 124,000,000,-
000,000,000,000 times a second, steps up its frequency by about
2,470,000,000,000,000 pulses in going from the first "shell" or
energy state to the second, then up by different amounts in
passing to the third, fourth, fifth shells, and so on, each state
or orbital position being a measurable quantum of frequency
above the next with "nothing" in between.

Since the days of de Broglie, you notice, the electron has not
been considered to move in an orbit but rather in an *orbital* — a
word more expressive of a generalized, statistical, wavelike path
than a well-defined line, indeed, of a path fundamentally uncertain in some details though mathematically true for all its
fuzziness, and fully consistent with observation. The paradoxical
profundity of the vague and wavy orbital in its ψ essence will
come up for discussion in the next chapter, when we look into
the famous uncertainty principle, which seems to be a cornerstone of natural law.

Meantime, let it be said that the waving electron may still be
regarded as a particle so long as this is not taken to imply it has
an exactly knowable "orbit" — for its particle aspect is in fact
sometimes both useful and important. In the light of
Schroedinger's wave equation, matter in the electron can be
most reasonably visualized as occupying the known wave forms
and following the orbitals that cut perpendicularly across the
nodal surfaces. At least the mathematical "correspondence" between wave and particle works out that way, and its statistical
conclusion indicates that the body of an electron is "most often"
to be found where a wave's intensity is greatest, giving matter
a probability texture that should ultimately explain it more completely than ever before.

Putting off the presentation of probability until the coming

chapter, however, I can only say here that the whole modern
atomic theory has been built up, to a great extent, upon
Schroedinger's wave mechanics yet without rejecting any of the
proven *workable* parts of Bohr's model, parts that are now collectively relegated to the atom's aforesaid and useful "particle
aspect." The evidence is indeed overwhelming that every atom
is somehow made of durable waves that vibrate continuously in
hierarchies of energy — neat terraces of binding resonance between ψ frequencies. Although we have described some of the
simpler dimensions of the simpler waves of the very simplest
(hydrogen) atom, all atoms have comparable wave patterns,
and the bigger, heavier ones could be likened to complex musical
instruments or even whole orchestras on which many notes are
being played simultaneously as chords from the contrabass levels
to the outermost shell's altissimo. And of course, atoms vibrate
as a whole also, and complete molecules generate their own
cohesive wave systems, as do entire crystal lattices in beautiful
interweaving integrated regularities, and all larger objects and
organisms — including men, stars and, for all we know, the universe.

It is in these and comparable ways, as we are becoming increasingly and redundantly aware, that all matter tends toward
its natural rhythms, ranging from the simple mechanical oscillation
of pendulums and springs and falling drops of spray to the
farther-fetched ups and downs of weather, where sunshine increases evaporation which thickens clouds, bringing rain and coolness which retards evaporation, clearing the sky for more sunshine . . . from electric oscillation of capacitance–inductance
–capacitance–inductance to the chemical rhythms of the heart
regulated by enzyme feedback — to such ecological interaction
as the shark-sole frequency of the sea in which the abundance of
soles provides such ample food for sharks that the shark population
increases rapidly on its sole diet until the resulting scarcity of
soles starves off enough sharks to enable the sole population to
increase again to supply the next generation of sharks . . . even
to our impalpable waves of radio and television that the senses
cannot directly detect but which we mentally accept as real be-

cause *something* must convey the forms we finally hear and see, just as a "ψ essence" can be said to wave wherever matter is.

If it still seems incredible that an electron cannot be a simple "billiard ball" of ultimate smallness, one may reflect that such a jot of simplitude could hardly have meaningful continuity in time or place, for it could no more be identified twice than you could take in the same breath twice (since some of each breath becomes part of your body). Does the moving spot of light from a flashlight continue to be the *same* spot? An elementary *particle* obviously cannot be tagged or painted red or recognized as an identity from moment to moment. Yet a wave, being in its nature vastly more complex than the undifferentiated chunk of particle, can easily be imprinted with a recognizable, individual label. What is the coded signal from a lighthouse but a name-tab? Three flashes two seconds apart followed by a single flash separated by six-second intervals — what could it be but Malaga, Spain? Or when you recognize your mother's voice by telephone, do not the electromagnetic and sound waves carry a positive identification?

The "billiard-ball" concept of matter thus turns out to be actually more unearthly than an assemblage of waves, and it does not satisfy the newer, truer equations of physics. Very careful experiment has repeatedly shown that an electron's orbital is not deformed by perturbations in the way Uranus' orbit is deformed by Neptune — that the waving radiations coming out in expanding spheres from such an electron basically *are* the very stuff the electron is made of.

The wonder of such a discovery that radiation really is a material cannot possibly be fully grasped by a human mind, nor is mystery dispelled solely by compounding it upon more mystery. So it is hard to know whether the relation between quanta and continuity could in any sense resemble the relation between, say, apples and applesauce. Or if there is a "surface" between matter

and nonmatter, exactly where is it? And assuming we have begun
to know what matter is made of, what is nonmatter made of?

These deep questions seem to go on and on. But we will try to
tackle them as best we may. Mathematics is of enormous help,
but it is often hard to decide whether it represents reality in
the way de Broglie's mathematics turned out to do. One wonders,
for instance, whether abstract terms themselves may have a
structure in objective nature? We have learned that energy grows
according to its pitch, a principle of music, and that momentum
literally has a wave length, but are these beautiful thoughts part
of the material universe? How do they relate to structure? We
know that a man can eat meat, wheat, salt or *any* of a thousand
things out of the animal, vegetable and mineral kingdoms, all
of them serving as structure of his body cells. But body cells
contain millions of atoms. What about the structure or sub-
structure of a single atom? Can something as small as an electron be made out of *any* material available? And does an electron's body include de Broglie's phase waves whose velocities may
have *any* value so long as it is not slower than that of light?

It will take a lot of doing to find answers to such problems,
which are as much philosophical as scientific — and which have
been voiced down the ages since God challenged Job about the
"wisdom in the inward parts?" — a challenge that echoes to this
day in the laboratories as, "How does the electron choose its path?"
or, "Are effects really caused by 'causes'?"

If answers there are, they must be found at last, I suppose, in
the ubiquitous patterns of energy and thought, somewhere in the
interflow of waves that crown the flood rivers of abstraction —
somewhen among the consonances and equations that pulse the
sleepless symphony of the worlds.

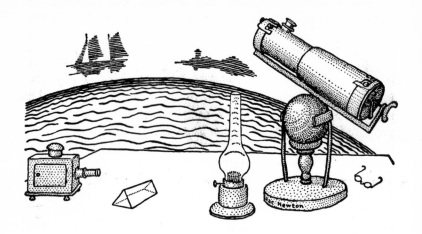

12. Of Light and Color

MY INSTRUMENT PANEL AND ALL THE WALLS of this space station are illumined by powerful built-in fluorescent lighting. This is necessary because out here in the void there is no twilight. I mean everything not in direct sunshine or artificially lit is shrouded in jet-black shadow because of the lack of what you'd call normal atmospheric diffusion. And earthly eyes obviously have not been prepared by evolution for such harsh contrasts.

As a matter of fact, until I got away from Earth I did not really know what total light could be. For of all the familiar phenomena of Earth, light now seems to me more nearly absolute than anything else. Not only does it travel mysteriously in the vacuous dark, its velocity the almost unbelievable constant that has been made a cornerstone of modern physics, but its immateriality is probably the most measurable connecting link between the physical and mental worlds.

Light is also the common stuff of vision, the messenger of form and, along with the rest of radiation, the swiftest-known medium of energy transport in the universe — its speed the limit of the propagation of material influence anywhere, its accomplishments far beyond human comprehension. Eight minutes ago the light you now see reflected from the butterfly's wing was actually inside the sun, where each photon of it is calculated to have spent something like ten thousand years wildly milling about on its way to the solar surface. The strange potency of even a little burst of light is shown by the fact that a single flash from a photographic flash tube can kill a sick rat, while a slightly longer exposure from an ordinary light bulb can stop a cocklebur from flowering or trigger a bird into singing a song before setting forth on a 10,000-mile flight! Moreover, as we shall see in the next chapter, any stream of light from a candle ray to a star beam is sufficiently substantial that, if unsupported, it will literally fall of its own weight or bend under stress. And it may be twisted like a cable or pumped (through valves) like a gas. It can even make itself felt in familiar economic units as was suggested by the engineer who figured out that light on Earth now costs approximately $400,000,000 a pound delivered.

In ancient days, men naturally wondered what light is and why it behaves so capriciously. Such an authoritative explanation as that God had said, "Let there be light" and there was light, was not sufficient for all. Nor could the real sun, promoted to godhood on six continents, satisfy every man's curiosity merely with his warmth and light, which often came to be worshiped as a kind of divine bestowal or manifestation. And so it happened that the imaginative Greeks became the first people to consider light as a subject suited to the scientific treatment.

Empedocles it was who proposed in the fifth century B.C. the modern-seeming theory that the radiating particles of light must have a finite velocity! This idea could hardly have been based on observation but, more likely, on reasoning and intuition, the most respectable sources of philosophical doctrine in those prodigious days. And Aristotle in his turn added that, if light takes time to move, "any given time is divisible into parts, so that we should assume a time when the sun's ray was not as yet seen but was still traveling in the middle space . . . before it reaches the earth."

This semimystical hypothesis was a great forward step toward the understanding of light — so far forward, in fact, that it could not be confirmed or disproved for nearly two thousand years, not even by the first scientific attempt to measure the velocity of light in 1667 with a method suggested by Galileo in which men flashed lantern beams vainly back and forth from distant hilltops. Yet only eight years later, in 1675, the Danish astronomer Olaf Roemer got the first definite evidence that Empedocles and Aristotle were right. For some ten years Roemer had been keeping very precise records of the eclipses of Io, the innermost of the four then-known moons of Jupiter, who disappears routinely behind the giant planet every 42 hours, 28 minutes. Roemer noticed that Io had the peculiar habit of being a little late in her rendezvous during each half-year in which the faster earth pulled away from Jupiter yet always perked up and became correspondingly early whenever the earth began to overtake him again. On the basis of this evidence, timed by his new pendulum clocks, the thoughtful Dane concluded that the light from Io to the earth must take just about "twenty-two minutes" to traverse the diameter of the earth's orbit!

o      o

Such an unexpected gift of a precise scientific measurement of light's velocity, albeit of a fantastic magnitude, was naturally very exciting to all the scientists of the day. And to no one more than Christian Huygens of Holland, who had long been experimenting with lenses and lately had taken to searching for an explanation of why light moves in straight lines, and of how its rays can cross completely through one another without apparent hindrance.

Roemer's discovery, if it meant anything, reasoned Huygens, must mean that light literally travels. And travel, of course, implies the "transport" of something tangible from place to place. Yet in view of light's unaccountable ability to cross its beams without mixing them, how could light possibly be a transport of actual matter?

If Huygens could not fathom light as a material, however, neither could he conceive of its being completely immaterial. So he let the paradox simmer in his mind for a while until, following a suggestion of Robert Hooke's, he saw a way to resolve it by postulating light as a "successive movement, impressed on the intervening matter." In this way light "spreads," he wrote in his *Treatise on Light*, "as sound does, by spherical surfaces and waves: for I call them waves from their resemblance to those . . . formed in water when a stone is thrown into it and which present a successive spreading as circles."

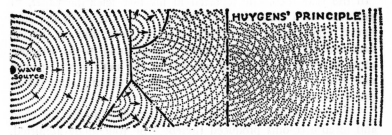

On this premise Huygens brilliantly developed the wave theory of light into an important concept still known as Huygens' principle, which recognizes that each point of any advancing wave front is in effect the source of a fresh wave, while all such fresh waves together continue onward as the advancing front. It explains why a loud sound originating, say, a mile outside and beyond the open door of a room produces something like a fresh sound source (as far as persons in the room are concerned) at the doorway.

But Huygens did not find light to be so amenable as sound to his principle, since light does not disperse evenly through a room and, unlike sound, moves in straight lines, creating sharp shadows. To explain shadows, he had to presume that light waves are extremely small and, to account for their capacity to carry across interstellar space, he considered also that an "infinitude" of them at each instant "unite together in such a way that they sensibly compose one single wave only, which, consequently, ought to have enough force to produce an impression on our eyes. Moreover," he added, "from each luminous point there may come many thousands of [successive] waves in the smallest imaginable time, by the frequent percussion of the corpuscles which strike the ether at these points: which further contributes to rendering their action more sensible."

It was a bold but reasonable attempt to explain one of the most baffling phenomena in nature. Young Isaac Newton, meantime, in Woolsthorpe had been engaged in some significant research on the same general subject, using both lenses and prisms. "In the year 1666," he reported in his first scientific paper, "I procured me a triangular glass prism, to try therewith the celebrated phaenomena of colours. And in order thereto, having darkened my chamber, and made a small hole in my window-shuts, to let in a convenient quantity of the sun's light, I placed my prism at its entrance, that it might be thereby refracted to the opposite wall.

" It was at first a very pleasing divertisement to view the vivid and intense colours produced thereby," he touchingly admitted, but a few minutes later began to apply himself more "circumspectly" to the question of what made the light separate into these colors, a mystery that naturally involved the deeper question of what sort of stuff or granules or atoms composes the ultimate inmost parts of light.

" Then I began to suspect," wrote Newton, " whether the rays, after their trajection through the prism, did not move in curve lines, and according to their more or lesser curvity tend to divers parts of the wall. . . . I remembered that I had often seen a tennis ball struck with an oblique racket, describe such a curve line. For, a circular as well as a progressive motion being communicated to it by that stroke, its parts on that side where the motions conspire, must press and beat the contiguous air more violently than on the other, and there excite a reluctancy and reaction of the air proportionably greater. And for the same reason, if the rays of light should possibly be globular bodies, and by their oblique passage out of one medium into another, acquire a circulating motion, they ought to feel the greater resistance from the ambient ether, on that side, where the motions conspire, and thence be continually bowed to the other."

Although he was unable to detect the "curvity" he suspected of his "globular" particles of light, Newton did soon realize, by placing prisms and lenses in many relationships, that at least the separation of colors in refraction is really a sorting of light into its fundamentally different "rays, some of which are more refrangible [bendable] than others," the "least refrangible" producing "a red colour" while the "most refrangible" show "violet." Thus he concluded that "colours are not qualifications of light derived from . . . reflections of natural bodies, as 'tis generally believed, but original and connate properties, which in divers rays are divers."

And "the most surprising and wonderful composition of all," he found, "was that of whiteness" because it could be made by remixing "all the colours of the prism . . . in a due proportion," thus confirming ordinary "white" sunlight as literally compounded of many parts. Even "the odd phaenomena of . . . leaf-gold, fragments of coloured glass, and some other transparently coloured bodies, appearing in one position of one colour, and of another in another," Newton reasoned, "are on these grounds no longer riddles. For those are substances apt to reflect one sort of light and transmit another; as may be seen in a dark room by illuminating them with . . . uncompounded light. For then they appear of that colour only, with which they are illumined, but yet in one position more vivid and luminous than in another, accordingly as they are disposed more or less to reflect or transmit the incident colour."

Thus, described in their expositors' own words, arose the two principal and opposing theories of light — Huygens' wave theory and Newton's corpuscle theory — which were to compete, sometimes bitterly, for dominance in optical science for two hundred years before they could be happily combined at last into a comprehensive whole by Einstein and others in the twentieth century.

At first Newton's easy-to-visualize explanation of light's straight rays and sharp shadows as due to the very fast courses of corpuscles of light was generally accepted, partly on the strength of his growing reputation as the inventor of a successful reflecting telescope and later as the author of the universal laws of motion and gravity. But as the eighteenth century came and went, more and more evidence appeared to support Huygens' wave idea — particularly new aspects of refraction and diffraction.

Refraction means the change of direction any radiation takes when passing obliquely from one medium into another in which its speed is different. Newton, of course, saw that oars appear bent where they enter water and knew that light can refract also on entering glass, but he could think of no way to account for it other than to guess that light (like sound) travels faster in liquids and solids than in air, and that was hardly a convincing explanation.

Diffraction, on the other hand, is the wave effect produced at the edge of shadows made by light coming from a single point. Although much less obvious than refraction, it too was known to science as early as 1665 in the form of a mysterious series of tiny fringe bands of alternating bright and dim light, a phenomenon particularly annoying to lens makers because it limited the resolving power (thus the practical magnification) of their optical instruments. However, neither Huygens nor Newton paid much attention to such an apparently minor detail, and it remained for thinkers of succeeding generations to begin to wonder if diffraction could possibly be caused by waves of light bending around the edges of whatever cast a shadow — even as sound waves behind a door or sea waves around the end of a breakwater.

The culmination of this classic issue between corpuscles and waves came with the famous "interference" experiment of Thomas Young, the English scientist, in 1800, in which he passed light from a single point source through two tiny parallel slits on its way to a screen. The fact that the striped diffraction pattern, produced when both slits were open, darkened certain parts of the screen that had been lit up when only one slit was open showed that there must be some kind of interference between the two light paths — which no one could logically explain except by the wave theory of light. The phenomenon may be compared to a silencer that dampens sound by matching the crests of one set of waves with the troughs of another, for some light from one slit obviously must be combining with light from the other at such a distance that the two wave frequencies were 180° out of phase, inevitably canceling each other and producing a band of darkness!

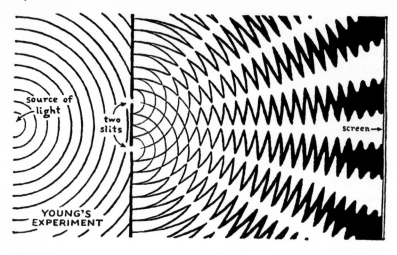

After several similar experiments by Young and some later ones by Augustin Fresnel, the wave theory of light became so firmly established that the corpuscle concept was pretty well discredited. Yet, clinging desperately to Newton's coattails, corpuscular light managed to get a "final" hearing when the French scientist Armand Hippolyte Louis Fizeau devised a way of mechanically measuring the speed of light by reflecting it back and forth between the teeth of a rotating wheel, a method which another Frenchman, Leon Foucault, improved the following year by substituting a revolving mirror for the toothed wheel and providing test tanks for comparing light's speed in water with that in air or other materials. By such means, in 1850 a "crucial experi-

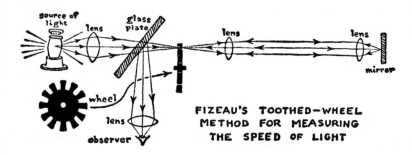

ment" was performed by Foucault to determine "once and for-ever" whether light is "a material body" or "a wave of disturb-ance," the issue to be decided solely by whether light's velocity proved to be greater in water, as Newton predicted, or in air as Huygens' calculations required. It happened at about the earliest date in the zooming evolution of technology that could muster the precision to cope with such a sophisticated comparison and the scientific world was agog for the verdict — which turned out to show quite definitely that light is swifter in air than in water, thereby effectively ruling in favor of Huygens and the wave theory.

From then on, so far as the velocity of light was concerned, only technical refinements were needed to narrow it down to its present established value of 186,282 miles a second, which has been repeatedly checked to within a fraction of a mile a second by many methods, including the latest (suggested by a Russian in 1958), which requires nothing but an electronic flash tube, mirror and photoelectric cell. In this system, the mirror serves only to re-flect the tube's flash back to the photocell, which is rigged to fire the tube automatically again, repeating the flash over and over at a frequency that by simple calculation, gives the speed of light.

One might think it futile to hope for any more direct observa-tion of the motion of light than that, but astronomers occasionally are privileged to view a traveling parcel of light at such vast range that it appears to be standing still and can be clocked as easily as a moon or a comet. The first time such snail-like light was noticed was in August 1901, close to an ebullient " new " star known as Nova Persei. This exploding sun had been discovered the previous February 21st by a Scottish parson just after it had increased 60,000-fold in brightness (from 14th to 0.0 magnitude) in two days. And by August it had sprouted a " faint nebula " that, on close examination, showed a continuous, growing texture of concentric rings, each of which kept expanding at an angular rate between two and three seconds of arc per day. As no proper motion among stars even one fiftieth as fast as this had ever been known, it was quickly deduced that the rings must be periodic outbursts of light that were illuminating successively more and more distant parts of the nebulous surroundings of the star — in other words, the rings were actual rhythmic flashes of light moving outward through space in a stately procession at 186,282 miles a second!

Even on Earth, light has recently been observed moving in comparable parcels which, in this case, had to be deftly snipped off by a pair of electrically controlled polarized filters and photographed by a camera with a similar shutter system that could expose its film for only one hundred-millionth of a second. But by such means, Dr. A. M. Zarem of Stanford Research Institute caught a beam of light scarcely ten feet long spang in mid-passage, its shining presence "frozen" by the camera like a veritable fleeting flick of time itself, while both its ends (front and back) could be seen fading mysteriously away into the surrounding darkness!

Such a vivid demonstration of the moving reality of light hardly needs further confirmation, but I must mention the strange phenomenon of "aberration" discovered by James Bradley, England's Astronomer Royal, in 1726 when he was searching for clues as to the distance of stars. Finding astonishing and unmistakable evidence that stars all over the sky shift their positions with annual rhythm up to a maximum of 20″.47 near the ecliptic poles, he realized this difference could not possibly be the parallax of distance he was looking for, as it was in exactly the wrong direction, not to mention its being clearly independent of any randomness in the stars' distances. For a time, he suspected it might be the effect of nutation, a nodding of the earth's axis when the attracting forces of sun and moon periodically try to pull earth's equatorial bulge into the plane of the ecliptic, but it turned out to be due solely to the speed of light in relation to the earth. In

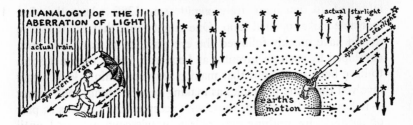

brief, just as an airplane pilot flying through a shower of vertical rain sees the rain slanting almost horizontally against his windshield, so an astronomer on the earth revolving through a continuous shower of light from the stars sees the starlight slanting at an angle that depends on the relation between the perpendicular component of his orbital velocity (perhaps 18 miles a second) and that of light (186,282 miles a second), thus making all telescopes aim slightly ahead of the true direction of the stars they see, in effect just like a gunner "leading" a duck with his gun.

An entirely different aspect of light that has long occupied scientists is the magnification of visual images. The ancient Greeks observed that glass spheres filled with water could enlarge anything seen through them, and Ptolemy elucidated the optical properties of various materials in his famous *Optics*, which offered, among other things, a complete table of refractions for different angles of incidence. Although these surprisingly advanced discoveries in ancient science could hardly have been generally appreciated at the time, they do suggest how lenses with a focal length of nine millimeters came to have been in use in Pompeii in A.D. 79, probably for what Seneca described as the "magnification of writing."

After a little further development by Muslim and European scholars (including Roger Bacon in England), the practical manufacture of optical instruments was at last permanently established in northern Italy about A.D. 1286 when the first spectacle maker opened shop. One might think that the telescope should have quickly followed the eye glass, or at least have been developed by such an inventor as Leonardo, but it does not seem to have been so obvious that making very near things look bigger involved the same principles as making very far things look nearer — not even in the eyes of those who accepted the heavens as part of nature — for nothing approaching a telescope appeared until about 1590.

Then out of Italy (probably Naples) telescope making evidently spread to Holland from where, in the year 1609, in Galileo's own words, "a report reached my ears that a Dutchman had constructed a telescope . . . and some proofs of its most wonderful performances were described." Eagerly garnering material on "the telescopic principle" from this source, the only one he knew, Galileo spent a few months in "deep study of the theory of refraction" before preparing a "tube" of lead 9½ feet long by 1⅔ inches in diameter, "in the ends of which I fitted two glass lenses, both plane on one side, but on the other side one spherically convex and the other concave. Then bringing my eye to the concave lens I saw objects satisfactorily large and near, for they appeared one third the distance off and nine times larger than . . . natural."

Within a few more months, having constructed a second telescope "with more nicety, which magnified objects above sixty times," and a third that "magnified nearly a thousand times . . . I betook myself to observations of the heavenly bodies . . . with incredible delight." Almost immediately he discovered that the moon's face is "full of hollows and protuberances," that "the planets present their disks round as so many little moons," that there are "four sidereal bodies performing their revolutions about Jupiter — the four Medicean satellites, never seen from the very beginning of the world up to our own times," that "two huge protuberances" extend out from the two sides of Saturn, that in every direction there are "stars so numerous as to be almost beyond belief," including at least 80 new ones close to Orion's belt and 40 unsuspected Pleiades, while the Milky Way is revealed as "nothing else but a mass of innumerable stars . . . the number of small ones quite beyond determination."

The following year, adapting his telescopes to very short working distances, Galileo effectively founded the history of the compound microscope, while the 1,600-year-old simple microscope or magnifying glass reached something of a culmination of its long development at the hands of Anton van Leeuwenhoek later in the same century. A Dutch genius and great pioneer of the microcosmic world of life, Leeuwenhoek ground and polished his own exquisite single lenses, with focal lengths ranging down to a twentieth of an inch, through which he discovered in 1674 the strange "little animals" we now call protozoa and bacteria.

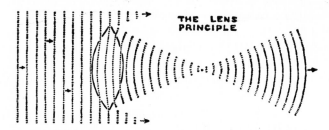

THE LENS PRINCIPLE

Thus the seventeenth century turned out to be tremendous in the history of light, not only in measuring light's velocity and explaining its nature but in the practical matters of using refraction and reflection, with the aid of lenses and mirrors, to magnify things out of other worlds, both far and near, into the consciousness of this one. And telescopes and microscopes have been improving ever since as their designers learned that the sharpness of an image depends not only on bringing light to where there ought to be light but on bringing darkness to where there ought to be darkness. With light waves tending to spread in all directions, the latter task is the more difficult. But it has been accomplished in ingenious ways, one of the latest developments being the electronic amplification of light through the principle of resonance or sympathetic vibration (see pages 386–87).

When the successive accomplishments of the famous 40-inch, 60-inch, 100-inch and 200-inch reflectors demonstrated that a practical limit was being reached in the size of visual telescopes on Earth, not only did radio waves come to augment light waves in our new radio telescopes (see page 191), but electronics offered a way to convert light into electrons (forming a "picture" by fixing static electric charges on a nonconducting surface) that is far more efficient than chemical photography. This was important because the twinkling of stars (due to refraction among the shifting densities of the air) inevitably blurs their images on time-exposed photographic plates, and "night sky glow" (from chemical phosphorescence in the upper atmosphere that sheds twice as much light on earth as all the stars combined) greatly reduces the contrast between a dim star and its background glim, effectively limiting detectability by photographic emulsion to stars within the first twenty-four magnitudes. According to Jeans, photons from even "a sixteenth magnitude star can only enter a terrestrial telescope at comparatively rare intervals, and it will be exceedingly rare for two or more quanta to be inside the telescope at the same time." But while it takes some thousand photons to activate the smallest developable grain of emulsion, less than ten photons will eject an electron from a photocathode metal surface, thus producing a static electric "print" with sensitivity improved a hundredfold. From here, the contrast between image and background may be vastly increased by electronic means, whereupon a television-type scanning beam can read off the amplified picture and transmit it to a screen for viewing or photographing.

By similar methods, it is calculated that a 200-inch telescope should be able to see as far into space as an unaided telescope with a 2,000-inch reflector, which would mean being able to photograph the creases in a newspaper held at least fifty miles away. Of course a 2,000-inch (167-foot) reflector of solid glass is out of the question on Earth at present, but here in space, free from the stresses of gravity, no doubt very large weightless optical reflectors (perhaps of some sort of lacquered sheeting) will be constructed for future observatories in which they can float unsup-

ported in continuous focus upon unwinking stars set deep and
fast in the glowless pitch of "eternity."

Eternity, admittedly, is a questionable word to apply to the
travels of starlight in outer space, and perhaps I should not have
used it. For if starlight really has anything like an eternity
in which to travel, there logically arises the question: why is our
night sky so dark? And why is the sky always dark as seen from
up here? Why isn't it dazzling with the light of the infinitude of
stars?

This rather insidious puzzle was first posed seriously in 1826
by the German astronomer Heinrich Olbers. When he was answered, "Why shouldn't the sky be dark with all the stars so far
away that only a few of the nearest ones are even visible?"
he agreed that the light of the average star is very feeble but
pointed out that, if stars in general can be presumed to be about
evenly distributed through boundless space, the number of them
at any radius or distance must be proportional to the square
of that distance (for the same reason that the surface area of any
sphere is proportional to the square of its radius), which just
counteracts the known fact that the intensity of light from any
star (or other source) is *inversely* proportional to the square of its
distance away. Thus the remoteness of stars should exactly balance
their plenitude and, if you think of them in the ancient fashion as
fixed in concentric spheres, something like the skins of an
onion, each additional sphere or star layer (say, a thousand
parsecs thick) should shed just as much light as the nearer
layers of equal thickness inside or outside it, these spheres of
equal light coming to Earth in endless succession from greater and
greater depths of space until the stars in back are completely
blocked from earthview by the stars in front, leaving the whole sky
as bright as the "disk" of the sun.

Seeing that the sky, fortunately, is not that bright — which
would incidentally burn us up as surely as if we were inside the

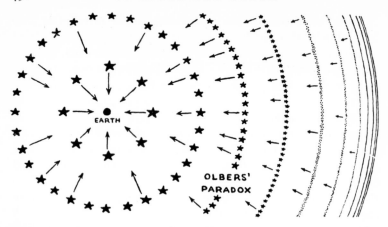

EARTH

OLBERS'
PARADOX

sun — one cannot suppress the suspicion that something must be rather wrong with this line of reasoning. In Olbers' day, as a result, astronomers concluded that the stars could not be distributed at random through space but must be concentrated largely in the Milky Way, and this presumption "solved" the question for the time being. However, when the twentieth century opened up the vastness of transgalactic and supergalactic space, it inadvertently opened up Olbers' paradox all over again.

Naturally new theories arose once more to deal with it: that the universe may be still so young that the majority of its starlight has not yet had time to reach us — and, in the 1920's, that it is expanding on the large scale at a rate that may be called explosive. The latter hypothesis, based on the most careful spectroscopic observation, appears, to a pretty conclusive degree, to have finally resolved the mystery. At least there is now a consensus among astronomers that starlight fades out into infrared invisibility at a range of a few billion parsecs (say 10,000-000,000 light-years), where the average galaxies are presumably retiring at about the speed of light (in relation to us) which, as we shall understand in the next chapter, effectively cuts off any prospect of their light ever reaching us here.

Along with such cosmic revelations, if the investigator into light should also condition himself to expect an intermittent assortment of odd earthly and unearthly phenomena to keep popping up, the explaining of which will add to his store of knowledge on this difficult subject, he is not likely to be disappointed. He might look, for example, at the commonplace specks of sunlight on the ground under a large tree on a summer day. I don't mean big patches of light but rather the small single light spots that come and go as tiny gaps among the leaves open and close to let darts of sunshine through to Earth. One might think these isolated flecks of light would be of all sorts of random shapes as the haphazard apertures chance to appear in the quivering foliage, yet surprisingly they all turn out to be the same: all smoothly rounded — in fact, they are exactly similar ellipses. How come?

It is a question known to have been asked by Aristotle in the form: why does a square hole admit a round image of the sun? And the explanation, first hinted at by Francesco Maurolico in the sixteenth century, is that every tiny opening between leaves, even though square or irregular, acts like the aperture of a pinhole camera, which will take remarkably sharp pictures without a lens. In fact, the sun, being no mere point but a round disk half a degree across, as it appears from Earth, is being "photographed" by the tree so that its round image appears wherever the shafts of its light get through to the "film" of Earth. In confirmation of this, during a partial solar eclipse all the little sun pictures are observed to be crescent-shaped and completely inverted (as required by optical theory) in respect to the real sun.

Something comparable happens also in the case of shadows of small objects. You have heard of the *umbra* of total eclipse when the moon passes before the sun, this being the very dark, cone-shaped, full shadow, which is surrounded by the much larger and fainter semishadow or *penumbra* of partial eclipse. Such a distinction among shadows is likewise attributable to the sun's not being a mere point, and the penumbra, which spreads out as it reaches farther from its source, obediently forms an increasingly realistic sunshadow picture — which explains why a butterfly's shadow becomes round like the sun as he flies higher above the

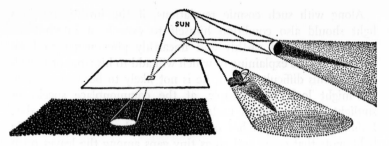

ground — and why the shadows of your outstretched fingers tend toward the shapes of claws during a semieclipse.

Such phenomena are pretty easy to reason out because the main light rays involved go in straight lines without reflection or refraction. But when you investigate what happens in mirrors, light begins to get more mysterious — which may explain why women and magicians regard the mirror as one of their important tools.

Did you ever wonder why a mirror makes your reflected right hand into a left hand, in effect reversing things sideways right and left, yet without reversing things up and down? Why should a mirror have a preference for swapping hands but refuse to swap heads for feet? The puzzle is not made easier by the fact that there is a kind of mirror that does not reverse right and left, and which both Plato and Lucretius described as a rectangle of polished metal bent into the concave form (shown on the right, below.) In such a mirror you see yourself as others see you and a printed page reads perfectly normally.

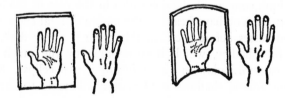

The explanation involves the laws both of reflection (which is really a special case of refraction) and of symmetry, which we

will deal with near the end of this chapter. Reflection's familiar
law — that the angle of incidence must equal the angle of reflection — solves the simpler mirror problems quite readily, for re-

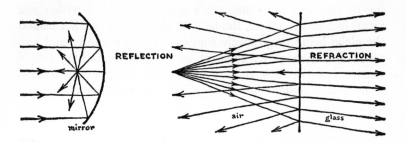

flection is essentially a bouncing process and a rubber ball truly
reflects off a floor. Reflection's relationship to refraction, moreover,
may perhaps best be illustrated by the shooting competitions that
used to be held on Lake Koenigsee in the Alps where I once
spent a summer. Surrounded by high mountains, the lake is so
calm that a special feature of the sport was to have the marksmen
aim not directly at the target but rather at its reflection in the
water, counting on the bullets to rebound from the surface to hit
it. This, amazingly enough, the bullets apparently did — and fully
as accurately as if they had been shot straight through the air all
the way.

But the oddest thing about the phenomenon is that it was not
a case of simple reflection of bullets off the top of the water. For
a scientist who hung a series of screens in the lake proved that
the bullets penetrated well below the surface where, obeying hydro-
dynamical laws, their pressure of friction upon the liquid depths
forced them into smooth curves upward until they emerged into
the air again at exactly the angle they had entered! One may
well ponder whether photons reflecting off a mirror move in some
such manner while in contact with the vibrating electrons of its
polished surface.

In any case, the angle law is enough to account for every kind
of reflection, from the so-called "universe" mirrored in a garden

globe to the glass strands that conduct light into the stomach for photographing ulcers. By simply tracing the incidence-reflection angles upon the mirror globe's surface, you can see why it acts as an optical instrument with an ideally large "aperture," presenting to your eye the whole earth and sky confined within one visual face of the sphere, the parts of the universe farther behind the globe being progressively compressed into narrower and narrower distortion at its apparent edges, leaving nothing totally missing but the little spot of background lying exactly behind it — which becomes relatively smaller as you withdraw farther and farther away.

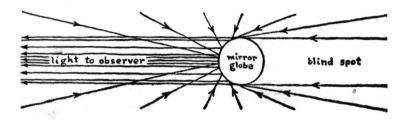

The glass strands, on the other hand, carry light around sharp curves by letting it reflect back and forth internally from surface to surface dozens or hundreds of times in the manner of short-wave radio impulses that bounce from ionosphere to ground to ionosphere to sea as they follow the curvature of the planet. And

the gastroscope that illumines the stomach is only one of many applications of the new "fiber optics" using hair-thin strands of optical glass as light carriers. Great bunches of glass fibers are assembled to bear precise images through difficult routes, a method that works as long as the fibers keep in the same relative positions even if they have been tied in knots. And fiber messages can also be coded by scrambling — disconnecting and twisting the bundle a certain number of degrees — and later decoded again at the other end by countertwisting it the same number of degrees.

Still another aspect of light reflection is the phenomenon of polarity or a predominance of direction in light's vibration. This kind of polarity does not occur in the case of sound waves, which are longitudinal, but it is often a major factor among transverse or crosswise waves such as those of light. Just as a whale can swim either by flipping his tail up and down or wagging it sideways, light waves have been found to oscillate in different directions, sometimes more in one than another — which affects the quality of the light somewhat as the timbre of a violin depends on whether you pluck or bow it. When light vibration has an excess of 3 percent in one direction, we say the light is 3 percent polarized. A fair proportion of starlight is polarized 10 percent and most light from the blue sky a good deal more, because of reflections off innumerable dust particles in line with the sun.

The easiest way to see light's polarity without using special polarized material is to look at the reflection of some blue sky in a flat piece of glass with a dark backing. Where light strikes this glass at an angle of about 30°, the reflected light will be almost completely polarized. That is to say, all of it that is in the common plane of incidence and reflection will leave the glass at an angle exactly equal and symmetrical to the one at which it arrived, thereby denying itself any lateral vibration in that plane — which would mean it could vibrate only outside, and at right angles to, the plane. Thus the various natural (transverse) oscillations of the light waves will be sorted (polarized) all into the one direction.

If you hold the glass so that it reflects the blue sky from straight above you at about a 30° angle, meanwhile turning successively to each point of the compass, you will see that the reflected sky is brightest when you face toward or directly away from the sun (letting the naturally polarized vibrations reflect intact) but darkest when you stand sideways (cutting them off with counterpolarization). This shows that most of the zenith light is polarized to oscillate perpendicularly to the plane that includes the sun, the zenith and you.

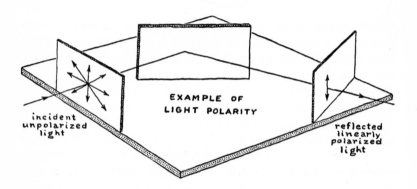

EXAMPLE OF
LIGHT POLARITY

incident
unpolarized
light

reflected
linearly
polarized
light

With a little practice, you can even see sky polarity with your unaided eye, particularly by staring at the zenith for several minutes in clear twilight when the whole sky may pervade your consciousness as a polarized network. Then you should become aware of a remarkable retinal vision known to science as Haidinger's brush, an hourglass-shaped figure of faint yellowish light squeezed at the waist between a pair of blue "clouds" and always aligned with the sun. It can be seen much more clearly through green or blue glass, and there are various optical instruments which can accurately measure its angle, such as the new sky compass for Arctic navigation that shoots the azimuth of the sun even when it is far below the horizon.

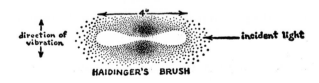

direction of
vibration

incident light

HAIDINGER'S BRUSH

A still more striking, and more unearthly, example of light polarity is the monstrous "jet galaxy" called M 87 in the supergalactic womb of Virgo. Its central "blue jet" is 2,500 light-years long, evidently bursting with the most powerful cosmic rays known, and the light of it arrives on Earth about 35 percent polarized in a unique bluish continuum, something like that of the Crab Nebula (blasted forth by the supernova of A.D. 1054), only ten million times bigger. Some astronomers have speculated that the extraordinary polarity of this potent starlight may derive from its passage through space clouds of needle- or disk-shaped dust that has been uniformly oriented by the force lines of a vast galactic magnetic field.

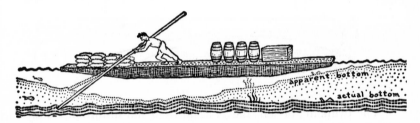

After touching on such varied aspects of reflected light, it may be as well now to mention the more general subject of light's refraction: the familiar bending of its rays that appears to "lift" the bottom of the canal before and behind your barge, that widens the setting sun to your earthly vision, that twinkles the stars, that spreads mirage lakes upon the desert or floats enchanted castles in the sky.

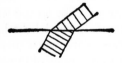

All these are variations of the aforementioned curving of light, when one side of a beam of photons is slowed down relative to the other side by encountering a denser medium, just as a column of soldiers tends to veer left when the left side of the column is slowed by marshy ground, waving girls or any other impediment.

Thus the slanting, convexed rays from the canal bottom seem to lift it everywhere but directly below your eyes where there is no slant to refract it.

The case of the setting sun is similar except that the medium is air gradually thinning into space instead of air and water joined at an abrupt surface. As the light from the "lower" part of the sun passes a longer distance through the earth's curving atmosphere than the "upper" sunlight, inevitably the "lower" sun appears raised by the refraction curves to a greater degree than does the "upper" sun. Thus the top and bottom of the sinking sun are optically squeezed together, giving it its characteristic look of lateral distortion.

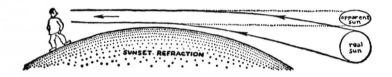

The twinkling of stars differs again from sun distortion mainly in that the cone of light to your eye from these distant suns usually subtends an angle of not *half* a degree but something less than a *millionth* of a degree. This is to say that the apparent width of the average single naked-eye star about equals the width of a dime viewed from a thousand miles away. Such a tenuous cone of light is bound to be seriously distorted, indeed intermittently cut off by the slightest atmospheric turbulence, by the innumerable flowing "bubbles" or strands of relatively warmer air called striae that rise wavelike on the wind. Such local differences in air density naturally bend light by refraction, and that is why stars twinkle, particularly when they are low in the sky so that their light passes through more of the lenslike striae. You can see the same effect when looking from near the ground at distant railroad tracks in the sun, for the lively striae just above the hot surface make the tracks seem to twist and shimmer and sometimes actually wink like stars. You can see it negatively in the shadows of high towers too, which often squirm and tremble from the irregular refraction. You can even measure the striae (usually between four and sixteen inches thick) when a searchlight many miles away shines its beam against a white wall, revealing the undulating shadow bands of demarcation — or by timing the successive blinkings of the Pleiades, like valves of an engine, as each wave of distortion drifts by.

The kind of refraction that creates the common inferior mirage of an illusory "lake" upon sun-baked ground is produced by the great contrast in temperature between the hot surface and the air that may be 25° F. cooler only half an inch up. Since the density of the air varies with the temperature, light rays bend fairly sharply in such disparate layers, letting you see the down-dipping rays of the sky after they have skimmed low over the hot ground, then curved up to your eye, striking you exactly as if they had been reflected off calm water. Thus it is the sky that you really see refracted upon the distant highway or sunny plain, not water, just as it is the sky that you really see reflected upon the surface of a far-away real lake — which explains why the two phenomena look so alike.

cooler

hotter

INFERIOR MIRAGE

But in contrast to the down-dipping light rays of the common inferior mirage over a warm surface, there are the opposite, up-arching rays of the rarer superior mirage over a cool surface such as the sea in spring or a frozen plateau. The reason the superior mirage is less common is that it requires not only a cool surface but increasingly warmer layers of air as you go higher above it: a condition meteorologists call an *inversion* of the usual decrease in temperature with altitude. When horizontal light is slowed by

warmer

colder

SUPERIOR MIRAGE

lower, cooler, denser air, its rays naturally arch or bow themselves convexly across the sky, sometimes leaping clear over intervening obstructions like the horizon — which produces the startling optical effect of islands or mountains rising spectacularly into
view from positions previously hidden behind the earth.

When there is a cool layer of air *between* warm ones, many
light rays may reach your eye from the same part of a distant
knoll but by traveling different routes, some of the rays curving
under the cool lenslike air, some going through it, others arching
over it, all these visual lines, inferior and superior, meeting at
your eye from their vertically various directions to give you the
impression that the knoll is greatly elongated vertically — a kind
of visional tower. Or the opposite may happen: rays from the
different altitudes on the knoll may curve and merge toward one
another through a warm air stratum between cooler layers until
they reach your eye almost as one ray, giving the knoll a very
condensed, stubby look. Or the rays from top and bottom of a
ship may actually cross each other, making the ship look upside
down in a natural mirror image of reality upon an absurdly inverted horizon.

SOME UNUSUAL MIRAGES
lines of light and sight   **object**   **appearance**

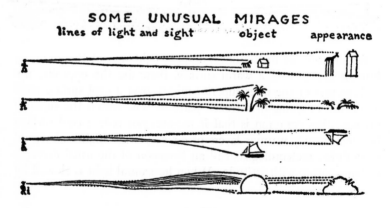

Almost anything can occur as the flexible paths of light grope
their way among the ever-changing folds of density and temperature. The setting sun can turn into a stepped pyramid or a crim-

son pineapple, often sliced into layers with nothing between —
and a few cliffs or crags perched above the far shore of a still
sea may be glorified by vertical elongation into majestic castles in
the air interspersed with soaring towers, minarets and battlements
— bewitching fairylike scenes that spasmodically crumble and evaporate, then form anew like dreams, producing a deep sense of
nostalgia, a profound and trancelike wistfulness — the fata mor-
gana!

Leonardo once wrote in his notebook that "as soon as there is
light, the air is filled with inumerable images to which the eye
serves as a magnet." It was a rashly imaginative attempt to explain vision, yet, fantastic as it seemed, it was nowhere nearly
fantastic enough to be literally true. For Leonardo had no way
of observing the still secret world of the microcosm or of knowing how to deal with things beyond the generalizations of common
experience. It is true he had an approximate idea of how a stone
curves when thrown through the air. And a cannonball's flatter
trajectory was not completely strange to him, since the cannonball could usually be seen in flight from the cannon. Also one
might discover where it landed and, on occasion, where it passed
through a tree, flag or windmill blade on the way — thus, by inter-
polation, its whole passage. But should one assume that smaller,
subtler or more elusive forces must necessarily follow the laws of
stones and cannonballs?

Galileo did not think so, as we learned from his principle of
similitude (see page 233), and, even though high-speed photography and powerful microscopes have since made it possible successively to observe Brownian movement, molecular and atomic
gyrations, even (by magnetic spectrometer) the motions of protons
and neutrons inside the atomic nucleus, science cannot yet pre-

sume it safe to generalize any basic physical laws over such a range of sizes.

Faraday, you will remember, found he could not generalize Newton's macrocosmic laws of motion to explain the microcosmic behavior of electromagnetism but had to postulate unheard-of "tubes of force" extending invisibly outward from a terminal or a magnet like tentacles that reached with diminishing though unending strength to the uttermost limits of the universe. That was the original concept of "field," a mysterious immaterial force that could influence matter and which Faraday, not having been trained in mathematics, envisioned or invented as the most logical way to give form and continuity to an evident cause and effect of nature.

Maxwell was too young then and too imaginative to be one of the many scientists who scoffed at Faraday's "amateurish" unorthodoxy. Instead, he grew up to develop Faraday's field idea into its modern mathematical structure that defines electrical and magnetic flux in terms of components of force and direction through the now famous Maxwellian equations $\nabla \cdot E = \rho$; $\nabla \cdot H = O$; $\nabla \times E = \dfrac{-\dot{H}}{c}$; $\nabla \times H = i + \dfrac{\dot{E}}{c}$. And, strange to relate, among the ensuing mathematical implications was the odd requirement that whenever an electric field is put into motion or retarded, it must not only set up a magnetic field at right angles to it but must send out (perpendicuar to both) an impalpable electromagnetic wave that travels through space with the speed of light and has other important properties derived from Huygens' wave theory of light.

This unprecedented development struck Maxwell as exciting in its potentialities. Could such electromagnetic waves — it they turned out to exist — really be a kind of light? Was light, in fact, a form of vibrating electromagnetic energy which might have other forms at other frequencies? Maxwell definitely concluded so, but his health was failing and, try as he would, he could not succeed in detecting any kind of space waves in his few remaining years and died before he had vindicated his theory. Yet only seven years later, in 1886, a young German physicist named Heinrich Hertz, who had thoroughly studied Maxwell's equations under the great Hermann von Helmholtz, proved the close relationship between light and electricity in a now famous experiment in the physics lecture hall in Karlsruhe. Using a Leyden jar (condenser) whose electrical discharge was well known to be not a one-way current but a rapidly alternating oscillation, Hertz rigged it up with a spark coil (model-T Ford type) so that the powerful sparks jumping back and forth between the two brass knobs of his foot-long broken-rod transmitter would, he reasoned, send out the mysterious waves predicted by Maxwell. He had

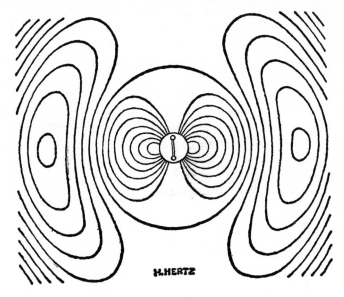

H. HERTZ

brilliantly calculated the exact shape these theoretical waves should have as the current, oscillating at a frequency of slightly more than 500 megacycles, broadcast its subtle "influence" outward in all directions, and he saw no reason why his receiver, a similar divided brass rod with a delicately adjustable spark gap between a knob and a sharp point, set up at the other end of the hall, should not show some kind of electrical response — assuming the waves indeed possessed any sort of material reality.

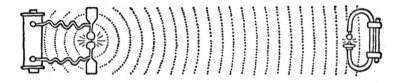

It was a tense moment, therefore, when Hertz put out the lights in the great room and, letting his eyes adjust themselves to the dark, turned to peer intently at the receiver's spark gap. Was there anything there to be seen? Could it really be — yes, a tiny blue spark flashed between the knob and the point whenever the transmitter was switched on. So it was true: electromagnetic waves were a proven part of the actual physical world at last!

Further experimentation soon showed that the new waves, though of lower frequency, were like light waves in basic character, traveling at light's speed and penetrating straight through some substances (nonconductors such as glass) while making others (conductors such as iron) cast "shadows." Hertz was delighted to find he could focus his waves with big "mirrors" of galvanized iron, polarize them by reflection and refract them with large "prisms made of coal-tar pitch." In his official report he added, with scarce-restrained glee, "They go right through a wooden wall or door and it is not without astonishment that one sees the sparks appear inside a closed room."

Honors were showered upon Hertz from all over Europe, and the reflected fame of Maxwell in consequence grew almost in proportion — for all had turned out as Maxwell foretold: sunlight, candlelight, glowworm light and electric current were "of a kind."

Hertz was soon experimenting with the photoelectric effect (see page 455) and might well have discovered the electron before J. J. Thomson if he had not developed bone cancer and died on New Year's Day, 1894, at the age of thirty-seven, evidently without having ever taken seriously the growing talk of long-distance communication by "Hertzian waves" — a world-revolutionizing development that Guglielmo Marconi would bring into exciting reality with his first wireless messages the following year!

The advent of practical "instantaneous" communication across trackless space in fact proved so stirring to the human imagination that it was accompanied almost simultaneously by a whole series of related discoveries; x-rays in 1895, radioactivity in 1896 with its constituent alpha, beta and gamma rays, and at the same time experiments with cathode (negative) and positive "rays" revealing the first subatomic particles, followed by the quantum theory in 1900, which threw an entirely new light on all these developments. Thus was to end the comfortable, 300-year-old mechanistic era so inspiringly launched by Galileo and Kepler and so solidly established under Newton with his neatly geared universe of orderly understandable motion. And thus, into the vacancy, was to dawn the new age of restless unsubstantiality and profound abstraction.

Several of the key steps in this great change-over seemed to come entirely by accident, as when Wilhelm Roentgen, a physics professor at the University of Würzburg, experimenting with a platinum plate fixed inside a large vacuum tube in which a raylike electric current of electrons was shot against it, noticed that a screen covered with fluorescent salt (that just happened to be near) started to glow every time he switched on the tube. Since it was known that the stream of electrons (then called a "cathode ray") could not penetrate the glass walls of the tube, it was evident that some other kind of radiation must be being produced, probably by the electrons from the negative (cathode) terminal as they hit the metal plate. Roentgen tried blocking off the screen with a fat "bound book of about one thousand pages" but it still "lit up brightly" and did not diminish much until shielded with plates of copper, silver, gold, platinum — or when virtually blacked out by lead more than 1.5 millimeters thick. Later, venturing to hold his bare hand in front of it, he was thrilled to see the screen clearly reveal "the darker shadow of the bones within the lighter image of the hand itself."

Finding he could not reflect, refract or polarize his new rays by any of the usual methods, Roentgen guessed that they might be ascribable to "longitudinal vibrations in the ether," but so much mystery attended them that he rather wistfully named them "x-rays." Even after the medical profession eagerly adopted x-rays as a prime tool for diagnosis of internal injuries, seventeen years were to pass before their true nature as high-frequency electromagnetic waves was to be established in 1912.

By that time, many scientists had tested x-rays with diffraction gratings (surfaces on which thousands of very fine parallel slits have been scored per inch), looking in vain for the successions of spectra that visible light of all wave lengths diffracts by these means. Then unexpectedly, Max von Laue, another German physicist, came to realize that if x-rays were waves at all, they must be a lot shorter than had been suspected, and he suggested that man-made gratings were too coarse for the job but that "a grating provided by nature in the form of crystals might catch waves less than a thousandth as long."

Sure enough, as soon as von Laue had worked out the mathematics of his theory, other physicists confirmed it in a sequence of astounding experiments in which precisely controlled beams of x-rays passing through the almost unknown three-dimensional lattices of zinc sulfide, calcite, phosphorus, uranium, mica and other substances diffracted the beautiful and characteristic patterns of each crystal upon photographic plates as a kind of unheard music, triumphantly proving thereby that the wave length of x-rays is scarcely one ten-thousandth the wave length of light. Or, putting it another way, not only had the deduced regular spacings of the crystals "taken the pulse" of the x-rays, but the x-rays simultaneously returned the favor by revealing the exact chemical interrelationships of each crystal.

And as the culminating act in this drama, a brilliant young English physicist named Henry Gwyn-Jeffreys Moseley succeeded in measuring the x-ray diffraction patterns of practically the whole

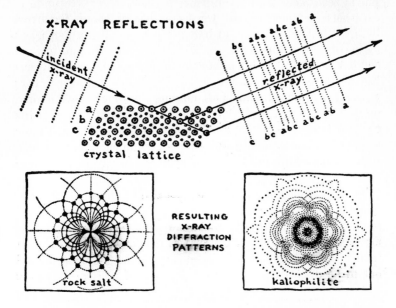

table of elements, discovering a hitherto unknown order in the square roots of their vibration frequencies that precisely conformed to the periodicity of the series of atomic numbers from 1 for hydrogen to 79 for gold — an exquisite and sweeping confirmation of the ancient, but no longer legendary, music of the spheres. The only flaw history seems to have allowed in connection with this noble accomplishment is the heart-rending irony that Moseley was prevented from testing the elements beyond gold only by the British army's recruiting office, which perfunctorily called him into His Majesty's service in 1914, just in time for some hasty training in the use of the rifle and bayonet before shipping him to Gallipoli to be impersonally cut down by a Turkish bullet at the age of twenty-eight — a sickening recapitulation of the senseless martyrdoms of Archimedes in the fall of Syracuse and Lavoisier under the Revolutionary Tribunal of France.

Another "accidental" discovery was that of Henri Becquerel, the French physicist, who, in trying to solve the mystery of x-rays by looking for them in phosphorescent salts of uranium, realized one day in 1896 that his photographic plates, wrapped in heavy light-protective paper, became exposed *in the dark* whenever they were left near the uranium. This puzzling phenomenon was cleared up only after Pierre and Marie Curie two years later isolated the element radium that "radiated" energy "millions of times" more vigorously than uranium and whose experimental use enabled Ernest Rutherford and others to analyze "Becquerel rays" into three components (α, β, γ) that seemed to correspond roughly to the smoke, flame and heat of a fire: (1) the moderate and positive alpha ray (later identified as a shower of helium nuclei) serving as the smoke; (2) the more penetrating negative beta ray (actually a stream of electrons) as the flame; and (3) the extremely penetrating and lethal gamma ray, which, like heat, turned out to be essentially a nonmaterial aspect of matter. Thus the

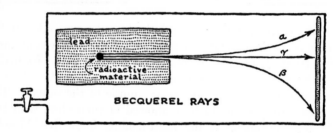

BECQUEREL RAYS

last is the only one of the three that is, strictly speaking, a ray, being in fact a very short electromagnetic wave of radiation, specifically only about a hundredth as long as an x-ray wave and emanating straight out of the atom's nucleus. This means that radioactivity is a dispersal of elementary particles along with high-energy radiation, and it turns out that, at any given moment, half the remaining dispersable energy of any radioactive element will be released within a constant period called its half-life. Which may explain, for example, why a waning supernova loses half its luminosity every 55 days, that period being the half-life of radiating beryllium 7, a radioactive isotope that disintegrates to form lithium.

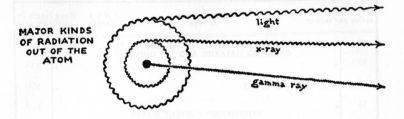

MAJOR KINDS
OF RADIATION
OUT OF THE
ATOM

light

x-ray

gamma ray

By the time most such phenomena had been sifted out, the whole spectrum of electromagnetic radiation, including visible light, was becoming pretty well established as a continuous scale of wave frequencies — a thought-provoking analogue of the musical and atomic scales, only much vaster, being not just seven or eight octaves in extent but stretching over more than 70 octaves plus several overlappings — all the way from the very long "double-bass" radio waves that vibrate only a few beats a second through the "tenor" of infra-red rays, visible colors, "alto" ultra-violet waves and "soprano" x-rays up to the shortest and highest pitched of "altissimo" gamma waves at frequencies in the quadrillions of megacycles per second.

It is, of course, a tremendous, not to say fantastic, spectrum and one which would surely have delighted Newton as well as Pythagoras, Aristotle, Galileo, Huygens and many another great pioneer of science. Its mere existence speaks great truths about the interrelationships of the world and the nonmaterial nature of its inmost texture. And our new realization that man's unaided eye cannot see even one full octave of the seventy known to exist is as heathfully humbling to the human ego in its way as was Copernicus' demotion of the earth from the center of all creation to the third satellite of an average star.

Viewed in the perspective of the whole sweep of radiation, then, invisible ultra-violet waves 3,700 angstroms long are harmonically close to and in the same "key" as invisible infra-red waves 7,400 angstroms long, being exactly one octave higher with all humanly visible light neatly bracketed between. Maybe that is why the opposite red and violet ends of the visible spectrum seem to join into a natural color circle through magenta and crimson-purple. Certainly this single obvious octave of frequen-

THE RADIATION SPECTRUM

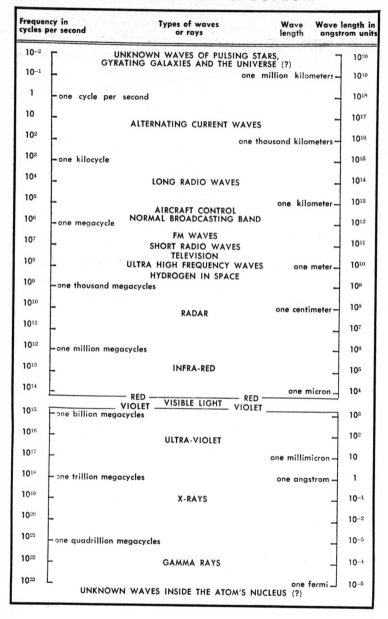

Frequency in cycles per second	Types of waves or rays	Wave length	Wave length in angstrom units
10^{-2}	UNKNOWN WAVES OF PULSING STARS, GYRATING GALAXIES AND THE UNIVERSE (?)		10^{20}
10^{-1}		one million kilometers	10^{19}
1	one cycle per second		10^{18}
10			10^{17}
10^2	ALTERNATING CURRENT WAVES		
		one thousand kilometers	10^{16}
10^3	one kilocycle		10^{15}
10^4	LONG RADIO WAVES		10^{14}
10^5		one kilometer	10^{13}
10^6	one megacycle AIRCRAFT CONTROL NORMAL BROADCASTING BAND		10^{12}
10^7	FM WAVES SHORT RADIO WAVES		10^{11}
10^8	TELEVISION ULTRA HIGH FREQUENCY WAVES HYDROGEN IN SPACE	one meter	10^{10}
10^9	one thousand megacycles		10^9
10^{10}	RADAR	one centimeter	10^8
10^{11}			10^7
10^{12}	one million megacycles		10^6
10^{13}	INFRA-RED		10^5
10^{14}		one micron	10^4
	RED VISIBLE LIGHT RED VIOLET VIOLET		
10^{15}	one billion megacycles		10^3
10^{16}	ULTRA-VIOLET		10^2
10^{17}		one millimicron	10
10^{18}	one trillion megacycles	one angstrom	1
10^{19}	X-RAYS		10^{-1}
10^{20}			10^{-2}
10^{21}	one quadrillion megacycles		10^{-3}
10^{22}	GAMMA RAYS		10^{-4}
10^{23}		one fermi	10^{-5}
	UNKNOWN WAVES INSIDE THE ATOM'S NUCLEUS (?)		

cies contains all sorts of striking color intervals, beautifully analogous to music, like the harmonic fifth of red and violet, the
fourths of red-blue and orange-violet, the complementary thirds
of red-green and orange-turquoise and any number of chords
beginning with the simple major triad of red-green-violet. Color
chords, however, as you must have noticed, are not seen by the
eye in a musiclike multiple form but rather as single blended
tones: most often dull brown or gray or some other averaged
pitch of light.

If you ever thought the key of a plucked harp string takes
too much effort to visualize in abstract numbers of vibrations
per second, you can be certain the color or pitch of light is many
millions of times further removed from easy comprehensibility.
Should you glance for just one second, for example, upon an
ordinary yellow dress, the electrons in the retinas of your eyes
must vibrate about 500,000,000,000,000 times during the interval,
registering more oscillations in that second than all the waves
that have beat upon all the shores of all the earthly oceans in
ten million years. And if the dress were green or blue or purple,
the frequency would be that much higher. Or if x-rays were
used instead of light, it would be increased a full thousand times.
If gamma rays, a million times!

This quantitative explanation of radiation that portrays color
as the look of frequency is probably close to what Newton was
seeking when he experimented with his prism in 1666, for it
explains every kind of iridescence from rainbows to the changing hues of oil upon dirty harbor water. By now, of course, the
rainbow has long since become well known as a series of refractions through all raindrops in sight that are aligned at certain
angles (particularly near 138° and 129°) from the sun, each color
being formed very precisely as an individual frequency cone of
directions for each eye that sees it.

But oil iridescence is quite different in origin. It is the result

of interference between the light rays reflected from the upper
and lower surfaces of the oil film, these two sets of waves
creating a phase disparity that amounts to a particular frequency
and varies directly with the oil's thickness. Perhaps you have
noticed that the delicate rainbowlike colors of oil freshly dumped
on water always disperse as the oil spreads out its irregularities
and thins down into a layer of uniform thickness and color.
Then, if the oil is not prevented from continuing its spreading
and thinning, its color gradually rises in frequency from red to
yellow to green to blue to violet in conformance with the decreasing wave length of the interval between the oil surfaces, finally
disappearing into ultra-violet when the film is too thin to be
picked up by any wave of visible light. After this, it can be seen
only while its slipperiness still reduces the friction of the wind
enough to keep it a smooth, unrippled slick amid surrounding
relative roughness.

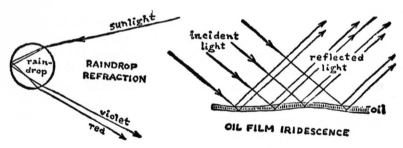

This matter of the oil film's becoming too thin to be seeable is
related to the fact that most crystal lattice patterns were too fine
to be discovered before von Laue thought of looking at them with
x-rays — and to the inability of any sort of waves to accept
modulation or gather information while the waves themselves are
as long as the things they encounter. This is why a pipe between
rooms can be used as a speaking tube to convey intelligence so
long as the waves are much shorter than the tube, but waves
long enough to tune into it immediately turn the pipe into a
whistle.

On the other hand, if you are walking at night along a beach with heavy sea waves rolling in, at any place where the waves suddenly diminish you can be reasonably sure there must be a reef or something big out at sea that absorbs or reflects the waves' energy, thereby sheltering you in its "shadow." But if, instead of a reef, there should be only a thin pole out there sticking rigidly from the bottom up through the waves, you would never notice its effect at the beach. For quite obviously its thickness would be much too small in relation to the big waves to impress any very lasting influence upon them. Even if there were thousands of poles, placed close enough together to add up to a kind of reef, the resulting shadow could not hint of any individual poles. Only if the sea were nearly a flat calm but laced with tiny ripples from some whispering wind could single poles cast shadows that would appreciably persist to leeward. And it would happen then only because the length of the ripples had become smaller than the diameter of the poles.

The principle here, you see, is that of the artist who wants to paint a Persian miniature. He does not choose a barn brush but looks for a fine camel hair suited to the delicate texture of his work. And just so do the white clouds, made of water droplets whose diameters are greater than the wave lengths of light, disappear from sight as soon as their droplets evaporate (break up) into separate H_2O molecules too small to modulate the light.

X-rays, however, are fine enough to "see" water vapor in "empty" air — for instance, in samples of air taken fresh from a cloudless sky. On the other hand, although clouds can be easily seen with ordinary light, their microscopic droplets are too small to affect most radar waves, which are proportionately so long they are blind to them, while the much larger drops of falling rain can be "seen" collectively by radar yet do not provoke any reaction from the still longer waves of broadcast radio.

I mention such relationships because they give some idea of the meaning of transparency, which occurs when light (or other waves) pass through a substance without being appreciably influenced by it — which is to say, without being harmonically related to it or tuned in on it. And conversely, they show the meaning of opacity, which is the stopping of the waves to an extent that leaves a shadow whose sharpness, significantly, is strictly proportional to the shortness of the waves.

Opacity also means either reflection or absorption of waves, and commonly both, since something must happen to waves that are stopped — which something is a prime key to the appearances of things. Light waves are absorbed, for instance, when their frequency is in resonance (sympathetic vibration) with the atoms or electrons of anything they meet. As the atoms of most solids and liquids vibrate at frequencies of somewhat less than three hundred million megacycles (300,000,000,000,000 vibrations) a second, which is in the infra-red frequency range, the infra-red radiation of ordinary heat is absorbed by tangible objects in general. And as electrons and other *sub*atomic particles have much higher frequencies, in fact, considerably higher than those of any visible light, short ultra-violet as well as most of the longer x-ray radiation is also readily absorbed by virtually all materials.

Thus there are two main absorption bands of opacity in the electromagnetic spectrum — in the longer infra-red range and in the shorter ultra-violet and adjoining x-ray ranges. But this leaves prevailing transparency in three other zones: in the low-frequency bands of radio waves (which pass fairly easily through nearly anything but metals), in the very high-frequency regions of x-rays and gamma rays, which penetrate almost everything and, more obviously if less completely, in the intermediate (between infra- and ultra-) frequency range of visible light where many substances like glass, quartz, water, alcohol, glycerin, gasoline, salt, fluorite, diamond and various plastics are manifestly transparent. This middle band of transparency, moreover, is in effect extended a little way into its bordering frequencies by such devices as rock-salt lenses for the shorter infra-red waves and quartz prisms for the longer ultra-violet ones.

If you wonder now why metals are so opaque, not only to light and radio waves but to any radiation of lower frequency than short x-rays, it is easily explained in that they have loose electrons in their outer "shells" capable of vibrating in response to all but the very highest frequencies. And it is these same loose electrons, you may remember, that earlier explained such phenomena as the magnetism of iron, the conductivity of copper and, perhaps even more significantly, made it possible for Hertz to jot down a certain brief note during his famous experiments with electromagnetic waves. In this note, I am told, Hertz recorded that whenever he let the light from the flashing sparks of his transmitter shine directly upon his receiver, the tiny answering sparks in its gap became slightly brighter.

Even though Hertz's mind was evidently too occupied with other things at the time to sense much significance in this curious effect, the phenomenon could have been none other than the very photoelectric emission of electrons by light incidence that Einstein would make famous nearly two decades later when he published his concept of photons in 1905. This brilliant intuition of Einstein's was actually an extension of Planck's five-year-old quantum theory into the shattering postulation that the energy in a light beam does not spread out evenly into the universe along with the fields of its electromagnetic waves (as leading scientists then supposed) but is concentrated instead into the almost infinitesimal packets called photons.

Millikan's contemporaneous photoelectric experiments, indeed, had shown that if a piece of metal, insulated from the ground, is negatively charged with electricity, the charge (excess electrons) will leak off through the air when light shines on it — and the more so if the light is of a short-wave color such as violet or ultra-violet. What could this mean but that pieces of matter called electrons were being knocked away by pieces of light, and in proportion to the number of them? And what were pieces of light but the units Einstein called photons?

Einstein's photoelectric law, it is true, does not specifically banish or deny the existence of light waves, since a photon is considered to have a frequency, and its energy (directly proportional to its frequency) is transferable in a mysterious wavelike way to and from electrons, but every step of Millikan's painstaking investigation consistently and triumphantly supported the existence of photons and quanta, most of all through the ejected electrons' speed and kinetic energy which were completely independent of the light's intensity yet always in exact agreement with the formula of Einstein.

Likewise, as Einstein pointed out, a little-known but "crucial experiment" had confirmed the quantization of light as early as 1902, when Phillip Lenard proved that a sensitive screen being withdrawn from a light source does not continue indefinitely to absorb less and less radiant energy but instead, when its rate of absorption has stepped down to a certain extreme minimum, it refuses to go any lower until it suddenly drops to zero! Was such granulated energy consistent with the diffraction wave patterns of light? Einstein evidently accepted both without really explaining or reconciling them.

But how could light be both particle and wave? If some atom in space, for example, radiates just one quantum of light, the wave theory says that after one second this energy will be spread very thinly over the surface of a sphere 186,282 miles in radius with the original atom at its center. And then the quantum of light may happen to be absorbed. But we have found that a quantum cannot be divided. By definition and by all tests it must be absorbed as a unit by a single localized atom. So arises the awkward question, how can all the light energy spread over a sphere thousands of times bigger than the earth be gathered up instantly into a single atom? Could any mortal mind really believe such a miracle is part of normal everyday nature?

The puzzle amounted to a big enough dilemma to prevent the general acceptance of space-localized quanta until 1923, by when Arthur H. Compton had discovered that reflection can lower the frequency (or increase the wave length) of radiation by absorbing some of its energy. This he observed while watching x-rays deflect off carbon and other light elements, a process in which the reduction in frequency ranges from zero on upward as the angle of deflection correspondingly increases. And Compton demonstrated mathematically that this is exactly what one should expect from Einstein's photon theory if photons are really material objects that have momentum enabling them to "bounce" off electrons or other particles according to the mechanical laws of billiard balls. In a very glancing blow, he noticed his x-rays were only slightly deflected in direction and gave up little energy to the electrons they hit. But in a nearly head-on collision, they were knocked away at a sharp angle after relinquishing much more energy — a fact made obvious by their considerable drop in frequency.

The compton effect, as it came to be known, practically clinched the photon as a proven material particle — incidentally explaining fluorescence as a slightly lagging "reflection" at lowered pitch and phosphorescence as a longer delayed "reflection" (really an absorption followed by a re-emission) that also reduces the radiation to a lower-frequency color.

But there were lots of other aspects of light that still needed clarification, including some that had been under intensive scientific development for decades. Did you ever read about the singularly unfortunate position philosopher Auguste Comte put himself into last century, when he rashly announced that man must reconcile himself to "eternal ignorance" of the composition of the stars?

His words had hardly been spoken before the astronomical spectroscope eloquently refuted him in what has been called the language of the atom. It was a language in refracted colors that explained, among other things, exactly what the stars are made of, how hot they are, whether they are coming or going and, rather conclusively, that they are chemical cousins of the sun and earth.

The letters of this atomic alphabet had been first remarked by William Hyde Wollaston in 1802, followed by a poor glass-polisher's apprentice named Joseph von Fraunhofer in 1814, in the form of mysterious dark lines among the separated colors of sunlight refracted through a prism. After Fraunhofer, starting at red, had designated these lines A, B, C, etc., it was discovered that each one originated in the absorption of light of its own frequency by a particular kind of gas in the atmosphere of the sun or the earth and, within a few years, every chemical element was shown to possess its own indelible, spectral signature: a fixed set of absorption and emission lines and bands that are as insolubly keyed to it as the lines of your fingerprints are keyed to you. Thus Fraunhofer's red lines A and B (at wave lengths of 7,594 and 6,867 angstroms respectively) proved to come from the earth's most plentiful element, oxygen. His red line C (6,563Å) is made by hydrogen, his yellow lines D are sodium, green E is iron, blue F hydrogen again, violet G both iron and calcium . . .

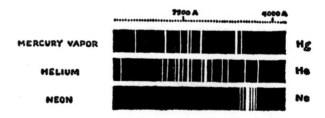

Probably the easiest way to visualize the workings of such absorption lines is through the analogy of music. If you have three tuning forks in a room, each keyed to a different note in the major triad C – E – G, and this same chord is played in the next room with a large peephole opening between the rooms, your three forks will start to hum the chord by sympathetic vibration through the air. But if another E fork is placed exactly in the peephole and the experiment repeated, the original E note will be found missing from the resultant dyad, which will now consist only of C and G, the middle fork being silent because the new E fork in the peephole hums in its stead, having absorbed most of the energy of E frequency as it tried to pass through the opening. The three original tuning forks in this analogy correspond, of course, to the spectroscopic screen and the missing E note to the dark line of a frequency that did not arrive because it was absorbed by its resonance with some substance it passed through on the way.

Analyzing such spectral fingerprints geometrically, and concentrating on those of the simplest element, hydrogen, an obscure Swiss mathematics teacher named Johann Jakob Balmer became so fascinated with the riddle of their musiclike intervals that by 1885 he had succeeded in working out a "ladder" or climbing sequence of the frequencies of all the known hydrogen lines, each frequency being a definite fraction of the ladder's limiting frequency (3,287,870,000 megacycles a second) beyond which the sequence does not go. And these fractions in turn formed a beautiful harmonic series, each denominator a cardinal square in natural succession, each numerator four less than its denominator — $\frac{5}{9}$, $\frac{12}{16}$, $\frac{21}{25}$, $\frac{32}{36}$, $\frac{45}{49}$, $\frac{60}{64}$, $\frac{77}{81}$ . . . — a kind of Bode's Law for hydrogen, smallest of the inner spheres, since, if one recalls the mysterious number 4 that Bode added to each doubled planetary distance (see page 85), one may well wonder, could Bode's 4 be in any sense related to the 4 that Balmer subtracted from his denominator?

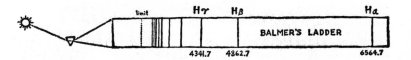

be found missing
limit   Hγ   Hβ   Hα
BALMER'S LADDER
4341.7   4862.7   6564.7

Whatever the truth might be, few spectroscopists had ever heard of Bode, and Balmer's Ladder appeared to be nothing but a mathematical curiosity even to the leading physicists of the day. Yet as more and more spectral frequencies of more and heavier elements were measured in succeeding decades, it became increasingly obvious that every element has its ladder or ladders and most of them are much more complicated, though no less beautiful, than Balmer's Ladder for hydrogen. Furthermore, an unexpected Rosetta stone of the atom's language with a complete key to the meaning of the spacings of the rungs in each ladder suddenly turned up when Niels Bohr proved just before World War I that the relationship between these colored lines corresponds exactly to the quantum intervals of the electron shells within the atom.

Thus the descent of an energy-radiating electron downward and inward, shell by shell, orbital after orbital, from a higher to a lower energy state as Bohr explained it (see pages 338–341), had its perfect visual expression in these dainty footprints of light down Balmer's Ladder! It was a breath-taking revelation of actual quantum divisions in action — one might say a glimpse into the electron's secret garden — a vision significantly comparable to, and no less lovely than, the sight of Saturn's giant rings resting palely, placidly upon the black counterpane of space.

As the dynamics of the atom further unfolded, it became evident that the series of spectral lines Balmer studied is not only quantized but comes specifically from the light emitted by the hydrogen electron in dropping from the third, fourth, fifth and higher energy levels to its *second* shell near the atom's nucleus. And this led to the realization that the wave lengths of all radiation producing visible light are functions of the distances between the atom's shells down to shell 2, the drop from shell 3 to shell 2 radiating as red light, from shell 4 to 2 (the first overtone) as blue, from shell 5 (the second overtone) as violet, and so on. Yet all visible light is such a tiny part of the spectrum that other kinds of "light," normally invisible, were bound to be discovered as instruments for their detection came into use — which is how it happened with the so-called Lyman series of ultra-violet light emanating from the narrow limits of shell 1, with the Paschen series of short infra-red light from the not-so-narrow shell 3, the Brackett series of longer infra-red from wider shell 4, the Pfund series of still longer-waved radiation from still wider shell 5 . . .

Each of these invisible rainbows of spectral music, you see,

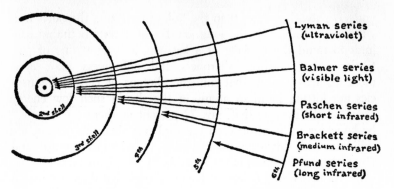

Lyman series
(ultraviolet)

Balmer series
(visible light)

Paschen series
(short infrared)

Brackett series
(medium infrared)

Pfund series
(long infrared)

is a world unto itself that took legions of scientists on several continents many years to develop. Special towers and observatories were built for spectroscopy of the sun and stars, modern counterparts of Stonehenge, Cuzco and the great pyramids of Egypt and Mexico, and their powerful series of prisms, lenses and reflectors magnified and widened the spectrum into literally a hundred thousand lines and bands that now reach a total linear spread of more than a mile. Even the very simple Balmer series on visible hydrogen has become an extension ladder of thirty-one rungs, some of them traceable to hydrogen's extra shells called "virtual" orbits because the hydrogen electron never attains them under earthly atmospheric conditions but only when the atom is vastly expanded in vacuous space. And some of them originate not with the single H atom but with the H_2 molecule and its added frequency of rotation about an axis perpendicular to the line connecting its two H nuclei, not to mention the interference beats from their combined vibrations.

If the visual light of simple hydrogen can produce so many lines, is it any wonder that a hundred elements, with their much more complicated and multiple systems of electrons create several thousand times more? The problem of deciphering such units, which further research is ceaselessly subdividing into still smaller units, is patently greater than the task of analyzing the notes in a symphony. Indeed, if the long low B♭ of a certain timbre conjures to mind the blowing of a bassoon, a spectral line of particular color, position, sharpness and diffuseness may, even more explicitly, mean that sunlight photons of certain frequencies are hitting hafnium atoms in the sky in such low energy states on the average that, say, 72 percent of them are absorbed by knocking an electron each outward one shell, 20 percent are colliding with higher state electrons to rebound onward and (by batting an electron inward one shell) release an extra photon, while the remaining 8 percent having energy that does not match any energy difference between two electron levels are simply passing through the hafnium without reaction.

Winding up this subject with a few sample rules of spectral analysis, I will add that when the characteristic absorption lines of iron are found in starlight, the source star must be at least as hot as molten iron. And the star's color or frequency will show directly whether it is red hot, yellow hot, blue hot, ultra-violet hot or to what degree it may be putting out x-rays or gamma radiation. Broad bands, whether from Earth or sky, indicate a solid or liquid source since overlapping and blended (i.e., broad) radiation is an unavoidable output of the denser states of matter, while thin separated lines tell of the lonely freedom of gas molecules or isolated atoms that rarely interfere with one another. And the qualities termed *sharp, diffuse, principal* and *fundamental* are clues to the subtle subshell differences described in Chapter 10 (see page 340), just as the Stark and Zeeman effects (particular splittings of lines) indicate electric and magnetic fields respectively, while the doppler effect (a change in frequency) shows whether the source is approaching or receding. The last phenomenon, known as the red-shift in the case of spectral lines from remote galaxies, is our main evidence of the expansion of the universe (page 215). It is the spreading of waves or lowering of frequency that is familiar, in the realm of sound, as the descending pitch of a passing train's whistle, and its appearance now likewise in the electromagnetic realm is virtual proof that all moving stars and galaxies compress their light toward the short violet

waves ahead of them while trailing it out in long low-pitched red
waves behind.

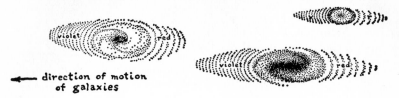

direction of motion
of galaxies

Here is a good place, I think, to glance back upon the full
scope of the radiation spectrum, for by now, we should have
perspective enough to see beyond it at both ends. If in a long
view of the ocean, say, one could regard the tides as nothing but
extremely long, low ocean waves of a super order and very slow
period, so might the end waves of radiation be conceptually
extended into other orders of space and time: down into the
deep infra-bass frequencies of slow-flashing variable stars and
whole gyrating galaxies, and — why not? — up into the still less
understood ultra-altissimo frequencies that quite possibly vibrate
somewhere far inside the inmost hearts of atomic nuclei.

This spectrum, as you surely realize, is not only much more
than light. It is much more than radiation in the usual sense.
Indeed, it is fundamental to all matter, to all energy and to all
the interactions between things and things in the world. Somehow one cannot help but feel it is at the heart of the mystery of
the particle-wave duality of matter — which remains to this day
almost as mysterious as ever. There is no doubt that a German
professor named Max Born had thoughts along this line when
he was teaching physics at the University of Göttingen in the
1920's and trying out ways of expressing all the abstract and un-
visualizable aspects of the atom. Balancing one attempt against
another in his efforts to define the photon or check the elusive
electron's position and velocity for every instant of time, he took
to the tactic of cornering his facts by statistical methods. As it
seemed to be impossible, for example, to pin down an electron,
why not try pinning down a billion electrons, he thought. A man
might be able to get a real grip on a billion electrons. And then

afterward, in the hope of coming somewhere near putting his finger on a single electron, he could divide his results by a billion.

Of course, such a statistical electron would not be strictly real. It would be just an *average* electron, a composite Mr. Wavicle from Atomville, a sort of actuary's norm. Applying its calculated mean to any actual electron, one would obtain not a sure position nor a true term of existence but rather a *probable* position and maybe a kind of life expectancy.

This turn of thinking inevitably brought the classical theories of probability into modern focus and raised not a few philosophical eyebrows at the newly discovered pores of uncertainty inside matter. Just what was this demi-dawn in the world's interior that offered mankind yet another fundamental lesson in humility, this abstract kingdom of chance that loomed through the gloaming of the germs? Is chance, they asked, really the antithesis of certainty or law? Is Lady Luck but another name for ignorance?

One might conclude so on reflecting how many people annually pray for rain, whose atmospheric sources are still shrouded in confusion, yet how few think of praying for an eclipse or a sunrise, which are comparatively much simpler to understand. The immeasurable thus we naturally attribute to chance, or God, and only the measurable, the clearly calculable, to science or human reason. As we cannot correctly measure the impulse we give the roulette wheel, we consider its spinning energy a matter of luck. Raindrops fall "at random" because we cannot accurately measure their formations. Even the postman's methodical rounds through a crowded city street are apt to appear random to the eye of a pilot flying half a mile overhead. And are not the coursing stars but studs upon a kind of great roulette wheel named the zodiac?

While the ancients are not known to have considered stars to have been sown at random, there is some reason to think that stars are actually about as random as molecules. Yet if their randomness seems the greater for their large numbers, it may be their numbers again that ultimately overcome their randomness. For laws of chance activity on a large scale have a remarkable degree of certainty about them, as is now well established. We call it pure chance, for instance, whether a tossed coin falls "heads" or "tails" because we do not know how to predict such alternatives. Yet we are very sure, in the long run, that the number of heads must nearly equal the number of tails. This is about the simplest possible expression of the law of probability — a kind of paradox in which a few large simplicities are literally composed of a host of small complexities — in which, as numbers increase, uncertainty steadily approaches certainty.

On a slightly more sophisticated scale, if we flip six coins, we may get anything from six heads to six tails and, by doing it hundreds of times, we discover the results form what is known as a probability curve. This is based on the fact that, out of the 64 possible ways in which the six coins can fall, one way produces all tails, six ways show 5 tails and 1 head, fifteen ways 4 tails and 2 heads, twenty ways 3 of each, fifteen ways 2 tails and 4 heads, six ways 1 tail and 5 heads, and the last way shows 6 heads. It can be expressed in numerical probability terms as:

Number of heads	0	1	2	3	4	5	6
Probability	1	6	15	20	15	6	1

or graphically as in the curve on the next page, which is strikingly similar to that produced by a "probability board" made to display the random distribution of falling shot.

A century ago, Maxwell startled the scientific world by using a similar distribution curve to confirm the famous law discovered experimentally by Robert Boyle in the seventeenth century that "the pressure of a gas is inversely proportional to its volume." Maxwell did it by analyzing the presumably haphazard velocities of molecules for the first time, plotting them on a graph according to Gauss' "law of error" derived mathematically from probability theory.

From here, Ludwig Boltzmann took an important step further with his "law of probable population densities for molecules,"

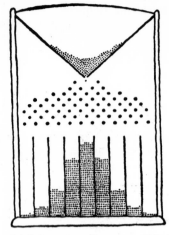

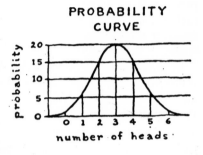

PROBABILITY
BOARD

PROBABILITY
CURVE

which has since become a kind of common law of the atmosphere.
Perhaps of more general application in chemistry than any other
principle, Boltzmann's law is the basis for calculating the evaporation rate, the energies of molecules — for practically our whole
modern conception of air in which every molecule hits multi-
tudes of other molecules a total of some three billion times a
second while traveling an average of $\frac{1}{160,000}$ of an inch between collisions. And although each oxygen and nitrogen molecule, each H_2O, each CO_2, each argon, neon, helium and krypton
atom is much freer than a rolling die to go its own way — any
way "luck" will take it — the net effect of them all in vast quantities is as dead certain as death itself. If this were not so, any
air might explode or collapse any time, and no man could be sure
of his next breath.

The workings of probability in our familiar macrocosmic realm,
however, are in some ways quite fantastic — certainly not in accord with horse sense or any sort of common intuition. In a
simple game of coin tossing that lasts for weeks or years, for
example, you might think that, if the coin is perfectly impartial

and the tossing truly random, first one player will be ahead in the score, then the other, the lead seesawing frequently between them to give each a winning edge about half the time. But this expectation is entirely wrong! The most careful probability research proves that in 20,000 tossings it is about 88 times more probable that one contestant will lead in all 20,000 cases than that each player will lead in 10,000. And "no matter how long the series of tossings, the most probable number of changes of lead is zero."

In the microcosm, on the other hand, the functioning of probability turns out to be not only different from in the macrocosm but, significantly, even farther removed from common sense. When, for example, in macrolife two golf balls are tossed at random into a bin whose bottom is partitioned into two equal compartments, there is one chance that both balls will fall into the first compartment, one chance that both will fall into the second and two chances that a ball will fall in each compartment. In the microcosm, on the other hand, substituting atoms for balls and quantum states for compartments, the chances turn out not 1:1:2 but 1:1:1.

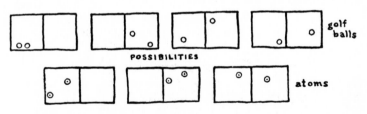

A curious difference, you'll agree! And it struck one of Professor Born's bright young graduate student assistants as a very important clue to the true nature of matter. His name was Werner Heisenberg and he not only played the piano in his off hours but had been "playing" with both the wave and particle concepts of matter at the university, "going from one picture to the other and back again," as he put it, in an attempt to find out if "nature could possibly be as absurd as it seemed to us in these atomic experiments."

The probability workings of atoms henceforth offered a way, in Heisenberg's fertile mind, of measuring the queer lack of individuality of any elementary substance — of expressing the difficulty (or was it really an impossibility?) of keeping track of which of identical molecules is which. Perhaps golf balls, he speculated, if they could be made smaller and smaller until they faded out of sight, would ultimately turn into something like marks or dollars in a bank account, which soon lose their tangible identity and become only "things to balance the books by." Thus the first ball in the first compartment and the second in the second compartment would be no different from the second ball in the first compartment and the first in the second. Each set of combinations would not only seem like the other but would literally *be* the other — having lost its identity materially as well as abstractly.

Of course, such an eerie hypothesis is not rigidly expressible in classical language where you are more or less stuck with words like "particle," "wave," "energy," "velocity," "time," "position," "frequency." These expressions represent concepts thunk up by us huge inhabitants of the macrocosmos, while atomic reality is not macrocosmic and seems not even to conform to our language which, when inappropriately used, unfortunately but undoubtedly tends to convey contradictory and ambiguous meanings.

Recognizing this, young Heisenberg saw a promising new light on Bohr's old correspondence principle, which had attempted, not very convincingly, to reconcile the classic and quantum worlds, and which Prince de Broglie had pretty well by-passed with his startling wave concept of matter — a concept that Schroedinger, in turn, unbeknownst to Heisenberg, was just now (1925) working into a full-fledged modern theory of the atom. What Heisenberg saw was that atomic events have a strange independence or integrity of their own — that they do not accept partitioning by space or time into parallel or successive events.

For a convincing example, he could review Thomas Young's famous experiment in 1800 (see page 421), which revealed the interference of light when it passed simultaneously through two slits in a screen. Even after he reperformed the experiment with modern apparatus, using the fewest possible photons of light, he observed that each photon, in effect, still must go through both slits — that the investigator who asks which slit a particular photon really goes through does not receive any answer. Quite obviously, the question in that form just does not make quantum sense. In Heisenberg's own words: "We have to remember that what we observe is not nature herself but nature exposed to our method of questioning." For, if you ask *inappropriate* questions, why should nature feel any compulsion to give you *appropriate* answers? No more does the plumber respond very efficiently to the lady who phones him for "a thingamajig to fix the tub in my bathroom" without any hint that there is a leak and that the job will need a hacksaw, two 8 by ¾-inch nipples and a ¾-inch union.

It is plain, then, that on entering the microcosm, we have sacrificed a good deal of our capacity to describe what we encounter in familiar classical language. But, on the other hand, we may have gained a fresh chance to describe in some more suitable (and still largely undiscovered) language wholly new features heretofore unknown to our macrocosm.

Heisenberg naturally turned to mathematics as the most likely available source of this needed language. In particular he turned to certain abstract principles that were already nearly a century old and had been developed by the famous mathematicians William Rowan Hamilton of Ireland and Arthur Cayley of England. Hamilton was an especially appropriate choice from the standpoint of language, for he had been a prodigy reputed to have mastered thirteen languages by the age of thirteen, among them Latin, Greek, Hebrew, Sanskrit, Persian, Arabic, Chaldee, Syriac and sundry Indian dialects. At twenty-two he was appointed a professor and, in another of those mental projections that in retrospect seem to have a divine prescience, he borrowed a principle from Pierre de Fermat, who had observed of refracted light that "the ray pursues that path which requires least time," and perfected it mathematically as if in preparation for the undawned, undreamed atomic age and the even less dreamed advent of relativity. It was the ancient metaphysical *principle of least action*, developed also by Pierre de Maupertuis (who applied it to animal motion and plant growth) and by Leonhard Euler. But Hamilton formally adopted it for optics and dynamics, explaining that light navigates space as a sailor navigates the ocean, by just naturally seeking the great circle or shortest path — the easy, economical route of *least action*.

Hamilton used a simple mathematical notation of p for momentum (mass times velocity) and q for position (in terms of coordinates), by which he could express the dynamics of any particle in p's and q's. And with rigorous logic he forged and proved a link between the sciences of light and dynamics, incidentally using weird nonarithmetical quantities that multiplied by unheard-of rules which often made p times q come out different from q times p.

$$\triangleleft \cdot \downarrow \mathring{\gamma} \, \varphi \, \ddagger \, \Lambda$$

There is no need further to confuse you, or myself, with a lot of abstruse mathematical language we haven't learned the vocabulary or grammar of — so suffice it to say that Heisenberg took to Hamiltonian mathematics like a cat to fish. And as he tried to analyze an electron's behavior in p's and q's, separating these factors into their simple constituent sine ∿ waves by Fourier's method (see page 391) to get at the heart of the wave-particle paradox, he half-expected that the resulting list of sorted wave frequencies would match up in some normal, or at least reasonable, way with the frequencies of the radiation spectrum. When the two sets of frequencies apparently would not agree, he wondered why. If matter and light are essentially just two aspects of the same thing, should they not somehow correspond or have some kind of matchable relationship? It was, of course, Bohr's old correspondence problem in a subtly different context.

At this point, Heisenberg suddenly caught himself. "Perhaps," he reflected, "I am asking the wrong question again." And a slight shift of focus immediately came to mind: if Fourier's analysis (a classical relation) and Balmer's Ladder (a quantum relation) will not correspond in the obvious way, why not try an unobvious way?

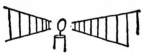

So Heisenberg began casting about for fresh concepts. He tried to avoid thinking of electrons moving around orbits, since no one had ever seen an electron and, as de Broglie pointed out, any "orbits" one of them might or might not be presumed to move along could hardly be other than fictitious, to say nothing of being descended, more than likely, from ancient astronomical tradition. He mused instead on the well-observed ladders of light, which are about the solidest facts yet established in the atomic realm. And he got to thinking of them as profound spatial intervals, as irregular geometrical abstractions — sometimes simply as relative distances stretching this way or that way across the universe. When a man matches up distances in down-to-earth life, however, comparing the distances, say, between towns on a map, he has an interesting range of choices as to how he may go about it. "Might such an idea possibly give me my opening," wondered Heisenberg. At first the man may think only of a linear representation of distances, as, Berlin to Leipzig 90 miles, Leipzig to Nürnberg 145 miles, Nürnberg to München 95 miles. But eventually something will probably spawn a bigger or more sophisticated concept in his mind — perhaps a tabular form with its added dimension, its superior flexibility and wealth of information, not to mention a strangely fascinating symmetry about one diagonal axis. The tabular form may be expressed as:

A Mileage Table

Name of town	Berlin	Leipzig	Nürnberg	München	Name of town
Berlin	0	90	135	330	Berlin
Leipzig	90	0	145	240	Leipzig
Nürnberg	135	145	0	95	Nürnberg
München	330	240	95	0	München
Name of town	Berlin	Leipzig	Nürnberg	München	Name of town

Could this, by any chance, be what was needed for a meeting of the classical and quantum worlds? It was certainly neat and suggestive. It was a square table and just happened to suit Heisenberg's listing of his p's and q's, using frequencies and amplitudes in place of towns and miles. There didn't seem any point in worrying about just what it all might mean so long as it worked. After all, Heisenberg was barely twenty-four years old and would have plenty of time for checking up and philosophizing later.

Without any clear idea of where he was going, therefore, he plowed ahead into what turned out to be quite a complicated system of square tabulations of momentums and positions. And, sure enough, he found that, when he had laboriously devised a logical way to multiply momentum p tables by position q tables, $p \times q$ almost never equaled $q \times p$.

How old Hamilton (who died in 1865) would have exulted over this! And Professor Born eagerly pointed out to Heisenberg that Arthur Cayley, who had generalized Hamiltonian algebra and ex-

plored the frontiers of geometry, had also managed to invent
a visionary "matrix calculus" in 1858 that was as if made ex-
pressly for Heisenberg — a curious theoretical technique for handling square number "matrices" such as the new p and q tables.
In Cayley's day, this was about as esoteric and other-worldly a
field of endeavor as could be imagined, with no real, practical,
or even potential application in sight. And yet it was exactly the
field Heisenberg would be reopening sixty-seven years later in the
process of reconstructing the whole foundation of physics! By
what slim odds could such a "coincidence" have occurred
through random luck alone?

Professor Born and Pascual Jordan, a mathematical colleague,
now became so intrigued by Heisenberg's matrix discoveries that
they set to work to dig to the bottom of the mystery and, after
"much extraneous assumption" while diligently minding their
p's and q's, finally came up with the peculiar equation
$p \times q - q \times p = \dfrac{h}{2\pi \sqrt{-1}}$ which says that the difference between the two ways of multiplying p and q is nothing but
Planck's constant h divided by 2π times the imaginary number
$\sqrt{-1}$. Wasn't this perhaps more than a little odd, to put it mildly?
For 2π is simply what you multiply the radius of a circle by to
get its circumference but, since there aren't any known numbers
that can be multiplied by themselves to obtain a negative product,
how can -1 have a square root?

The mystery went very much deeper than this, of course, as
all mathematicians (including Heisenberg) well knew, and the
word barely had time to spread abroad before many another
theoretical physicist was drawn into the fray, notably the great
Bohr and Pauli and that extraordinary but then still unknown
Englishman, Paul Dirac. A year younger than Heisenberg, Dirac
had just begun to wonder if he had enough aptitude to finish
his engineering course when the news struck him like a bolt
from Olympus. Instantly he forgot about becoming an engineer
and threw his whole soul into the challenge of basic matter,
quickly and independently developing an abstract generalization
of Heisenberg's theory that more than equaled the combined

work of Heisenberg, Born and Jordan. Like the Göttingen trio, he found the magic combination of h, 2π and $\sqrt{-1}$ in one lightninglike flash of revelation that was "the most exciting moment" of his life — but, more important, he saw beyond the "scaffolding" of Heisenberg's huge, square tabulations and deep into the essence of the p's and q's. He discerned that p's and q's were actually a new kind of number that followed quantum, instead of classical, rules and convinced physicists that henceforth they would have to deal with both kinds of number. Calling the new ones "q numbers," he demonstrated with rare elegance that what they stood for included not only Heisenberg's p's and q's but also such abstract dynamical quantities as time and energy that had been represented in the square tables.

Thus the scientific world, which had been increasingly wondering what could ever replace Bohr's ailing correspondence principle, suddenly found itself in 1926 with not one but four new theories of matter, all profound, revolutionary and promising. It was an unprecedented turn of history, and the four physicists, deBroglie, Schroedinger, Heisenberg and Dirac, would all soon be rewarded with Nobel prizes — and Dirac with the chair of Newton as well.

Their four theories, moreover, were by no means wholly at odds with one another and came to be classified logically in two pairs: (1) the wave theories of de Broglie and Schroedinger, which descended from mechanics, and (2) the abstract particle theories of Heisenberg and Dirac, which developed more from optics. Besides this, there was the deeper binding influence of old Hamilton, who had boldly combined mechanics with optics in his mathematical theory, and whose "wave dynamics" had helped Schroedinger almost as much as his "particle dynamics" had served Heisenberg and Dirac.

Then one day Schroedinger had an inspiration about the abstract new quantum rules that govern the multiplication of p's and q's. He suddenly realized that these new numbers are not *quantities* at all but *commands* that mathematicians call "operators." For example, while 2 is a number, the command "multiply by 2" or the command "subtract 5" is an operator. This explains why the order of multiplication makes a difference in p's and q's for, if you apply these two operators (above) to a number, say, 8, the first order $(8 \times 2) - 5$ results in 11, while the second order $(8 - 5) \times 2$ results in 6.

$$\sqrt{-1}$$

Operators also put sense into the square root of -1, which had too long been a mystery. It is said that in the year 1572 a reckless Italian mathematician named Girolamo Cardano first put the apparently meaningless root of a negative number on paper, explaining that it provided an irrational and fictitious way of solving the otherwise impossible problem, "What two numbers add to make 10 and multiply to make 40?" The two numbers of his rather complex answer came out as $5 + \sqrt{-15}$ and $5 - \sqrt{-15}$, a "fictitious" solution that nevertheless proved itself mathematically.

During the next two centuries mathematicians were surprised to find $\sqrt{-1}$ and other roots of negatives increasingly useful, despite the great Leonhard Euler's appraisal of them as "neither nothing, nor greater than nothing, nor less than nothing, which necessarily constitutes them imaginary." But at the beginning of the Napoleonic wars a fancy-free Norwegian surveyor named C. Wessel tried $\sqrt{-1}$ out as an operator. Since the military command "about-face" results in a symmetrical 180° reversal of direction, evidently he thought the negative number -1 might be considered a kind of "about-face" of the positive number 1. It seemed a pretty far-fetched idea at first but it exactly fitted $\sqrt{-1}$ for, if you regard $\sqrt{-1}$ as the command for a 90° "right-face" or "left-face" turn, then $\sqrt{-1}$ times itself would be a 90° turn upon a 90° turn, which would make the product -1 or a 180° "about-face." Even the right-left ambiguity of direction is logical, as all square roots have an ambiguous sign. And

of course the −1 of "about-face" fulfilled twice (or squared) results in the original 1 or forward direction.

Simple as this concept is — in fact *because* of its simplicity —
it has had a profound influence on the evolution of mathematics.
Today $\sqrt{-1}$ is such a seasoned tool it is commonly written only
in its abbreviated form *i*. Most of this developed long before the
day of Schroedinger, of course, but it was through Schroedinger
and his new interpretation of the *p*'s and *q*'s that the *i* and the
operator principle generalized wave mechanics enough to induce
Heisenberg and Dirac separately to adopt Schroedinger's ψ essence of space. Whereupon, largely through Dirac's abstract insight, almost all the other important aspects of quantum mechanics
were assimilated into one unified system. The mathematical ramifications of this combination — including such features as a "spinor
calculus" devised to harness the spin of the electron's "waves
of probability" — are rather technical to go into here, but I cannot resist mentioning that Dirac presided henceforth in Newton's
professorship at Cambridge with such astringent calm and sphinx-
like restraint that his students jocularly honored him with their
own special unit of professorial reticence, the *dirac*. By definition: "one *dirac* = one word per light-year."

The mathematical language and structure that thus crystal-
lize our present quantum mechanics, while obviously very important, can hardly give the average pedestrian much idea of what
this stuff we call matter really boils down to. So let us try to
see what can be visualized out of all these particles and waves
and shells and spins and orbitals and probabilities. Is there more
to matter's abstraction than the thought of square tables of *p*'s
and *q*'s observed through "imaginary" *i*'s?

Before trying to pin anything more definitely down, however,
I think there is one additional check we should make. We should

try to be sure we are facing our limitations squarely. That is just what Heisenberg did in his determination to resist being led up any scientific garden paths. And, quite significantly, it led him instead to his famous, and now solidly established, uncertainty principle.

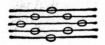

This principle is a mathematical expression of the limit of fineness of the atomic world, of the ultimate quanta grains of matter which cannot be further subdivided, of Leucippos' final "parts which are partless," of the unsharpenable bluntness of all material tools when they get down to exploring things as tiny as electrons and photons. Incidentally it casts profound light on why this world is quantized, why no action has ever been measured or computed to be less than one whole h.

Heisenberg could hardly have reached his great conclusion solely on the basis of any physical experiment, because, as you can well imagine, one cannot literally handle or measure the single electrons or photons that most clearly exhibit the uncertainty in question. Even to measure a giant molecule a million times bigger than an electron with the most delicate conceivable tool would be something like taking the temperature of a demitasse with a swimming-pool thermometer. The demitasse would be affected nearly as much by the thermometer as the thermometer by the demitasse — so the thermometer could not possibly register the original temperature of the demitasse. Much less could a single atom be measured by any material instrument. Even less again could an electron or a photon. In other words, in the microworld the observer and his instruments inevitably become an integral part of the phenomenon under investigation — even as the elephant who knew no way to test the health of his friend the beetle without squashing him to oblivion.

So, instead of a physical experiment, Heisenberg conducted what has been described as a "thought experiment." This technique, used earlier by Einstein, offers the advantage of an "ideal laboratory" in which any sort of gadget or instrument or condition is permissible so long as it does not violate accepted basic laws of physics. Heisenberg therefore equipped his mental set-up with an imaginary electron gun that would shoot a single electron horizontally across a vacuum chamber so perfectly empty it did not contain a single air molecule! And he "observed" his moving electron by the light of an "ideal" microlamp that could emit "photons of any desired wave length and in any desired number," watching it through a perfect mental microscope capable of transmitting any part of the spectrum "from the longest radio waves to the shortest gamma waves."

According to classical principles of mechanics, of course, any particle of matter must follow an elliptical (Keplerian) path, even as a planet or a pebble, and the fact that it is observed with the aid of light should make no difference. But in actuality, as we now know in this quantum age, light does make a lot of difference in the case of an individual electron — for as soon as a photon strikes it, the electron rebounds with changed velocity and, if subjected to many photons, it inevitably follows an unpredictable zigzag course.

In order to simplify the problem of keeping track of the electron's path, therefore, Heisenberg thought of reducing the frequency of his magic lamp so low that the photons striking his electron would have minimum energy, as in extremely long radio waves. Thus they would virtually cease deflecting it (energy being proportional to frequency), allowing it to go practically straight and at a fairly measurable velocity and momentum. But here arose a new difficulty. The longer the wave length of the "light," the less accurately it could "see" or locate any object — for the same reason that long sea waves are little influenced by a thin pole sticking out of the water, or that infra-red waves are blind to many things noticed by x-rays. Thus Heisenberg found himself faced with a baffling choice: either he could speed up the frequency of his photons to throw more energetic light on the electron, defining its precise location every time a photon knocked it off at some unknown speed and direction — or he could throttle down the photon's energy to stabilize and measure the electron's speed and direction at the expense of having less light to locate it by. In other words, he could accurately determine either position or momentum so long as he did not try to do both at once. He could have p or he could have q. He could not have $p + q$. And no combination of the two could amount to more than a peculiar compromise value for pq, the product of these two mutually exclusive parameters, a composite uncertainty that (it turns out) "can never be smaller than h/m or Planck's h divided by the mass of the particle."

Such is the real and mathematical essence of the principle of uncertainty. It is not just a problem of measurement. It is not a mere mental quandary, nor a plaintive ploy on two symbolic letters p and q that happen, most appropriately, to be mirror images of each other. Rather it is something like the dilemma of a photographer trying to shoot a fast-moving celebrity in a dark alley. Unless he has a flash outfit, he must make a hard choice between (1) using a fast enough shutter speed to stop the motion, which will not quite admit enough light to expose his film, and (2) using a slower shutter to gain sufficient light with the virtual certainty of blurring his subject.

It is a perverse paradox, a perpetual plight of the microcosm — the peculiar pq symmetry of mutual mathematical exclusion that knows many forms. If an electron is shot through an ideally tiny hole in a rigid screen, for example, its position in the hole at an exact time can be determined with great precision but not its momentum at the same instant. Yet by suspending the screen on an ideally sensitive spring scale, the electron's momentum can be precisely ascertained by the motion of the scale — only, however, at the price of uncertainty of the electron's position in a hole that is no longer rigid. Here again the total uncertainty can never *in principle* be less than h/m which, in effect, means that the electron's path cannot be regarded as a *line* but is rather a *band* of uncertainty nearly as wide as the radius of its "orbit."

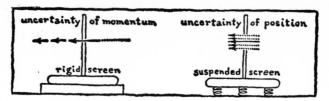

And from this it follows that a tiny grain of dust weighing one milligram should be measurable simultaneously to within a trillionth of a centimeter in position and to within a trillionth of a centimeter per second in velocity, yet no closer in either of these respects without suffering a compensative loss in the other respect. One might perhaps profitably liken this to the newly discovered macrocosmic symmetry of errors in space travel which, at high rocket speeds, makes errors in velocity more tolerable and errors in aim less tolerable whereas, at low speeds, the opposite is found true.

In any case, such symmetries of exclusion keep turning up as physicists continue exploring the abstractions of the quantum world, and probably most, or all, of them are aspects of one another. Have you ever considered, for instance, the curious symmetry between the incompatible qualities of precision and accuracy? Precision, technically, means "fineness of detail," while accuracy means "truthfulness," and an increase in either tends to be balanced by a decrease in the other. This relation is perhaps best exemplified by maps of various scales — scales whose range of usefulness turns out to be surprisingly narrow because of the practical need for both precision and accuracy in not too different proportions. If a map of the universe, let us suppose, should be drawn to show its features as looked at from infinity — taking an extreme case — the map could hardly help being absolutely accurate but also, unfortunately, it would have to be entirely blank because its precision could be no higher than zero at that unimaginable distance. If finite maps were later drawn to show smaller and smaller portions of the heavens on scales more and more magnified or — which is the same thing — with galaxies and stars seeming to come nearer and nearer, which (from the dynamic standpoint) would make their counterparts in real life appear to move faster and faster, accuracy would inevitably decrease as precision increased. And the ultimate map produced by this trend toward nearness and unlimited precision would presumably be one drawn with a perspective of infinitesimal closeness showing the minutest imaginable subatomic detail, virtually no part of which (because of the limitations of knowledge) could possibly be accurate.

ᕍ ᖾ
Ꮞ ᕵ

From such a symmetry of the unknown universe and the uncertain electron, one can range onward into all manner of significant symmetries. Time-energy is an important one, for any experiment that measures the energy of any particle or system takes a certain length of time to perform and tends to alter the system's energy. Moreover, it turns out that the shorter the time period the greater the effect upon the energy, so that the more exactly the time of measurement is known the less certain can be the energy quantity measured. And again, the product of both uncertainties is never less than h.

Probably the simplest kind of symmetry to visualize is ordinary structural symmetry which has the quality of remaining unchanged when reflected in a flat mirror. A cube is symmetrical in this sense. So is an average table or chair. But structural symmetry can be nicely divided into three geometric classes corresponding to the *point*, the *line* and the *plane* and associated respectively with the three classic kingdoms of our world: *mineral, vegetable* and *animal* (see illustration, next page). Thus a basic mineral form such as a star, a rain droplet or (to a lesser extent) a tourmaline crystal tends to be symmetric about the point of its center, a gravity-resisting vegetable to be symmetric about the line of its vertical axis, a mobile animal symmetric on either side of the plane that separates the right and left halves of its body.

But the third of these evolving symmetries includes the curious asymmetry of handedness or, more exactly, the mirror twinship of

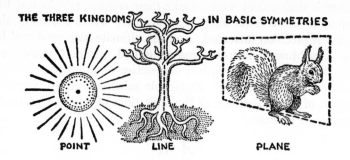

THE THREE KINGDOMS IN BASIC SYMMETRIES

POINT   LINE   PLANE

asymmetric parts in a symmetric whole. This abstruse distinction between rightness and leftness deeply perplexed Immanuel Kant, who asked, "What can more resemble my hand and be in all points more like it than its image in the looking glass? And yet I could never fit such a hand into the place of its original."

Handedness pervades the world — as much the microcosm as the macrocosm, not excluding (so far as we know) the galaxies, the supergalaxies nor, mayhap, the whole universe. As a geometric concept, handedness is found in abstract structures of four and more dimensions — in fact in structures of any number of dimensions. While a straight line, for example, is symmetric as a whole along its one dimension, a long segment of it followed by a short one makes an asymmetric (handed) pattern that may be mirrored by a point into a short segment followed by a long one. Three-dimensional crystals are commonly right- or left-handed as we saw in the case of quartz (page 288). And the vertebrate body, while bilaterally symmetric in general, has a leftward heart and a definitely handed spiral intestine. Even in the traditional realm of the soul, handedness has developed an asymmetric symbolism along the lines of mental and spiritual polarity, accounting for such familiar Biblical distinctions as those found in St. Matthew's account of the last judgment when "he shall set the sheep on his right hand, but the goats on the left" and the fortunate ones on the right "inherit the kingdom" while the outcasts on the left are condemned "into everlasting fire." Obviously, it is only this sort of handy symbolism handed down the ages that makes possible such a *hands*ome pun as "Be right or you will surely be left."

Most words of ordinary speech are alphabetically asymmetric, since they must adapt their linear structure to the complex needs of semantics. Yet there are a number of palindromic words like *level, redder, noon* and familiar names like *Ava, Bob, Dad,* that read the same both ways. And there are symmetric sentences such as, "Draw pupil's lip upward" or Napoleon's famous retrospection, "Able was I ere I saw Elba." There are even complete conversations: such as Adam's first remark, "Madam, I'm Adam," to which Eve, sitting up and taking notice, appropriately replied, "Tis I, Eve. I sit."

Word symmetry can be vertical as well as horizontal, however, an example being the ambidextrous gambler's telegram "DOC HID DICE — CHECK BOX BED" which reads as easily in a mirror as outside one. This is likewise true of the girl and boy names AVA and BOB, but here appears a curious horizontal-vertical distinction, a polarity that permits the feminine gender to reflect only horizontally and the masculine only vertically. I hardly need point out that the name of the notorious hermaphrodite HOXOH inevitably reflects both ways.

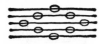

Music obviously lends itself to symmetry along the linear dimension of time, and Bach, Haydn and Beethoven all used temporal symmetry for contrapuntal effects, probably influenced by the somewhat harrowing fifteenth-century fashion for palindromic canons with complete dual melodies that imitated each other backward. And musical reflection in the vertical (nontemporal) direction can now be accomplished with startling ease by turning a player-piano roll upside down so that it plays forward but with treble and bass notes reversed. The ensuing un-recognizable melody, significantly enough, is just what would come out of a looking-glass piano if it could be played in the normal manner. And it often turns out not unpleasantly melo-dious despite the polar inversion which includes an unexpected transposition of major and minor keys. The classic example of such nether music is to be found in Bach's *The Art of the Fugue,* where the twelfth and thirteenth fugues are invertible. But Mozart wrote what probably is the tops of all turvy tunes with his doubly-dextrous canon featuring a second melody that is the first one both backward and upside down, thus handily (though un-handedly) enabling two players (one of whom may be Chinese) to read the same notes simultaneously from opposite sides of the sheet (with or without mirrors) in either direction!

The world is full of considerations related to symmetry, like the handedness of dice, there being two ways of placing the dots on each die's face so that its opposite sides always total seven — each way the mirror image of the other. And the fascinatingly knotty topological problem of proving that "a pair of mirror-image knots in a closed curve cannot be made to cancel each other by deforming the curve," no mathematician having yet succeeded with this obviously true but deceptively simple theorem.

If you feel you should shrug off all such matters as trivial, here may be a good place to recall that great thinkers from Pythagoras to Einstein have eagerly tackled equally humble questions — and not always victoriously. Certainly no man need be ashamed to look over Alice's shoulder into her mirror and to wonder, as she did, whether looking-glass milk is good to drink. Only half a century after her author's death, it was discovered that the milk we drink is literally endowed with handedness, being composed of counterclockwise or left-spiraling protein molecules which the enzymes of our bodies (with equivalent handedness) are able to digest. So our systems would undoubtedly react violently against right-handed looking-glass milk, if we ever could contrive to drink any. And, worse still, the recent discovery that many elementary particles have an even more fundamental handedness suggests that any physical contact between our world and a mirror one would inevitably trigger explosive annihilation wherever the irreconcilable right- and left-handed particles met!

What are we to make of this fantastic new idea of particle and antiparticle asymmetry? Of handed polarity?

If I said "new" idea, I must quickly qualify it. For in essence it is as old as history in both Eastern and Western civilizations.

The ancient Chinese monad of yang-yin ☯ symbolizes all basic dualities, including the light-darkness, positive-negative, male-female and right-left relationships of what Lao Tze called "Is and is-not coming together." And its simple and charmingly balanced asymmetry makes appropriate the fact that a pair of Chinese physicists (one of them named Yang) won the Nobel prize in 1957 for discovering (of all things) particle handedness!

Meantime the other side of the globe developed the Greek idea, expressed by Leucippos, that *"what is is no more real than what is not"* and that *"both are alike causes of the things that come into being."* He called his atoms *"what is"* and held that they move in the void *"what is not,"* which is a *real* void.

Such a concept of nothingness is more basic and understandable to man, including primitive man, than you might think. Even the Micronesians have a legend of "Lowa, the uncreated" who said "Mmmmmmmmm" and raised islands out of the unbroken sea to make the world.

And now the very front line of basic physical research directly faces the seeming ultimate in nadir fantasy: antimatter. Although this other-worldly stuff, composed of antiatoms made of negative (not positive) nuclei at their centers and positive (not negative) electrons moving around them, exists only theoretically so far, being extremely difficult to put together even in the best of laboratories in a materially opposite world such as ours, all its needed elementary antiparticles have been discovered separately, as you may remember from Chapter 10 (see page 327). And physicists now soberly admit that they see no reason why antimatter on a vast scale may not exist in other worlds somewhere in the universe.

Since particles and antiparticles have proved to destroy each other by explosive cancellation the instant they touch, antimatter could not possibly exist naturally on Earth, nor likely in the solar system if our sun and planets actually had the common origin now generally accepted. It is true a few physicists have speculated that the great Siberian meteor of 1908 and perhaps the older ones of Arizona and Quebec (see page 121) may have been made of antimatter, thus explaining the absence of tangible remains where they landed, but this idea has not been generally taken very seriously. Even the local Milky Way galaxy does not appear a logical place for antimatter. But distant galaxies and, more so, supergalaxies are so far apart they should not normally bother one another even if they were made of reciprocally opposite stuff.

The nearest to direct proofs of antigalaxies have been the violent radiation sources picked up by radio telescopes from a few points where galaxies are (or were) apparently colliding (see page 213), the vast energies recorded being unexplainable by present knowledge except as radiation emitted in the wholesale annihilation of matter. But if there really are two such antipodean kinds of galaxies, theorists are hard put to explain how they got that way — how matter and antimatter were born and what force ever could have separated or kept them apart.

One theory holds that antimatter may exert antigravity, somehow enabling the rival structures to repel each other. But their double origin is a more difficult problem and apt to bring up the old question of Lemaître's primeval egg of the universe in the ylem days of the Big Squeeze (see page 216). At least, it will be hard to prove that antimatter was *not* created along with matter. Both stuffs are eminently stable when not in each other's company, and the laws of symmetry revealed by the paired creation of particle and antiparticle in the modern laboratory strongly indicate that both should exist in equal amounts.

o O ʘ o o o o o o O ʘ o o o o o O O

Symmetry is far too big a subject to cover adequately here, as is also its application to particle life within the atom. But I might mention that since it is one of symmetry's strictest rules that heavy nucleons and their antinucleons are always born in pairs, no hermit antinucleon is likely to appear alone to explode a nucleon of ordinary matter, a destructive happenstance that, on the large scale, would amount to the cancerous infection of matter by antimatter and from which our material universe — for all we know — could completely vanish into radiation through progressive annihilation.

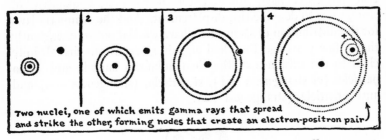

Two nuclei, one of which emits gamma rays that spread and strike the other, forming nodes that create an electron-positron pair.

Electrons and positrons are also born in pairs, as well as mesons and other momentary particles. Likewise do they "decay" and die in pairs — and generally in mysterious symmetrical ways. It is as if empty space, the void, is itself somehow symmetric, not to mention literally teeming with potentiality — indeed, with a dual potentiality. It is as if the most perfect vacuum is still chuckfull of what physicists call zero-point fluctuations, or abstract subquantum uncertainty. This could mean that *in principle* there is no such thing as absolute emptiness — certainly not an emptiness in every sense. In other words, the electron may well be born out of nowhere, physically speaking — yet, because of the demands of symmetry, it leaves something behind it — something it came "from" — a sort of a hole in nothing that can move around like an invisible bubble. If it sounds crazy to say this, remember that there are no words yet in existence (in any known language, even mathematics) that can adequately express basic physical truth. So as near as we can say or think it, a hole in nothing is something. And at least some aspect of nowhere is somewhere. That seems to be one of the profound discoveries of modern science and philosophy. It is unquestionably abstract, but exactly what part of it may also have what material relation — who can say? And again and again out of the depths it keeps asserting itself. *A hole in nothing is something.* It is the root essence of symmetry in physics.

The known ramifications of this "fact" are already too many to grasp. Under their influence some of the strange fleeting particles have been found to have such strange yet orderly displacements of their expected group centers of electrical charge that physicists have adopted the new physical quantity of *strangeness* to describe this displacement. And the symmetry laws for the distribution of strangeness have worked out so consistently that a few years ago they had already given us our first definite clues to the existence of the then unknown lambda and sigma particles (of strangeness − 1), xi particles (strangeness − 2) and anti-xi particles (strangeness +2).

Another symmetry law, known as the CPT theorem, governs the three rather drastic, symmetrical operations of charge-conjugation (C), space-inversion (P), and time-reversal (T), which, in combination, turn any material process into its counterprocess in antimatter as observed in reverse motion through a mirror. The "mirror" aspect of such symmetries, however, has little to do with a looking glass, for the subatomic image, instead of bouncing off a surface, merely converges, then diverges straight through a single point as in the simpler pinhole-camera type of reflection. And other rules may deal with the mirrorlike symmetries of size, handedness, energy, momentum (both linear and angular), acceleration, oscillation, singularity (vs. plurality), gravity (vs. antigravity), emission (vs. absorption), heat (vs. cold) cause (vs. effect), numbers (real vs. imaginary), relativity, and so on.

Pythagoras would be fascinated, perhaps completely enthralled, by the modern reasoning that has grown logically out of the very principles of harmony and balance he once introduced. I mean such hyper-Pythagorean logic as: that since the symmetry of a sphere is the greatest that is possible, the symmetry of any *one* state may be greater, and cannot be less, than the symmetry of any of its corresponding *many* states. That therefore the symmetry of the *many* is a subgroup of the symmetry of the *one*. Or: as effects grow out of causes and show equal or higher symmetry, cause-symmetry is a subgroup of effect-symmetry, past-symmetry is a subgroup of future-symmetry, etc.

In numbers, as we have already hinted, one important kind of symmetry works to give each ordinary number, say, 9, its "imaginary" double, usually written as $9i$, which means $9\sqrt{-1}$. This is the same as saying that, since every ordinary number (plus or minus) is the square root of something, a number symmetrical to it can always be imagined which is the square root of *minus* the same something. Thus as $\sqrt{4} = 2$, so its symmetrical counterpart $\sqrt{-4} = \sqrt{4} \times \sqrt{-1} = 2\sqrt{-1} = 2i$, the "imaginary" double of 2. Therefore i is a kind of master key to the symmetry of all numbers: 17 and $17i$, 52/63 and $52i/63$, 8.604 and $8.604i$ . . .

Such symmetry obviously depends partly on language, in this case the language of mathematics. But it is also deeper than language, for it involves two basic and alternative viewpoints, two profound aspects of the same thing — which just might be what Heracleitos of Ephesos sensed intuitively when he said that the knowledge of opposites is one. And if these opposites seem to be contradictory, who or what is to decide between them? I mean, when you open your door to a winter's night, are you

letting *in* the *cold?* Or letting *out* the *heat?* Is a bubble rising in
the sea a real thing-in-itself? Or is it mainly an absence of water?
And how do you evaluate a sculptor's marble? Are the solid,
positive chips he drops on the floor worth more, or less, than the
negative chips of antimarble emptiness he so carefully chisels
into the block to give it meaning and beauty?

At our present stage in history physicists are trying to unify all
the known fields of force (GRAVITATIONAL, ELECTROMAGNETIC and NU-
CLEAR) into one GENERAL theory. This naturally encourages
our budding periodic Table of Particles that is roughly comparable to Mendeleyev's periodic Table of Elements of last
century, and other probings into the seemingly endless patterns
of symmetry. One of the more significant recent efforts has
been Dr. John Grebe's discovery that the mass ratio between
muons and pions as well as between protons and sigma particles
is equal to $\pi/4$. This produces a new constant (1.1288)
based on $4/\sqrt{\pi}$, a tool that helps "explain" in the language of
symmetry many of the mass relations of particles.

Heisenberg, for his part, is working toward adding a new constant of nature to the established c of light's velocity and the
quantum h of action. "There must be a third such natural unit
of measurement," he says, "which is conceived in present-day
atomic physics as a length of the atomic order of magnitude — for
example, the size of the diameter of simple atomic nuclei. The
goal of atomic theory would be reached if one succeeded in
stating a mathematical structure that does not contain any arbitrary constants besides these three natural units of measurement
and from which the various known elementary particles with
their proportions can be derived."

Most physical laws boil down to the conservation of something
such as energy or momentum. And some, like the law of conservation of symmetry, are interrelated with other conservation laws
applying to various associated symmetrical properties: spin,

charge, nucleon number, handedness, strangeness, etc. Spin, for instance, is significant as one of the principal particle statistics, manifesting itself in magnetism and quantized behavior according to its own prim rules for each particle, pair or group of triplets, quintuplets, multiplets, etc. Since an elementary particle, whatever it may be, is certainly not a planet or a star but part of the microworld, it cannot spin in the easily understandable macromanner of Earth or sun. It cannot gradually slow down or speed up, and it knows no "seasons." Its poles sprout abstract appendages known as "axial cones of uncertainty." Yet, in its strange quantum way, it is affected by a "spin orbit coupling" analogous to the moon's tidal force, and it exhibits a curious interaction between its "day" and "year." Furthermore, if the spins of a lonely hydrogen atom's proton and electron, for example, happen to be aligned in the same direction (the two "north" ends parallel) there is a tendency for one of the poles to flip over until they are reoriented oppositely — and the resulting radiation

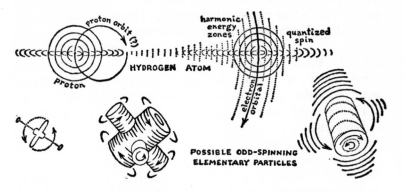

HYDROGEN ATOM

POSSIBLE ODD-SPINNING ELEMENTARY PARTICLES

from space is the main thing "seen" by radio telescopes. The spinning of a "cylindrical" particle, on the other hand, may possibly be self-symmetrical: it may spin in both directions at once, its ends somehow rotating oppositely on the common axis which thereby achieves a continuously slipping twist. Other spins and counterspins, nodes and antinodes, turn groups and mirror-turn groups and all of the confusing ferment of translational and breathing or pumping vibrations, are balanced reciprocally as in an abstract mirror.

It may have been the many such demi- and semiunderstood factors, relentlessly cropping up like weeds in the atom's garden, that prompted Heisenberg to declare recently that we have not yet got any convincing proof that basic functions have to be simple. "The final equation of motion for matter," he ventured, perhaps a little imprudently, "will likely turn out to be some sort of quantized nonlinear wave equation for a wave field of operators that represents generalized matter, not any specified kind of waves or particles."

Asked if the so-called elementary particles, whatever they are, might someday be divided into smaller bits, he replied, "How could one divide an elementary particle? . . . The only tools available are other elementary particles. Therefore, collisions between two elementary particles of extremely high energy would be the only processes by which the particles could eventually be divided. Actually they *can* be divided in such processes, sometimes into very many fragments (page 333); but the fragments are again elementary particles, not any smaller pieces of them."

Further insight into this paradox of division that is not division, it being more truly a transmutation of collision energy into new matter, comes from the now prevailing Heisenbergian view of the elementary particle as having no really concrete existence but only a tendency or probability of existing. "Shape or motion in space cannot be applied to it consistently," he says, and "certainly the neutron has no color, no smell, no taste. . . . Far more abstract than the atom of the Greeks, it is by this very property more consistent as a clue for explaining the behavior of matter."

Since the first photon that strikes an electron is "sufficient to knock it out of its atom," he explains, "one can never observe more than one point in the electron's orbit. Therefore there is no orbit in the ordinary sense. . . . It is of course tempting to say that the electron must have been somewhere between any two observations of it, and that therefore the electron must have described some kind of path or orbit even if it may be impossible to know which path." But this would amount to a complete disregard of the uncertainty principle and of the quantum nature of the microcosm. Uncertainty within the atom, we must not forget, is considered to be not just uncertainty of knowledge. Rather it is uncertainty of being — that elusive mutual exclusion of objective dimensions that seems to follow the lines of abstract symmetry. "Quantum theory does not contain genuine subjective features," continues Heisenberg. Although the mind must have its uncertainties, the uncertainty that is crucial to quantum physics is an uncertainty in the objective world. Indeed in a material experiment, the actual occurrences being observed *happen* at interactions between objects and measuring devices, not at registrations of these in the mind. "And since a device is connected with the rest of the world, it contains in fact the uncertainties of the microscopic structure of the whole world."

Even though Einstein had a somewhat different view, being loath to abandon his hope of achieving "a theory (of matter) that represents things themselves and not merely the probability of their occurrence," he eventually had to concede that "we must give up the idea of a complete localization of the particles," adding that "this seems to me the permanent upshot of Heisenberg's principle of uncertainty."

As for the real nature of ultimate matter, perhaps Einstein's best attempt described it as abstract fields "having modes of action in which there would be pulselike concentrations of fields, which would stick together stably, and would act almost like small moving bodies."

Obviously one does not need to ask what these fields or their "bodies" are made of. For what word could be used but "matter" or "energy" or some synonym equally wanting in final clarification? And if you would resort to such geometric idealism as "points in space," not only are "points" of very questionable reality but what could you actually mean by a point in space anyhow? You could hardly claim to pin down in space something which, by definition, occupies no space. Nor could a finger, needle or instrument hope to split a quantum distance, even in principle. Furthermore, how many points does a quantum hold?

Even if some instrument somehow could point to a single point in space at a single point in time, could anyone determine that that point remains exactly where the instrument located it, or exactly when, if ever, it had been there? Time too, we notice, is as indefinable as space and in the same basic way. A billionth of a second is about the most precise interval yet measured by man, and obviously there must always be some limit of measurement in this finite world.

So space and time become conscious human concepts amalgamated largely from measuring devices built of matter, not the reverse. Like a newspaper picture, which is an over-all concept formed of a white background containing a pattern of microscopic black dots, so are time and space the over-all relationship between events. And the nature of our minds synthesizes the structure of the world (dots, events . . .) into meaning (pictures, time, space . . .).

This is a way of saying that very likely fundamental entities of some sort exist independently of time or space or other illusions of limited perspective. Just as a thought can seem to be in two places at once because it is really no place, so may a single unit of matter exist in two places at once or a single event happen both before and after another event, as we shall see more clearly in the next chapter. Indeed, time and space now stand exposed by the success of relativity theory as probably not truly fundamental — and physicists no longer marvel when an electron (framed in the mirror of symmetry) is discovered "meeting itself coming back from a place it hasn't been to yet."

If we are here edging into a realm of thought that has more of metaphysics than physics in it, never mind — for physicists are coming to realize that, if they throw metaphysics into the fire, their own subject will soon smolder also — that not only philosophy but mathematics contains undecidable propositions and logic is far from unique.

It seems to be true, furthermore, that the abstract aspects of quantized matter that show up more and more prominently as we dig deeper into fundamental questions are more to be trusted than the old concrete easy-to-see illusions of classical theory. Certainly one cannot build a television station on sheer common sense. There is a real and growing difference here, you might say, between abstract and concrete things — a difference that is perhaps most easily exemplified in money transactions. If Amos owes Basil a dollar and Basil owes Amos a dollar, the abstract debts clearly cancel out to a result of zero. But if Amos has a dollar in his hand for Basil and Basil has a dollar in his hand for Amos, there are two concrete dollars which do not cancel out. Now if your imagination will allow you to think of light falling on an object as a shower of dollars descending upon a poor village, influencing it this way and that in a kind of wave motion, we can point out that the dollars will be more like real photons of light if those of opposite influence cancel each other abstractly rather than accumulating concretely.

The same holds for electrons or any other elementary particles of matter. The main difference between radiation and other matter is that radiation spreads spherically while other matter moves in a line, but each seems to boil down to the abstraction that Bertrand Russell calls "a string of events." Of course, our world contains some continuous series of events (say, a wave of water or a sunbeam) that do not all belong to the same piece of matter, in which case the change from one "event" to the next could not be considered simply as a particle in "motion." But in Russell's words, "strings of events exist which are connected with each other according to the laws of motion; [and] one such string is called one piece of matter."

Evidently "the unity of a piece of matter is causal," he goes on, "an observed law of succession from next to next. . . . If a tune takes five minutes to play, we do not conceive of it as a single thing which exists throughout that time, but as a series of notes, so related as to form a unity. In the case of the tune, the unity is esthetic. In the case of the atom it is causal."

There may be nothing at all to matter except just such causal series of events. And be the events "particles" or "ψ waves of probability" or "laws" or "symptoms" or just abstract relationships of unknown meaning, it makes little difference. You can call them anything. They are the "wisdom of the inward parts" in Job. When there are enough of them to create molecules and when the masses of molecules reach the dimensions of statistical illusion, the smooth flowiness of water will appear (if the molecules are called H_2O), or the transparency of air (if N_2, O_2, A, etc.) or something else.

But while statistical illusion increases with magnitude, there is an opposing increase in energy with minitude — which means a growing potency as we approach the nucleus of the atom. Energy being vital as the medium of passage between physical cause and effect, most phenomena become apparent only at a certain threshold of energy. That is why atoms that encounter one another at low energy behave like billiard balls, clicking each other's surfaces, their complicated interiors coming into play only at higher energies, the nucleus of the atom yielding to nothing less than 100,000 electron volts. Which explains how we can keep discovering deeper secrets of nature as we penetrate to higher and higher energy thresholds with no foreseeable end to the sequences of unexpected phenomena that ever become attainable from behind the endless veils of mystery.

Of all these shifting aspects of matter, however, undoubtedly the hardest to grasp is the factor of abstraction, which seems inversely proportional to size. As the macrocosm fades into the microcosm, indeed, the statistical certainty of masses always dwindles inexorably toward the uncertainty of single units. Macrofact devolves into microprobability. It is something like seeing a friend walk off into the distance. Exact knowledge of where he is and of what he is doing decreases. You cease knowing him so directly and you begin to know him more indirectly. Soon you know him only through telephones, letters, chance acquaintances, rumors . . . Sense has been replaced by symbolism.

Another way to express it is that there is no inherent "realness" to matter. There is instead an element of latency in things. Length and duration utterly depend on measurement, which utterly depends on an observer. These are aspects of things, just as mass and energy are aspects of the same thing. A piece of matter, therefore, no longer stands for something absolutely solid, nor something that keeps an identity, nor even "a hypothetical thing-in-itself known only through its effects." It is the "effects" themselves. We really do not know what makes electrons or protons or photons do whatever they do. We only know their effects. To us the effects *are* the electrons and protons and photons: the matter. In other words, as a particle or wave acts, so it *is*. Oscillation through space *is* light. Agitation of molecules *is* heat. Abstraction *is* reality. Matter *is* manifest behavior, palpable or deducible occurrence. And this may be the prime clue as to what the Apostle Paul meant when he said, "The world was created by the word of God so that what is seen is made out of things that do not appear."

Of course, he may have simply been referring to the established concept of atoms, which compose things without themselves appearing. On the other hand, he more likely intuitively had in mind the more mysterious spiritual aspects of composition: macrocosmic potentiality through the overcoming of quantum limitation, plural definition out of singular uncertainty, the beauty of unified structure, of binding energy, harmonic synthesis, love . . .

No one will deny that it takes more than four separate wheels, two axles, some springs and a body to make a cart. Or more than body cells to make a horse or a man. If you were given three or four individual notes on a harp, would it be possible to imagine the sound of a musical chord before you had ever heard one? If not, the whole of a piece of music must somehow be incalculably greater than its parts and, in a larger perspective, the whole of any composition perhaps infinitely more than the sum of what composes it. It hardly seems that this could fail to be the answer to why hydrogen and oxygen can convey no idea of water until the mysteriously intricate abstraction of combining them has been introduced. And, by the same reasoning, if a train runs one day along the single track from Irkutsk to Novosibirsk and if a train also runs one day back along the same track from Novosibirsk to Irkutsk, the combination of both trains running on the same day can surely amount to an event far different than the sum of their two separate runs, which, in the quantum world, would logically be a cancellation. It can, in fact, be a collision — with all that that implies of violence and woe and love and unfathomable consequence.

Thus the world that arises in a grain of dust, the sky that floats in a bubble of air, the waves of ocean and hill that can no more hesitate nor halt than a photon can stand still — and for the same reason — along with our thoughts and the mystery called God, what else is there? In the ceaseless struggle of matter and life and spirit that composes the universe, the clash and traffic of every parcel is a basic part — the eternal triangle of two pluses trying to cancel the same minus, the cross seas of probability that rise and meet and fade away, the symmetries that do not quite balance, the spins that know a bias, the polarity that yearns.

13. of space, of time

THIS SPACE STATION, I am coming to think, is just the place to contemplate space. And also time — and relativity. For our place up here seems nearly no place, my watch has turned quaintly arbitrary and the earthly calendar is about as pertinent as the old timetable of a railroad that once existed on some legendary continent.

Do you remember the ancient fable of the monk who wandered pensively a little way into a wood, only to hear a strange bird break into an ecstasy of song? And somehow the exquisite loveliness of the song carried him out of his world — for, when he returned to his monastery, the gateman knew him not. And he was amazed to find the place full of strangers who, as their old records proved, had lived there most of their lives and were equally astonished to discover their long-forgotten brother returning unchanged from an absence of fifty years!

Such tales, we are beginning to learn, are closer to the quick of life and modern physics than you might think. Before the advent of relativity earthly scientists would hardly have considered such a Rip-Van-Winklesome disparity in time fields as possible even in theory, but today they have accepted the principle that time is by no means the universal flow of sequence it always seemed. Rather must it depend on relative motion, and its different parts move at different rates according to different points of view.

Meditating this, one may well wonder what sort of time exists at the center of the earth? And how much of time extends inside the atom? What becomes of it outside the galaxy? Or, if the earth's motion should somehow ever be reversed, would that change the direction of terrestrial time in any sense?

And what of space? How intimately related is space to time? To gravity? If space should shrink to a point, would time endure without it?

The answers to such questions are not easily come by. And the dearth of words to express them may be less than the dearth of minds to comprehend them. Yet human reason need not be considered a rigid chest of logical drawers, for it is in many ways more like a waving tree that is just coming into blossom. In fact, man's collective mind has been shown to grow while learning, continuously generating in itself new potentialities for thought which had formerly been unimaginable.

I should probably mention space before time because, of the two, space is the more obvious, the simpler to visualize, and therefore it probably developed earlier in history as a conscious concept. Language definitely supports this assumption, for we do not talk about a "time of space" yet rather of a "space of time," and such spatial words as "long" and "short" now also refer to "expanses" in time, as the ancient mariner's spatial distinction between things located fore or "before the mast" and aft or "after the mast," used on a moving ship, may naturally have evolved the temporal distinction between events happening "before" and "after" other events. What could it be but our natural bias toward space that started us saying "hereafter" or "thereafter" instead of the more logical "thenafter"?

Although time was not recognized as the fundamental param- eter of material change until late in the Middle Ages, the ab- straction of space appeared at least as early as the fifth century B.C. After millenniums of nothing more abstract than field area units like the Sumerian "little acre" or *še* (named for the bagful of seed it took to sow it), there suddenly appeared the mysterious, ethereal void of pure numbers — the classic space of theoretical geometry. Aristotle credited this creation to Pythagoras, the first man known to have asked, "Are days and miles necessary?" Num- bers can live without them, he argued. And so can circles, tri- angles, shapes of all sorts. And these things are real even though they exist in a peculiar ether of their own. Some of Pythag- oras' followers may have visualized this unearthly space of geo- metric form as somehow related to matter, for Archytas, the Pythagorean, is reported (by Simplicius) to have raised the ques- tion of whether or not there would be room enough at the end of the world to stretch out one's hand.

Leucippos, for his part, imagined space as having a porous structure, the "pores" conveniently serving also as his "atoms," which were thus automatically guaranteed their indivisibility since they occupied no space. Aristotle, on the other hand, took the surprisingly modern view that where there are no bodies, neither space nor time can have any existence. And his favorite pupil, Theophrastos, went a step farther in concluding that "space is no entity in itself but only an ordering relation that holds be- tween bodies and determines their relative positions." He may quite naturally have come to this soul-satisfying conclusion after considering the baffling problem of determining distances between moving ships at sea — or between the "wandering stars."

If space, however, proved inordinately difficult to measure, as Kepler was to demonstrate so exhaustively, time has turned out to be even more difficult. And not the least of its snags has been the near impossibility of visualizing it objectively. The Puri Indians, for example, knew only one word for "time" and modified it in tense by pointing backward for the past, upward for the present, forward for the future. Their "time" sense was also almost literally circumscribed by space in the fact that they looked upon the distant skyline of mountains that surrounded them as the outer rim of time, as much as it obviously was a boundary of space, and anything beyond this horizon seems to have been presumed drifting intangibly in a kind of forever.

More advanced peoples, meanwhile, ran into the more sophisticated difficulty of trying to devise a calendar that gave the year a fixed number of days, all neatly apportioned into regular months or seasons by the gyrations of a methodical but not otherwise any-too-reasonable moon. The fact that the earth actually takes 365 days, 5 hours, 48 minutes and about 46 seconds to go around the sun once and that there happen to be 29.5305879 days from moon to moon and 12.3682668 moons from year to year was too implausible to imagine, if not too ungodly to accept. Yet most peoples eventually had to admit the futility of trying to match the incommensurable sun and moon. The Egyptians, in fact, set up what was possibly the earliest, and certainly one of the most successful, calendars largely by ignoring the moon. Their year was timed instead by the sun, the stars and the flooding of the Nile. It had twelve months of thirty days which combined into three equal seasons: Flood Time, Seed Time and Harvest Time, each four months long. At the tail-end of this 360-day stretch they added a "holiday week" of five days to complete the calculated year.

The early Romans, on the other hand, struggled along with a carefree calendar of only ten lunar months, March through December, not bothering about the sixty-some days left over. "What earthly good are winter months anyhow?" But when the seasons kept getting twisted around, they grudgingly added January and February, plus, every other year, a thirteenth month, Mercedonius (literally "extra pay" for the legions), with whatever number of days the astronomers reckoned would best mollify the zodiac. The succeeding Julian calendar, decreed in 46 B.C. by Julius Caesar and modeled on the Egyptian with the refinement of leap year, was a vast improvement, even though its annual span averaged 11¼ minutes too long. This "negligible" amount, however, in the course of sixteen centuries, was enough to require a new adjustment of a week and a half when Pope Gregory XIII inaugurated our present Gregorian calendar (with its year still 26 seconds too long) in 1582 — an adjustment which touched off unprecedented "calendar riots" among the tradition-bound people of England, Germany and Poland, some of whom risked death in frantic attempts to save "eleven God-given days" from being "forever lost."

Years, months and days have not been the only perverse units of time, however, for, curiously enough, the Roman hour (which survived until the mid-nineteenth century when Ponchielli, perhaps significantly, composed his "Dance of the Hours") was of flexible duration because its definition as a twelfth part of the sunrise-to-sunset day required it to stretch to about 75 modern minutes in June and to shrink to a mere 45 in December, varying also, of course, in different latitudes even on the same day.

Redefining the hour as a twenty-fourth part of the complete average day+night 360° of earthly rotation was the obvious solution and a big step toward reasonableness. But it left the hour still not exact enough for modern scientific purposes. Even though the earth's turning can now be clocked against remote stars to an error margin of less than one part in a quadrillion, a coarser uncertainty remains because terrestrial motion is itself by no means absolutely regular. In other words, the earth perceptibly speeds up and slows down like a live thing, probably mainly because of nutation (see page 424), the complex gravitational effects of sun and moon which are always influencing her equatorial bulge to sway a little farther northward or southward as they shift their declinations. And there must be a plethora of other slight tidal, magnetic, thermal, geodynamic and unknown influences. At any rate, it has been observed that the earth slowed down enough to lose about ²⁷⁄₁₀₀ of a second between the years 1680 and 1800.

During the nineteenth century, however, she picked up nearly $3\frac{1}{100}$ of a second, then mysteriously lost a tiny bit between 1900 and 1920, since when she has been gaining again. There are shorter variations in her pace from year to year, of course, and also the inevitable longer-range running down of her spinning energy (see page 49), due mostly to over-all tidal friction, meteorites and erosion — all of them together slowing her by a whopping ten seconds each million years!

And if these are not enough fine points to consider, don't forget that the earth's nearly elliptical orbit alternately fattens and slims its form to its own very slow rhythm, the orbit now growing more circular as we approach the millennium of A.D. 26,000, when it is due to describe its most nearly perfect circle before slumping back toward the old biased symmetry. Every factor relating to the earth's energy or mass, indeed, has its effect, be it ever so subtle, on her rates of rotation and revolution — every little earthquake, storm or other shift of material alters her balance just so much — the melting of Antarctic ice, the Mississippi River carrying silt toward the equator, a new building rising up to augment the friction of the winds . . .

In view of the ponderable total of all these eccentricities of earthly motion, a man-made watch can be considered in essence an instrument for accurately interpolating between astronomical observations. If well made, it may run continuously for a quarter of a century ticking five times a second, 432,000 times a day, without replacement of a single one of its 180-odd parts, the smallest of which looks like a speck of dust and is actually a polished screw so tiny that a million of them will barely fill a demitasse. Its accuracy under normal conditions is often rated to within one part in 50,000, and I know of a navigation watch tested for 405 days in World War II, including travel in ships, planes, trains and submarine, that proved accurate to one part in 400,000, which means its errors averaged scarcely ⅛ of a second per day.

Mechanical watches and clocks are only one kind of timepiece, however. They were preceded by hour glasses and water clocks accurate to about one part in a thousand. Modern electric clocks, on the other hand, are timed by the alternating current of a power station, which may in turn be stabilized by the natural vibration rate of quartz crystals accurate to one part in a billion.

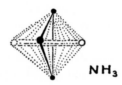

NH_3

The first atomic clock, built in 1948, reached farther into the microcosm by using the ammonia molecule (NH_3) as a timer, taking advantage of the fact that ammonia's single nitrogen atom naturally flips back and forth through its triangle of three hydrogens at a steady frequency of 23,870 megacycles a second. And newer atomic clocks use the lonely electrons in single hydrogen atoms, which vibrate between their two possible positions (page 261) with such imperturbability that, when amplified by the new *maser* resonance principle and applied directly to the regulation of a clock, they can stabilize its movement to one part in a quadrillion or an error of less than a second each thirty million years!

Such constancy, of course, is not only much greater than that of the turning earth. It is even greater than that of the "fixed"

stars of the constellation of Horologium (the clock), which, like other stars, are admittedly moving around on unknown courses among themselves. So atomic clocks are a lot more regular than they need to be just to interpolate our celestial time, their more important uses being measurement of vibrations and rotations in basic atomic research and checking such questions as whether the microcosm runs on the same time as the macrocosm.

In practice, the standard to which ordinary clocks are set in the western world is now called UT2, a new "uniform time" determined by the United States Naval Observatory, which reconciles it with the earth's uncertainty by "occasional step adjustments . . . on Wednesdays at 1900 UT (7 p.m.) . . . when necessary, of precisely plus or minus 20 millionths of a second." This is comparable to Bach's introducing his well-tempered or compromise musical scale in place of the ideal, but impractical, diatonic scale that preceded it (see page 396).

But where does it leave our standard second, which formerly was defined as $\frac{1}{86,400}$ of a mean solar day? There are means and means — but where is the mean of a well-tempered day? To settle this problem, a new standard second was recently set up by international authority and defined as $\frac{1}{31,556,925.974}$ of the tropical (equinox to equinox) year of 1900. Time reckoned in such 1900-style seconds is called "ephemeris time." Thus, you see, we have already got ourselves a few different and conflicting time rates, officially recognized — and all right down there on one planet.

Some physicists are currently in favor of defining a second solely in multiples of atomic frequencies, these being the most constant natural time intervals we know of — and never mind if the earth spends different numbers of atomic seconds going

through different astronomical centuries or its vernal equinox
starts sneaking toward April or February. The physicists indeed
are already using atomic wave lengths as their criterion of length
— since an international Conference on Weights and Measures,
meeting in Paris in October 1960, officially fixed the new standard
meter at 1,650,763.73 times the wave length of an orange spectral
line of krypton 86. So an atomic second, if also adopted as standard, would bring both space and time appropriately into the
same basic definition.

But there would be serious complications. Atomic vibrations
seem to have no vernal equinox, no reference point to set a
clock by. If our hydrogen clocks should somehow stop, where
would we set them after they got started again?

Also how could we check the constancy of light? That is no
minor consideration in science, and to define both space and time
in atomic vibrations is in effect like defining 186,282 miles as the
distance light travels in one second, and one second as the time
it takes light to go 186,282 miles. Under such a ruling, no matter
how fast or slow light ever got to be, the distance it would go
in a second would have to be 186,282 miles — no more, no less —
because of the definition. We actually have evidence that a new
ray of light starts off a little slower than full speed, warming up
to its constant pace of 186,282 m.p.s. (c) only after its initial
photons have in some mysterious fashion prepared or smoothed
the way for later ones. But measuring such velocity differences
would obviously be futile if our distance or time units should
stretch or shrink in the same ratio as the speed of light.

Yet, believe it or not, just such a ridiculous stretching and
shrinking of units — not merely by definition but in objective
reality — actually turned up near the end of the nineteenth century and so profoundly baffled physicists that it took a drastic
revolution, in the form of the theory of relativity, to clear the
mental air.

This was a scientific and philosophical cataclysm whose pressures had been secretly building for hundreds of years. It really started way back when physicists first began to wonder what is waving when a light wave "waves" through empty space. Sound, of course, had been pretty easy to visualize and diagnose as a vibration of molecules, and sound was found to travel faster in liquids than in gases, faster still in solids, for evidently the solider or more resilient the medium, the stronger its vibrations.

But light proved just the opposite. Its speed was found to be only three fourths as great in clear liquids (see page 422) and only two thirds as great in transparent solids as in air or a vacuum, ¾ and ⅔ being, you'll remember, the familiar harmonic ratios of the musical intervals of the fourth and fifth. And beyond these mysterious (perhaps coincidental) shades of Pythagoras lay the greater enigma of light traveling faster and faster through less and less, and fastest of all through an apparent nothing. If water waves wave water and sound waves wave air, what indeed could light waves wave as they speed from star to star?

Unable to believe that light radiates in absolutely nothing, scientists therefore postulated the seeming nothingness as actually a subtle somethingness. They called it *ether*, after the old Greek word for a supposedly similar ancient concept. Although intangible, invisible, presumably weightless and perhaps forever undetectable, the ether was assumed to fill the universe and to be present in all substances in greater or less degree. Nobody knew what it was, but the idea of it seemed so logical, even inevitable, that it quickly gained general acceptance as a basic material of creation. A preacher even "proved" its existence on the ground that it must be the reason for atoms gathering to make matter, since "where the carcass is, there will the eagles be gathered together." Maxwell's ensuing discovery that light is just one form of electromagnetic radiation, all of whose fields of force logically require a material structure, seemed to establish the ether more firmly than ever.

From here it was reasoned that, since the ether permeates all space and probably all things in space, at the same time binding all parts of the universe together, it must itself be integral and stationary — a sort of absolute frame of reference by which the motions of planets and stars might be judged. Did not the aberration of light, explained by Bradley in 1727 (see page 424), suggest just such a rigidity of space? Yet obviously, the astronomers could not expect to see the stars swimming through ether like goldfish through a bowl of stationary water, nor would a planet's speed be logically measurable by any sort of wind instrument of the airspeed-indicator type that shows motion in relation to a gas or matter. For an ether wind (not being made of liquid or gas or any tangible substance) must needs be an intangible wind and therefore it would have to be detected — if, indeed, detection were possible — by some much more subtle or abstract means.

This was a clear challenge to the ingenuity of nineteenth-century physicists, who very much wanted to know which bodies in the sky were really moving and, if so, how fast were they going and in what direction — and could there ever be, in a real sense, anything anywhere standing still?

One of the first attempts to measure the ether wind was made by astronomers who compared the refraction of light from a star when the earth was moving toward it with light from the same star six months later when the earth was moving away. In the first case, reasoned the astronomers, the eye is moving at about 18½ m.p.s. toward the light as the light at 186,282 m.p.s. approached its focal point in the telescope, while in the second case the eye is moving away at the same speed, and the 37 m.p.s. difference between +18½ m.p.s. and −18½ m.p.s. should make a noticeable difference in the nearness of the eye to the focal point. But no such shift in focal relations was ever detected.

The most plausible explanation offered for this failure at the time seemed to be Fresnel's old 1818 concept of the "ether drag," a theory that since ether is thicker in material bodies than in vacuous space, all objects tend to drag it along just as a ship drags

water, the resulting ether eddies canceling out much of the measurable flow of the ether wind close to the surface of the moving
object. To test this idea, a new experiment was clearly needed to
measure light's velocity in some fairly dense material that was itself moving in relation to the earth and presumably dragging its
own share of ether along with it. Such an experiment was performed by Fizeau in 1859 when he clocked light in both directions
(upstream and downstream) through swiftly moving water, demonstrating that a difference in the motion of the water definitely does
make a difference in the earthspeed of the light, a result regarded
as supporting the idea that ether is draggable.

But ether was by no means yet completely established, for what
evidence was there that the motion of water could not influence
light even without ether's help? Or, if ether clung to the earth,
how could aberration of light be explained? Clearly a much more
sensitive experiment would be needed to prove the ether beyond
any reasonable doubt, perhaps one in which the ether alone would
be measured with respect to light. And for this purpose the ailing
Maxwell, in the last year of his life, originated and proposed the
most crucial experiment of the century — in some ways the most
important test in all the history of science — an extremely delicate
optical analysis of light's velocity in different directions in relation
to the earth's motion through the postulated ether to see if some
sort of "ether wind" could be detected.

Although Maxwell died too soon to carry out the experiment, it
was actually performed two years afterward in 1881 by the American physicist Albert Abraham Michelson and again, with better
equipment and the help of Edward Williams Morley, in 1887.
On each occasion the velocity of light was timed both parallel
and perpendicular to the earth's orbital motion by an ingenious
arrangement of mirrors and light beams (see illustration), any
difference in the light speeds to be revealed by the very sensitive
interference pattern made by the two separated light beams upon
rejoining each other. On the principle that a swift river must
retard a swimmer's combined upstream and downstream speeds
more than his cross-current speed, a large difference in the light
speeds should show that the earth was moving rapidly through

the ether, a small difference that it was moving only slowly, the apparatus being delicate enough to record discrepancies at least as small as one mile a second. But on each occasion, to the consternation of the world of science, the result came out almost completely negative. There was no evidence at all of any ether flowing past the earth in any direction.

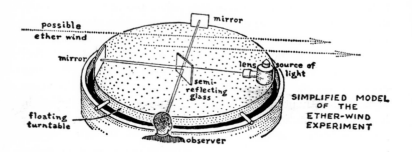

Michelson quite naturally interpreted this to mean that the local ether must be sticking fast to the earth, rotating and traveling along with it. If true, it would have been another vindication of Fresnel's "ether drag" hypothesis; such a rationalization, however, would still be up against the impasse of trying to reconcile itself to the long-established phenomenon of aberration of light, since any ether clinging to the earth would logically have to carry light with it (assuming light lives in ether), and there appeared no reason for such earthbound light to drift backward toward the earth's wake as aberrant light is always found to do.

Could the negative result, then, have meant that light in this case traveled not in ether at all but only in the stationary air, which hardly feels the earth's motion? Science emphatically said "no" — for although air has been found to have some effect on light transmission, light obviously does not require air as a medium for travel, nor is its velocity appreciably affected by it.

Yet something was certainly preventing the earth's motion through space from influencing the speed at which light strikes the earth. It seemed incredible that a velocity of 18½ miles a second in relation to the sun could not stir up the faintest whiff of ethereal breeze or other expectable effects of motion. It was like an airplane maintaining constant speed and direction over the ground regardless of all wind changes. There was little doubt about the fact, for many more "ether-wind" tests were made in succeeding years with new refinements in sensitivity — all to negative results.

In the first few years after the Michelson-Morley discovery, quite understandably, the whole thing seemed to most scientists to make no sense at all. It was only later that little by little some of the freer minds among them began to wonder whether the question answered by the experiment could really be the same question they had assumed had been asked of it. Come to think of it, now, perhaps they had been assuming too much. Should they have assumed that light is a wave motion in ether? Might they not better have been humble enough to ask the more elementary question: does light really move in waves, or in particles? Or in some other way?

Logically, if light is made of waves in ether, its speed of travel should be constant *relative to the ether*, while if it is made of particles shot from its source, its speed of travel should be constant *relative to the source*. Asked to choose between such alternatives, the Michelson-Morley experiment would definitely have had to pick the latter.

Yet there was something wrong with that answer also, for if light consists of particles, the particles shot out by two bodies moving at very different speeds would likewise naturally move at different speeds just as a bullet fired forward out of a jet plane goes at a different speed than a similar bullet fired from the ground. But astronomers well know that the light coming from the twin stars of a binary pair arrive on Earth at exactly the same speed regardless of which star is approaching and which receding or how great their disparity of motion. And the same with light from differently moving atoms in all stars. So starlight evidently disagrees with the particle concept of light.

The first explanation for the riddle that could withstand thoughtful criticism was pretty fantastic and with an Irish tang to it.

It was advanced rather quietly in the early 1890's by a professor named George Francis FitzGerald of Dublin. FitzGerald got to thinking about the flexibility of matter — of how a rubber ball is forced into a different shape upon hitting a wall or how a tethered balloon is distorted by the wind — and he saw no reason why the pressure of an ether wind might not also in some way distort matter, contracting it just a little in the direction of its motion through the ether. Anyhow, such a contraction in a single dimension could be made to explain the outcome of the Michelson-Morley experiment quite nicely and precisely: the arm of the apparatus moving against the ether (parallel to the direction of the ether wind) would be shortened (by ether pressure) just enough to compensate for the slowing down of light (by the same ether wind.) In other words, the shortening of the light's path along the arm would naturally and automatically be proportional to the slowing of the light during its round trip, since both effects stem from the same source (the ether), thus making all light slowed-by-1-percent travel all distances shortened-by-1-percent in the same old time and therefore nominally at the same old speed. Of course, the arm placed crosswise (perpendicular) to the ether wind would not be shortened as long as it held that position, since FitzGerald's contraction applies only to the direction of ether motion. Objects change shape, therefore, only

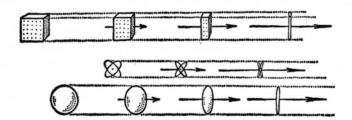

as they change ether orientation, cubes conforming to a rhomboidal foreshortening upwind-downwind, spheres becoming door-knob-shaped as their speed rises, all things always (no matter how they rotate) keeping their ether-shrunk dimension of motion parallel to the stream.

What could science make of this idea? Was it to be taken seriously? Or was it something dreamed up out of Alice in Wonderland, the recent best-selling fairy tale? Or just a bit of long-haired blarney?

Whatever it was, it certainly was ingeniously provided with a built-in booby-trap for the critics, because those who thought to disprove the reality of the contraction by measuring it soon realized that whatever footrules, eyes, lenses or other measuring devices they used would, according to the theory, contract along with everything else in the same dimension, thereby ensuring that each length of, say, 56.1 shrunken yards measured by a proportionately shrunken yardstick or retina would still number 56.1, revealing nothing as to whether there had, or had not, been any contraction.

More remarkable yet, FitzGerald's brash proposition was almost immediately up-graded toward respectability by the publication in 1893 of a similar but more complete theory by physicist Hendrik Antoon Lorentz in Amsterdam. Developed independently at about the same time as FitzGerald's, Lorentz's erudite hypothesis not only worked out the same one-dimensional contraction of moving matter in full mathematical detail (ratio of transformation $1 : \sqrt{1 - v^2/c^2}$, etc.) but explained exactly why it should happen in terms of the electric and magnetic fields inside molecules and atoms, even including distortions (from "spheres" to "ellipsoids") in the shapes of electrons, those still very mystical particles that had just been discovered by J. J. Thomson (see page 251) as kinds of negative beans in the positive soup of the atom. Electrical forces, pointed out Lorentz, are propagated like light, and "a moving electric charge should have a weakened field in the direction of its motion." For this reason, matter, which is held in shape by electrical forces between atoms, would naturally shrink in proportion to its velocity.

It was a theory, you may have noticed, based on old-fashioned absolute motion framed on a fixed empty space. Absolute motion was Newtonian motion, the common kind taken for granted in those days — albeit a motion that could, quite possibly, never be detected. Altogether the whole contraction idea was very peculiar, one cannot deny — yet temperature and pressure had long been known to contract matter, so why should not motion do it too? As no one arose to oppose the concept, it gradually came to be considered entirely plausible, even eventually to win a surprisingly general acceptance.

Only one man can I think of who definitely would not allow himself to swallow any such a contrived explanation — and that was a shy young patent clerk in Bern, Switzerland, who had been working up a few notions of his own on this and other aspects of science. But perhaps you may think such details of history not very important. So why bring this up? Who was this patent clerk anyhow?

His name — as the world was soon to find out — was Albert Einstein. He had been born to an ordinary Swabian family in Ulm, Bavaria, in 1879. Appropriately, perhaps mystically, like Newton's birth that came in the year of Galileo's death, Einstein's came precisely in the departure year of his great predecessor, Maxwell.

The sensitive little boy developed slowly, taking so long to learn to talk that his parents worried that he might be feeble-minded. At a Catholic elementary school in Munich he seldom could think of the "right" answer in class and was unceremoniously crossed off as an "odd duck" by most of the other boys, not to mention being sidelined as a "sissy" during sports. He hated playing soldier and cried when taken to see a military parade. He made few friends, impressed no teachers and seemed to care for nothing much but fooling around on the family piano, dreamily making up little chants or sentimental hymns of an afternoon which he would hum to himself next day on the way to school.

But he eventually grew to enjoy reading and one day, playing at navigation with a magnetic compass his father had given him, he discovered that (as he later put it) "something deeply hidden had to be behind things." His father, an unsuccessful manufacturer and salesman of the strange new electrical goods just coming onto the market, sometimes let him play with sample batteries and switches or hinted upon the secrets of mysterious-looking dynamos and transformers. His uncle, an engineer, also told him one day about "a funny science called algebra in which, if you go out hunting and hear some animal in the bushes but do not know what kind he is, you just call him X until he is discovered." Albert was intrigued. And, having no reputation to uphold, he did not mind asking all sorts of impulsive questions, even if they made him look foolish, for by nature and instinct he seems to have well understood the old Chinese saying: "He who asks a question is a fool for the moment. He who does not ask a question is a fool forever."

At twelve he got hold of a copy of Euclid's *Geometry* and puzzled over such mystic abstractions as the inevitable conjunction of the three altitudes of a triangle at a single point. It is remembered also that he was moody for days while pondering the Pythagorean theorem, of which, thirty years later, he was to recall, "It made me realize that man, by thought alone, can attain . . . order and purity." At thirteen he tackled Kant's *Critique of Pure Reason* and wondered what Kant meant about "space and time" being "forms of sense perception but not objective things." At about the same time, he discovered the rapture of playing Mozart sonatas on his violin.

But Albert was never happy in his gymnasium (high school) where he later remembered the teachers as being "like army lieutenants," always drilling with rigid formulas instead of whetting the students' appetites. At the age of sixty-seven in his autobiography he was to write that at this period he had indulged in "a positively fanatic orgy of free thinking coupled with the impression that youth is intentionally being deceived by the state through lies — a crushing impression. Suspicion against every kind of authority grew out of this experience — a skeptical attitude . . . which has never [entirely] left me." When his reaction to public education eventually caused one of the teachers to remark, "Your presence in the class destroys the respect of the students," he left the school and set off light-heartedly for Italy to join his bankrupt father, then trying to set up a shop in Milan.

He was enchanted with the carefree life of the Italians, the songs and jokes and gracefulness of villagers, and shortly renounced both his German citizenship and his legal membership in the Jewish religion. But neither in Milan nor in Pavia did his father's electrical shop succeed, so the young man increasingly felt the urgency of finding a profession.

Continuing to pursue the fundamentals of whatever and wherever his curiosity led him to, however, he did not bone up hard enough for his entrance exams to the highly rated Swiss Federal Polytechnic College in Zurich and flunked nearly every subject but mathematics. Although he managed to make the grade the following year, he remained rather indifferent to approved channels of thought and smiled indulgently over such unquestioned doctrine as that "in the beginning God created Newton's laws of motion." He seldom attended lectures but browsed freely in the library and daydreamed in the laboratory. Even after graduation as a physics major, he produced such a poor impression in the academic world that he was dismissed from three teaching jobs in succession and soon reduced to a hand-to-mouth existence. Nevertheless, he often found himself arguing far into the night about abstruse problems in logic with a quiet Serbian girl named Mileva Marec he had met in college and who, though studying to be a mathematician, was adventurous enough to accept his bashful and far-from-promising proposal of marriage.

The following year, with a baby son to support, young Albert tried harder for jobs in other fields — applying anywhere that some technical training might be of use — and counted himself lucky to land a berth processing patent applications in the Swiss capital. He had long been fascinated with new-fangled gadgets anyway, and here he was at the age of twenty-three, actually getting paid for examining and classifying them. Besides, his leisurely schedule allowed him a good many hours a day for browsing in the esoteric realms of space, time and energy — and almost every evening he could be seen wheeling a baby carriage along the street, halting now and then under a lamppost to jot down a row of mathematical symbols.

What was he thinking about in those days? It is hard to say, for Einstein himself not only could not remember afterwards but often admitted in later years that he found himself a poor source of information on the genesis of his own ideas. Even in his last important interview, only two weeks before he died at seventy-six, he insisted that "the worst person" to document any sequence of discovery is "the discoverer" himself. But we know that in Bern he must have meditated deeply upon the mysterious elusiveness of the "ether wind" and presumably explored ways its absence might be explained. Although he was later to become a close personal friend of Hendrik Lorentz, who "meant more than all the others I have met on my life's journey," at this stage Einstein had neither met Lorentz nor read any Lorentzian work more recent than his paper of 1895.

Instead, Einstein evidently was engrossed in his independent research, which was as much philosophical as scientific, wracking his brains to grasp what nature could possibly be trying to say through making the speed of light the same for all viewers regardless of motion. At one point, he told a colleague in the patent office that he did not think he could keep up such a hopeless search much longer. Yet somehow his innate faith in "the rationality of the universe" kept him going, and he never quite quit. Years later, reminiscing about his youthful quest, he spoke emotionally of "this huge world that exists independently of us human beings . . . that stands before us like a great, eternal riddle" — the "contemplation" of which perpetually "beckoned like a liberation."

The main difference between Einstein's thinking and the thinking of Lorentz and other scientists of the day seems to have been that Einstein instinctively hungered harder for the fundamentals of things, for the large view, the broad perspective, the simpler hypothesis. So deeply did he yearn for basic truth, in fact, that he resisted the corrosion of prejudice more successfully than anyone else and overcame the strong human temptation to take things for granted, to assume something true because everybody "knows" it to be true.

When all available evidence and logical reasoning forced him to conclude that "motion is never observable as 'motion with respect to space'" despite Newton's common-sense laws of motion based on long-accepted absolute space, he firmly decided that, having "no basis for the introduction of the concept of absolute motion," one no longer has the right to believe in "absolute motion."

It was an epic resolution of independent mind and spirit, an act of rare integrity born out of the inscrutable detachment of genius that Einstein himself would one day describe as a "solitude ... painful in youth, but delicious in the years of maturity."

But it was only a beginning — for to renounce absolute motion was one thing. To replace it with some truer breed of motion was another. And how to make a new motion stick in the face of such tests as Newton's famous "absolute-space" experiment: his hanging of a bucket of water upon a twisted rope so that, as it spun around and around, the water's rotating concave surface (pressed outward by centrifugal force) showed that "absolute space, in its own nature, without relation to anything external, remains always similar and immovable"?

Almost from the first, young Einstein, meditating over his baby carriage, was instinctively drawn to the idea of relativity — the concept that the only possible motion is relative motion. But it seemed elusively nebulous in the beginning. "Relative motion" —

relative to what? Would two or twelve or seventy thousand relative motions be relative only to each other without any fixed standard to judge them by — without anything anywhere really at rest in a frameless world? How disconcerting! And who would ever accept such a theory?

Einstein had not yet worked up much appetite for history but he must have been aware from reading Kant and other great thinkers that relativity was not a new concept. In point of fact, relativity had been a principle in mechanics for a long time. And was it not Heracleitos of Ephesos who opined that "the way up and the way down is one and the same"? And Empedocles who, pointing to the setting sun, remarked, "The sun does not really set. It is the earth that brings night by coming before the light"?

Even if such observations seem to some readers today as little more than witticisms, in the fifth century B.C. they were great leaps forward in human imagination. And some of the later Greeks, notably Zeno, maintained that, contrary to the fluid feeling it gives us, time is not liquid or continuous but, like a piece of wood, has a durable structure or grain. Zeno would have been heartened if he could have seen a modern watch, especially under a microscope to show that its hands do not move steadily but in tiny unavoidable jumps. And the quantum theory could hardly have failed to be congenial to him. In China also, at about Zeno's period, a Taoist logician is quoted as having said, "There are times when a flying arrow is neither in motion nor at rest."

Are such quantum thoughts anything less than probes toward relativity? By the end of the Middle Ages relativity ideas could be expressed more convincingly by Nicholas of Cusa, greatest philosopher and scientist of the early fifteenth century, who not only ventured to suggest that "all religions are essentially one" but introduced the "cosmological principle" of spherical symmetry in space with the argument that wherever in the heavens anyone may be placed, it naturally appears to him that he is in the center of the universe. Galileo brought the idea closer to home by pointing out that "uniform motion in a straight line has no discoverable effects," while Newton ruled that "the motions of bodies included in a given space [such as a ship's cabin] are the same among themselves, whether that space is at rest or moves uniformly . . . in a straight line."

Other thinkers echoed the relativity concept, from Leibniz's concession that "there is no real motion" through Huygens, Berkeley and Kant to Maxwell's balanced summary that "all our knowledge, both of time and space, is essentially relative." Such consistent conclusions could hardly have arisen from disconnected, subjective fancies but obviously reflected, instead, objective observations of nature over a long period of history. Certainly Einstein himself understood this by the time he modestly declared in 1921 that his theory of relativity "is not speculative in origin" but "owes its invention entirely to the desire to make physical theory fit observed fact as well as possible" — that "we have here no revolutionary act but the natural continuation of a line that can be traced through centuries."

Accordingly, it was almost inescapable that Einstein would have to begin where Maxwell left off. And, as Maxwell's greatest work was in the field of electromagnetism, quite understandably the very earliest example of relativity published by Einstein was not mechanical but electromagnetic. It appeared on the first page of his famous paper of 1905, *On the Electrodynamics of Moving Bodies*, and described "the reciprocal electrodynamic action of a magnet and a conductor."

Einstein had noticed that an electrically charged body (say, a piece of amber freshly rubbed with wool) was generally considered in a static condition as long as it remained "stationary." That is, when not moving in relation to the earth or some other sizable frame of reference, it merely retained a charge of "static electric-

ALBERT
EINSTEIN
1905

ity" (surplus electrons) without any current flowing. But if it were noticeably moving, the included motion of its electrons could be considered a flow of electricity and would, by virtue of its motion, create a magnetic field. Thus, as Einstein observed, there was a presumed "sharp distinction" between the conditions of rest and motion. Yet he realized — in what is said to have been his first clear conception of relativity — that if a man walks past a "stationary" piece of charged amber, the amber is given a relative motion in respect to the man and therefore acquires an electric current with a surrounding magnetic field *from the man's point of view.* In other words, electricity and magnetism are essentially relative along with their fields, and a magnet may be a magnet for one observer but not for another (see page 353), or a conductor may carry almost any strength of current, or none, depending solely on how you look at it.

Of course, this does not mean that such electrodynamic phenomena are imaginary or merely mental effects, for the man walking past a piece of amber may not sense its excess of electrons or be aware that it is amber or even that it exists. Its existence is really beyond and in spite of him. Which is to say that electrodynamics is, in a sense, an objective concept, yet it is also essentially relative and has a subjective aspect in that it changes according to the

motion of whatever frame of reference it is observed from or compared with — in the same way that heat is a kind of statistical
relative motion of molecules (see page 266) or the motion of
a rocket in space is measurable relative to the moon, earth, sun or
whatever you choose.

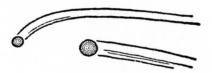

And this electromagnetic relativity was also separately suggested
by a kind of ether-wind experiment in its own realm conducted
after the Michelson-Morley experiment and known as the Trou-
ton-Noble experiment. The apparatus here consisted of a strongly
charged condenser delicately suspended so it could turn freely
and easily with any magnetic field on the presumption that it
might align itself perpendicularly to the earth's course through
the ether. Yet it showed no such tendency in the slightest degree,
a negative result that only added to the death knell of the
already discredited *absolute* motion.

So Einstein was confirmed in his conclusion "that the phenomena of electrodynamics, as well as of mechanics, possess no
properties corresponding to the idea of absolute rest." The only
kind of rest or motion anywhere in the world, then, simply had to
be *relative* rest or *relative* motion — rest and motion being, in
this new sense, exactly the same thing from different viewpoints
— and this as true in the microcosm as in the macrocosm, a universal law reaching from inside the atom to beyond the Milky
Way: Einstein's great discovery that he introduced quite characteristically as "this conjecture, the purport of which will hereafter
be called the Principle of Relativity."

It would have been a simple enough idea, too, once you got
used to it, except that it did not seem to be consistent with the
stubborn factual evidence of the constancy of light. For if all
motion is relative and anything can be considered at rest from some
frame of reference, why is light's speed through space fixed at 186,-

282 miles a second in relation to every body? Why cannot light be at rest relative to something? Or why cannot its speed be reduced at least from 186,282 miles a second to 186,272 miles a second as measured from a rocket moving along "with" it at 10 miles a second?

The queer constancy of c at 186,282 m.p.s., no matter what, appeared to Einstein as probably associated with the very meaning of speed. And, as speed is the quotient of space and time (25 m.p.h. = 100 miles $\div$ 4 hours), so might the essence of space and time be at the bottom of the mystery.

But what is the essence of space? Of time? How does one go about finding out such things in a relative world where nature has the viewpoint of no one in particular? Young Albert wasn't sure he knew, but he was curious and eager and he decided he would have a good go at it anyhow.

First of all, he determined to reject as much prejudice as possible from his thinking about space and time, including all ordinary common-sense and obvious mathematical assumptions like Euclid's famous axiom that "a straight line is the shortest distance between two points" or that a man walking at the rate of 2 miles an hour downstream upon a barge drifting 2 miles an hour down a river must be moving at 4 miles an hour in relation to the earth.

"Who can judge what is really a straight line?" he asked himself. "And who can say just when or where 2 and 2 will make 4?"

Almost any dimension is mysterious when you get right down to it, he reflected — even plain, old-fashioned miles on a map. What does distance really mean? How long, for example, is the west coast of Europe from Gibraltar to the North Cape? A good first guess might be four thousand miles — and that would be quite correct as measured on a small map by leaving out the Baltic Sea and making judicious short cuts over most fiords and river mouths. But five or six thousand would do just as well, merely by using a more detailed map and zigzagging in and out of more bays and inlets. Eight or ten thousand miles could easily be covered by choosing local maps of the coasts, twenty thousand by including sand bars and some of the larger rocks, a hundred thousand by tossing in individual stones with or without barnacles according to need, even millions or billions of miles by descending to grains of sand, and then on down to molecules or atoms. Thus, one must admit, distance is quite a flexible dimension and a material coastline can be of almost any length one chooses — without deviating an iota from reason or reality.

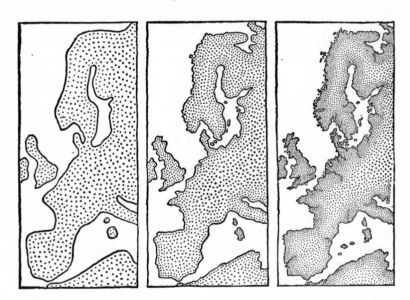

Time, likewise, seems to be a flexible dimension and closely associated with space. For, as clocks in Berlin tell time that is an hour "later" than in London, so do every fifteen degrees of earthly longitude equal an hour of earthly time. And just as minutes and seconds of longitude (which are angles) grow shorter (in miles) toward the pole, why may not minutes and seconds of time shrink proportionately from some correspondingly changing point of view?

Groping for a brainhold in the midst of such hard-to-visualize abstractions, Einstein found that the language of mathematics was much better than German, English or French for expressing and evaluating the concepts. And in working out his own solution to the Michelson-Morley discovery of the non-absoluteness of motion and rest, what should he come up with but the identical, the inevitable, formula of Lorentz: that the dimension of motion of any moving object must be "shortened in the ratio $1 : \sqrt{1 - v^2/c^2}$"! It was the only answer that would agree with the experimental results. Yet Einstein could not be content in attributing such a contraction to anything so limited as electrodynamic transformation in the atom, to the mere distortion of electrons' shapes and orbits. Rather must there be a more general explanation somewhere deep in the nature of relative motion — of shifting many-angled space and time. But where? How?

Perhaps the young father looked at the lampposts and people and houses along the street beyond his baby carriage and began to wonder if their apparent diminution in size with distance could be in any sense akin to the evident diminution of all matter in motion. He may have asked himself, if the shrinkage of distance is only an illusion, why should not the shrinkage of motion also be an illusion? Is one more real than the other? The dwarfing of a lamppost by distance can be precisely measured by its subtended angles, the area it presents to the eye being invariably proportional to the inverse square of the distance. If such an optical transformation of a lamppost, drastically obvious from the first glance, is illusory — how much more illusory must be the negligible shrinkage of an object in motion, such a diminution being normally too slight for any known technique of measurement, so slight in fact that the shrinkage of the whole earth's diameter at its solar velocity of 18½ miles a second totals scarcely 2½ inches!

It is quite possible that Einstein was fully conscious of the affront to common sense in such a comparison of the abstruse theoretical transformation due to motion and the patently illusory shrinkage of things receding into the distance, the latter a phenomenon every toddling child soon discovers does not *really* happen. But Einstein's nature just could not take things for granted, even though he saw how much easier it is to believe an error one has heard a hundred times than a truth one has never heard before. So he stubbornly determined not to let himself be taken in by any denials of people in the distance that their bodies had grown smaller than nearer people, not even if they pulled out tape measures to "prove" their bigness — for he just knew that the tape measures had shrunk along with the people. In a few cases he had even seen people go so far away that they became almost infinitely tiny — so tiny that they literally vanished from sight. What size *really* were these people? And how could they possibly protest any judgment made about them?

In a sense, Einstein might be said to have retained something of the direct simplicity of a child in his mental processes — for, like the little boy on his first airplane ride who asked, "Mama, when do we begin to get smaller?" he could accept the diminution of distance as having its own kind of legitimate reality. He could re-examine this so-called illusion and test it in the light of what no one considered an illusion and find the two essentially of a kind.

Einstein later personally inquired into the question of where or when a growing child acquires his concepts of space and time, and at least one psychologist, a Swiss named Jean Piaget, responded by demonstrating that a baby's first idea of space is "centered on his own body and on the location of successful actions." At this stage the baby has developed no clear sense of time or sequence, nor does any object have much continuity to him. When a six-month-old reached for Piaget's watch, for instance, Piaget flung a handkerchief over it, whereupon the infant withdrew his hand as though the watch had been taken away. Then a year-old baby, who had learned to look under the handkerchief for the watch, easily found it but, after seeing the watch subsequently placed in a box across the room, looked for it again under the handkerchief and was astonished that it was not there.

"The baby believes in an object as long as he can localize it," explained Piaget, "and ceases to believe in it when he can no longer do so." This attitude is amazingly similar to that of the modern sophisticated physicist who will accept a meson or a neutrino as real only when it is proved to occupy a known localized position.

Correspondingly, a baby's first conception of velocity appears to be based not on any comprehension of distance or time nor on the relation between them, but rather on the more primitive awareness of order or priority. To his newly budded brain, the object that arrives first is the faster, regardless of where or when it started. Nor does continuous travel necessarily carry the child mentally ahead on the map, as was dramatically expressed by the tired four-year-old who entered his third identical superhighway restaurant in one day, protesting, "Gee, Pop, we've been going all morning and all afternoon — and here we are again."

Even an old woman can retain enough naïveté, under some conditions, to fail to comprehend the simplest modern locomotion. This happened quite strikingly when the mother of Tenzing, the Sherpa who surmounted Mount Everest, was given her first train ride, from Jaynagar to Darjeeling, at the age of eighty-four. A few minutes after the train started, she suddenly asked her son in alarm, "Tenzing, where is that tree I saw in front of the window by the station?" After Tenzing laughingly explained to her what a train is, she sighed with relief, saying, "Never in all my life have I seen a whole house moving like this from place to place."

More common, however, is our normal confusion as to which thing is *really* moving when two things are seen changing their relative positions. "Is that other train starting to move now?" "Or is it us?" Looking down from a bridge at one's reflection in

a gentle brook, it is easy to get the impression that the water is standing still while you yourself are drifting through it. And the same holds for the moon sailing between thin clouds or a high tower toppling against the mist. The optical rule is that when a smaller object moves in relation to larger or surrounding things, no matter which is actually moving or which standing still relative to the observer, the smaller or enclosed object is what normally *appears* to be moving while its enveloping "frame" seems absolutely stationary.

Although this fact was established in a long series of visual tests by one J. F. Brown at the University of Berlin only in 1927, about a quarter of a century after the dawn of relativity theory, it sheds significant light on man's traditional notion of fixed space, accounting substantially also for the almost universal acceptance of Newton's postulate of the absolute — an assumption that Newton evidently made for practical reasons without much expectation that it could ever rigorously be proved true, but an assumption which nevertheless was in exact accord with a very general human illusion.

The persistence of such an illusion of the absolute through the era of railroad building last century obviously explains the apprehension many people expressed then that, even if passengers inside the new "steam cars" could be shielded from wind pressure, the mere fact that they would be moving at 30, or perhaps even 40 or 50, miles an hour might prove too much of a strain for the human constitution to withstand. Motion in relation to the earth's surface, in other words, was unthinkingly assumed to be absolute motion without regard for any other motions the earth itself or its part of the universe might be involved in. Where, indeed, were any astronomers or philosophers with perspective enough to point out that two blinks of a human eye, blinked one second apart, may be separated by something else than a second or by something other than time? For it was not yet realized that space too is inevitably involved in eye blinks. In fact, space is involved in all physical events to whatever degree any viewpoint may require. From the viewpoint of our moon, for instance, the earth's populated surface is spinning at about a quarter of a mile a second, so that two blinks of an average human eye would occur not just a second apart but literally a quarter of a mile apart. From the sun's view, the much higher orbital velocity of the revolving earth would stretch the length between blinks to about 18½ miles. While the views of remote stars, necessarily involving the sun's motion in relation to their own, could separate the blinks by hundreds of miles or, if far beyond our galaxy, by many thousands. Indeed, one might reasonably speculate that, from the extreme viewpoint of the opposite side of the universe (if the universe has sides), any second of time separating two earthly eye blinks could be literally transformed into 186,282 miles.

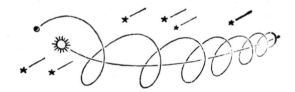

You may call this fantastic. It *is* fantastic from a common-sense earthly view, of course. But Einstein, pushing his hungry baby through the streets of Bern, could not afford to limit himself to common sense or even an earthly view. When a man explores such abstractions as space, time and the speed of light, it would hardly seem appropriate for him to confine his thoughts to any single star or planet. Besides, the very word *fantastic* in such a context could well be expected to unfurl a new dimension of its own meaning.

So Einstein let his thoughts soar freely into both space and time, disciplined only by the most universal and abstract logic. Ele-

phants were no longer "large" to him. Ants no longer "small." For that would have been looking at them through provincial human eyes, as if a mere man had a right to set an absolute standard of size. Instead, Einstein looked out of the sun and saw that elephants could be tinier than germs. And he looked out of the atom and saw that an ant could spread across the sky like a Milky Way! He taught himself that human words like *long, near, bright, hot, soft, loud, strong, soon* are all relative and therefore meaningless unless you assume some standard viewpoint, which need not be a human viewpoint. The same lamp that is *bright* by night is *dim* by day. The same full moon that now rises in the east before my right shoulder at 6 o'clock in the evening is setting simultaneously in the west behind your left shoulder at 6 in the morning on the other side of the earth. Neither space nor time, therefore, has any fixed absolute meaning, and Newton's "absolute, true and mathematical time" is just as outdated as his "absolute space."

Of course, you can point out that the different times of morning and evening on opposite sides of the earth are really different aspects of one time system and easily transposable from time zone to time zone, from longitude to longitude, angle to angle. And you can calculate that the exploding star we see now on Earth is not really still exploding *now* from its own viewpoint, since it has taken the light of the explosion more than a century to travel from the star to us. Yet the transposition of times and spaces is not nearly so simple as it first appears — for there is always the question of the relative motions of the two bodies. Where was the star, when a particular photon departed from it, in relation to the earth at the moment the same photon arrived? Such an interval, you must realize, is not simple. It is not just a distance. Nor is it just a period of time. Rather it is a compound containing factors of both space and time. It is what normally separates two *events* as distinct from two *places* or two *instants*. On the universal scale, neither places nor instants turn out to have meaning in themselves but only when combined into events. Thus there is really no such time as *now* except in some place. And there is really no such place as *here* except at some time.

Nebraska as a place, for example, means something to people now because the *now* makes it more than a place. It makes it an event. But if you throw away all ties with time, Nebraska evaporates into nothing. Where were the rocks and soil of Nebraska a couple of billion years ago? They certainly did not compose any river and hill skeleton we could recognize as Nebraska, and most of their elements must have been spread about the earth in liquid or gaseous form as parts of the primordial seas or steaming swamps or lava flows of that hardly imaginable period. Many of Nebraska's present atoms indeed had not then even arrived from the sun or from the space clouds that feed it. So Nebraska, in the cosmic view, has to be a time as well as a place if it is to mean anything. Strictly speaking, it is an *event* in earthly history.

That is part of why increasing remoteness from the *here* and the *now* add unsuspected distortions that dawned on Einstein only in irregular spasms, that led him to realize that neither space nor time alone is as universal, fundamental or constant as it seems — that, in fact, as the world must increasingly realize, space and time are only aspects of things. They are abstract points of view — dimensions of events — and, although related in subtle ways that are almost always taken too much for granted, each establishment of space or time is literally a separate function — an aspect that cannot be assumed to be part of the same system as any other space or time establishment.

Einstein indeed seems to have been the first human being ever to suspect that simultaneity between two events is a provincial illusion. Pointing to the significance of simultaneity in his 1905 paper, he wrote, "We have to take into account that all our judgments in which time plays a part are always judgments of *simultaneous events*. If, for instance, I say, 'That train arrives here at 7 o'clock,' I mean something like this: 'The pointing of the small hand of my watch to 7 and the arrival of the train are simultaneous events.' "

He admitted that observing such simultaneity was a reasonably accurate way for a person holding a watch to tell the time of an event happening next to the watch, but insisted that, on principle, the method could not be relied on for timing events far away from the watch, especially by someone moving in relation to the other things involved. The question, of course, has little to do with visibility or lack of visibility of the watch, which can be of any size from a vibrating atom to a whirling galaxy, but rather hinges on the relative nature of simultaneity itself — simultaneity being no more absolute than motion or fixity in space since, as Einstein noted, two events that are exactly simultaneous in one frame of reference may literally be far from simultaneous as envisaged from a differently moving standpoint.

COLLISION OF TWO OBJECTS

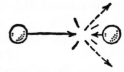
THE SAME COLLISION SEEN BY A MOVING OBSERVER

COLLISION RELATIVITY

THE SAME COLLISION SEEN BY A FASTER MOVING OBSERVER

I do not think there is any better illustration of this elusive truth than the story of the astronomically long freight train, traveling at celestial speed, which was suddenly struck by lightning at both ends. Although the damage proved slight, somehow a troublesome argument arose as to whether the two hits had been made "simultaneously" or not. First a reputable scientist, riding at the exact middle of the train, swore he had recorded the light of both bolts of lightning (with aid of mirrors) exactly simultaneously. Then an equally reliable observer, who had been standing on the ground at the exact mid-point between the strikes, proved he had recorded the flash from the rear of the train a sizable fraction of a second earlier than the forward flash reached him.

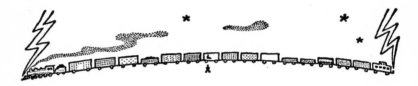

Most earthbound persons, if asked to settle such an issue, probably would incline to the view of the observer standing on earth who insisted the two lightning strikes could not possibly be simultaneous, their "simultaneity" as seen by the train witness being only apparent, not real, since the train had carried him closer to the forward flash by the time he received their "simultaneous" light from points that were (by then) no longer equidistant from him. However, as those who can accept the broader-minded relativity of motion will realize, it may be just as true to say that the train was standing still and the ground speeding by it as vice versa — so that the ground observer could have been "carried" beyond the equidistant point as easily as could the train observer. From Einstein's celestial view, in fact, the lightning flashes (along with their mid-point) are free to be considered an integral part of the train, or a part of the solid earth, or of any other frame of reference. Every observer may choose his own viewpoint. Was the observer on the train really moving toward the *place* the lightning had struck at the front of the train? Can you decide whether, after the lightning strike ended, its *place* of striking (the source point of its light) moved along with the train or stayed with the earth or, more reasonably, disintegrated into both these subjective components? Where, after all, can any *place* be if it is not where someone thinks it to be? Any viewpoint is true and right. No view is wrong.

Hard as it is to "get" such relative simultaneity through one's head, one somehow just has to take off from the accustomed runways of one's mind and fly one's imagination into the problem if one wants to understand relativity. For simultaneity is one of the first keys to the space-time relationship and a prime clue to the hidden subjective nature of these elusive abstractions that compose it. Just stop and figure it out now: if the answer to the question of whether lightning strikes the train twice at the same time or twice at two different times truly depends on whether the lightning is regarded as part of the earth world or as part of the train world, then simultaneity must be relative. And if simultaneity — a coincidence in time, involving space — is relative, obviously time and space are relative too. If this is true, it indicates that time and space have a deceptively subjective character — that somehow they flow and wimple and warp individually, fast or slow, this way or that, according to whether they are associated with a train or the earth — or something else. They are sensations of dimensions, indelibly but subtly related to your frame of motion or nonmotion, consider it which you wish. They are aspects of things, like angles of view or lampposts in Bern that you can make grow or shrink to any desired size merely by walking toward or away from them. Come to think of it, they are remarkably like Lorentz's collapsable atoms that are squeezed in line of motion by the "ether wind."

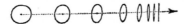

This very thought — or something closely comparable — when it flashed upon young Einstein in Bern surely must have given him a moment of profound exaltation, for he saw then that it could explain the Michelson-Morley mystery of "where is the ether wind"? — sounding the final knell of absolute space and time. This it may have been that he referred to half a century later when he explained to an eager young student in Princeton, New Jersey, "The mind can proceed only so far upon what it knows and can prove. There comes a point where the mind takes a leap — call it intuition or what you will — and comes out upon a higher plane of knowledge."

At any rate, Einstein suddenly realized that the formula of transformation dictated by the ether-wind experiment $(1 : \sqrt{1 - v^2/c^2})$ applies not just to the shape of matter or to the orbits of electrons but to the very nature of the space and time that enclose them. What did this mean? It meant that motion must have a shrinking effect not only upon moving objects but upon all the space involved in their motion — and upon all the time involved also. In other words, it was a very drastic and fundamental effect of motion.

But how could time shrink? Could it literally contract in speed of flow proportional to its relative motion — motion relative to any observer — just as space evidently could contract in line of motion? This was an eerie, unsettling idea, of course. But it added up mathematically. Its logic clicked. And it explained the case of the train struck by lightning as well as it cleared up the ether doldrum. It meant not only that a yardstick moving lengthwise must be shorter than a stationary yardstick but that a moving clock must run slow as compared with a stationary clock. If anybody should ask, "Stationary in relation to what?" the answer would be, "In relation to ANY thing or ANY observer — it makes no difference what." In a way, then, it was an illusory effect, Einstein realized, a kind of new perspective on time-space, yet as real as most fundamental things in this world, including matter itself. Certainly it was just as real as the lampposts he could see shrinking into the distance before his very eyes.

Let us try to *get* this relativity idea now — as straight and simple as it is possible to get it. It is really not so frightful once you catch on. It doesn't demand any mathematics, even though mathematics helps to prove it. It is elementary. If anything, *too* elementary. All you need is enough imagination to shake free from the earth and from your old notions about what is standing still and what is moving, from your comfortable assumptions that clock motion or the passing days or years are in any way inevitable.

The main thing to *get* is that somehow motion transforms things: it foreshortens their lengths and slows down their tempos. The foreshortening was dramatically revealed by the Michelson-Morley experiment last century, while the slowing down was directly proved in 1936 by H. E. Ives of the Bell Telephone Laboratories, who found that the very steady vibration frequencies of hydrogen atoms are invariably retarded by their speed in exact accordance with Einstein's equations. But this still adds up to be an illusory and relative effect, not something absolute that can be pinned down once and for all, no matter what. I mean that there is a kind of uncertainty principle about motion itself, and that no one can really decide what is moving and what (if anything) is not — so that there is deep doubt also about what is transformed and what (if anything) is not. In other words, while one yardstick is foreshortened by its motion relative to another, the other must also be foreshortened by its motion relative to the first, making them each symmetrically shorter than the other from the other's viewpoint. Which is like two men walking away from each other until each appears smaller to the other than to himself.

Something similar occurs in the time transformation: each of two relatively moving clocks running slower to the other than to itself. Which again is like two men walking so far apart that the legs of each appear slower in the other man's eyes than in his own.

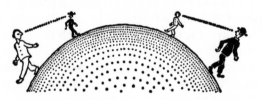

Thus the whole Lorentz transformation of motion can be exemplified by two rather arrogant men striding past each other, each of whom disdains the other as "smaller and slower" than *he* is. And this curious, symmetric relativity quite simply and logically solves the riddle of the missing ether wind. It solves it not only more fundamentally but more satisfactorily and much more elegantly than either FitzGerald or Lorentz could solve it. According to some of the more sensitive commentators, even the mathematics of it is beautiful, relatively speaking, and quite convincing — if you can be convinced by mathematics — in the way of showing you how the shortening and slowing effects of the earth's orbital motion, in relation to her other motion, exactly equate with Michelson's two perpendicular beams of light.

Even the queer constancy of the speed of light is clarified by the fluidity of relative time and space, for the constant c, of course, is not an *absolute* but a *relative* constant, being defined in miles and seconds that themselves must vary with relative motion. If a light flash, for instance, is sent out from a place where two men are passing each other, every point on its spherical wave will have advanced 186,282 miles from *each* man after a second by *his* watch even though the men are no longer together — this "miracle" of equidistance being possible because of the individual transformations of the miles and seconds of each man, which are functions of his relative motion. It is not, therefore, the fact that it is *light* that gives light its miles-per-second constancy to all observers. It is only the fact that its velocity is the *highest relative velocity of the transmission of influence in the material universe.* For if sound (or smell or touch) could travel 186,282 miles a second, its effects would presumably also reach each recipient at that same constant speed regardless of which way, or how fast, he was going. Indeed, not alone light, but electricity, heat, radio, x-ray and gamma waves all move at 186,282 miles a second because this is "the ratio of the electromagnetic to the electrostatic unit of electricity" — this is the relative speed at which the transformations of motion reach their natural limit — at which the contraction of space and slowing of time attain to zero — at which the increase of mass (another motion effect I must mention) reaches infinity. When space has thus (relatively) shrunk to nothing, when time has ceased to flow, and when mass has exploded to infinity, how can speed be further increased? Obviously, if you admit those limitations, there can be nowhere left to go nor time to go there in — quite aside from the nebulous question of whether any infinite force could ever have the motivation or capacity to accelerate any infinite mass. Indeed, without the very coordinates of speed (space and time), what in the world could any additional speed be made of?

And as for the increase of mass with motion, like the shrinkage of space and slowing of time, it has been amply proved by experiment, even before Einstein explained it — proved in the astonishing massiveness of the fastest (about .8 c) electrons emitted by newly discovered radium and uranium at the turn of the century. This mass increase means, in essence, that energy from the motion has been added, since mass and energy have turned out to be as much two aspects of one quantity as parallax and distance are two ways of describing the range of a star. Of such did Einstein abstract his $E = mc^2$.

2 + 2 = X

It is all pretty logical, you see — even if highly unearthly or, shall we say, a trifle uncanny. And it is decidedly explicable in the HOW sense, though perhaps you'd better not ask WHY. The WHYs of the most fundamental questions, as I've said before, are not satisfactorily answerable in this phase of life. Things work certain ways, according to the laws of nature as we find nature — just because things are the way they are or were the way they were. . . . What more may one say? Is there a "now" that is not "here"? Or were the Puri metaphysicians right in assuming that things farther away in space must also be farther away in time?

Concepts that are way down deep under our thoughts must be accepted almost blindly, it seems, like an axiom, on intuition or faith: a straight line that is the shortest distance between two points, the combining of 2 and 2 to make 4, or the objective reality of matter — things you feel in your bones, including even your skull bone, and which (if bones may be trusted) are true. Axioms, of course, cannot be proved. If they could, they would be theorems, not axioms. But that should not bother anyone, since axioms are deeper than theorems or thought, being made essentially of heart, not mind — of basic feeling, the very bed-rock of reason.

This at least is a way of saying that relativity is not logically so hard to understand, but that you must build its logic upon the right axioms if you want it to add up to something credible. You must somehow attain a certain minimum breadth of perspective as a foundation, which you cannot possibly do on reason alone. Rather, you must let yourself be swept off your mental feet, so to speak, in a kind of faith. For what is the use of learning the logical steps of relativity if you are not persuaded that relativity exists? In a word, the least of your problem is to *understand* relativity. The most is to *believe* it!

It may help here to reflect on the evolution of your own personal beliefs about the nature of the world. You can hardly be expected to recall much of how your intuition grew and changed as you discovered your environment — but surely your intuition *did* change. As a baby looking out from your crib, your life was almost timeless. You could not notice motion on the clock. Mother was just Mother. You had never seen her younger nor had you any reason to imagine her older. Neither had space ac-quired much meaning until you realized one day that things getting bigger were things coming nearer. You did not yet distinguish right from left except that the wall on one side al-ways had a window and the wall on the other a door. If you had had more capacity for generalizing, you might have assumed that right walls had windows and left walls doors.

Later, when you grew big enough to crawl around and notice new angles, you suddenly got a fresh intuition: the walls with windows were sometimes on one side of you, sometimes on the other. Like magic, right walls turned into left walls and you could make them do it. Little by little, this became easy. Then, some-time long later, you learned that a more reliable way to explain a right wall is to call it an east wall. The idea of compass directions in fact endowed you with an exciting new intuition that reached out all the way to the horizons.

At this phase, more than likely, your world was still flat. East was toward that hill over there and west was down that road, both directions continuing straight on as far as you could see. Up was up and down was down — unchangingly, inexorably, absolutely.

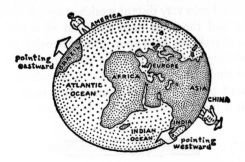

So it was a day of some shock and surprise when you finally caught on to the earth's being really a ball — which meant that "up" to you is the same way as "down" to a Chinese, and that "east" in Brazil points straight "west" in India. In fact, if you had lived in New York and had been given a thirtieth-century subterranean telescope that would let you look through the earth at Moscow, you might not have believed your eyes when you saw the Kremlin standing "horizontally" out of the "wall" of Europe as you gazed "upward" at it from "below."

The modern round-world concept in intuition, we must realize, was not only very little understood on Earth before the days of Magellan, but has taken centuries getting established since then, being still by no means accepted without question among all peoples. You see, it takes a lot of conscious effort to acquire such an intuition, particularly as the older, simpler intuition of a flat earth has not been finally disproved as wrong. When you come right down to it, the earth *is* flat — at least for a little way around you on the average. That's just as obvious as absolute space and time — which are also true intuitions in your immediate vicinity. Intuition thus turns out to grow in concentric spheres —

successive approximations of reality — consecutive awakenings to wider awareness . . . from Ptolemy to Copernicus to Kepler to Newton to Einstein. . . .

The earlier of such intuition stages, however, have seemed to be within the reach of average minds — not too steep for creeping credulity. I mean stages no further off than the round earth or the encircling moon and the planets. But when we get to Einstein's new leap upward into very distant worlds at speeds that drastically distort space and time, we need intuition of a different order. We need to stretch our homespun comprehension far enough to take in something wholly beyond any ordinary earthly experience. We need to study the workings of the newly discovered laws of nature without pride or prejudice until they make some logical sense — even if the foundations of the logic seem to be floating in emptiness.

I do not know whether, in attempting this here, we will err more in confusing the greenhorns of relativity or in boring the veterans, but the veterans at least can afford to skip over the next few paragraphs, leaving the greenhorns free to stumble onward in their full unmonitored innocence.

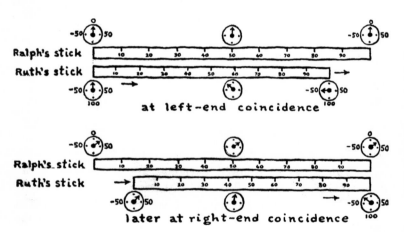

FROM RALPH'S VIEWPOINT

The Lorentz transformation, to take a clean-cut example, may be demonstrated by two meter sticks equipped with special clocks and moving lengthwise in relation to each other at half the speed of light $(c/2)$, which calls for a relativity foreshortening of 14 percent. Let us say the upper stick belongs to Ralph and is at rest relative to him, while the lower stick (moving to the right) belongs to Ruth and remains at rest relative to her.

The first picture shows the two sticks from Ralph's point of view, first as their left ends coincide at the zero instant $(t = 0)$ and next as the right end of Ruth's apparently shortened stick *later* reaches the right end of Ralph's — this occurring, curiously enough, at what turns out to be $t = -26$ by her nearest clock but $t = +28$ by his. You will notice that all Ralph's clocks agree with one another here, since they all represent his single, instantaneous view, but that Ruth's clocks differ (in his viewpoint) all down the reduced length of her moving stick. To him, this picture represents the essential facts of simultaneity.

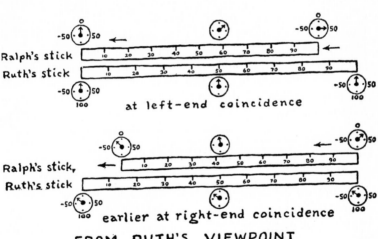

FROM RUTH'S VIEWPOINT

Ruth's viewpoint, shown in the second picture, is distinctly different. Although the left ends of both sticks still coincide at his $t = 0$ (which is her $t' = 0$), she regards his moving stick as the shorter and all his clocks as unsynchronized while hers are in perfect accord. Trusting her own view of time, she believes the right ends of the two sticks passed each other *before* the left ends met, the time of right-end coincidence being $t' = +26$ on his nearest clock and $t' = -28$ on all of hers. Thus, although both viewpoints agree that the other one reads clocks almost correctly, they almost never can admit that the other's clock is right.

I must point out that the two series of clocks could as easily be set to agree at the right ends as at the left ends, since the relationship is symmetrical. But that would not alter the more significant and fundamental fact that, when two bodies move past each other, each one sees part way into the other's past at the other's forward end or correspondingly into the other's future at the other's rear end, or both! Naturally, this has nothing to do with common sense and would have been regarded as completely daffy before Einsteinian relativity, yet it is now supported by a wide range of experiment and experience. And it even embellishes our previous analogy of Lorentzian transformation as resembling "two arrogant men," each of whom looks upon the other, in passing, as "smaller and slower," for the men must also tend to see each other's heads in the past (possibly with outdated ideas) and their behinds in the future (presumably sagging and gnarled with age). Could some such relativity of depreciation, ordinarily unnoticeable on Earth, be responsible in a slight degree for man's traditional disparagement of foreigners? Or even a hidden source of war?

Before we delve too deep into philosophy, however, there is another feature of very great importance in relativity theory which we must not overlook — that although distances and times vary with different viewpoints, they also combine naturally into the quantity called interval, which is the same from every view. Interval, you will recall, refers not just to space and not just to time but to the ubiquitous combination called space-time that actually separates events all the way from collisions of electrons to exploding stars. It is hardly possible to explain how a length of space and a length of time can each appear differently to differently moving observers, while their combined space-time interval remains the same for all, except by pointing out a peculiar mathematical fact: that the interval squared always equals the difference between its space squared and its time squared, a difference that is constant and unaffected by shifting observers' viewpoints or the relative proportions of space and time involved.

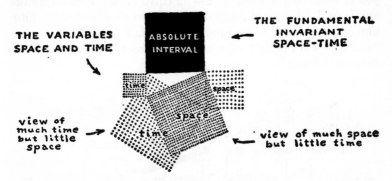

THE VARIABLES SPACE AND TIME

ABSOLUTE INTERVAL

THE FUNDAMENTAL INVARIANT SPACE-TIME

view of much time but little space

space

time

space

view of much space but little time

Which amounts to saying that the separation between two exploding stars is an absolute space-time quantity, regardless of whether you view it (from some relatively "slow"-moving planet) as composed more of space than time or (from a "fast"-moving rocket) as composed more of time than space (see page 585).

This Pythagoreanlike discovery appears to have stemmed from the exuberant mind of Einstein's old mathematics teacher, Hermann Minkowski, who made a stirring address in Cologne on September 21, 1908, promoting relativity into a system of "world geometry." In his third sentence, Minkowski boldly proclaimed that "henceforth space by itself, and time by itself, are doomed to fade away into mere shadows, and only a kind of union of the two will preserve an independent reality." It was his way of saying that the *interval* is the sole objective physical relation between events, the mathematician's fundamental invariant, the prime ingredient of world texture and probably one of the few absolutes left in our fathomless new ocean of relativity.

Incompatibly moving observers could thus look forward to ultimate agreement upon any interval as a whole, however they must
differ about contingent space and time. From this rock,
Minkowski made so bold as to associate a point in three-dimensional space with a corresponding point in one-dimensional time
in order to establish a four-dimensional *world-point* as the theoretical cornerstone of the interval. That is how he created what
he called "an image, . . . the everlasting career of the substantial
point" advancing through time — "a curve in the world: a world-
line." And "the world universe" was "seen to resolve itself into
similar world-lines" — even inducing physical laws potentially to
"find their most perfect expression as reciprocal relations, between
these world-lines."

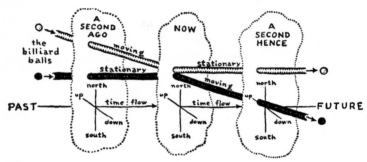

WORLD LINES OF TWO COLLIDING BILLIARD BALLS

Was this four-dimensional world of Minkowski in any sense
real — something one could get one's teeth into (real teeth, I
mean) — or was it a kind of mathematical trick to comfort the
theorists? Einstein himself had his doubts at first and is said to
have remarked that "since the mathematicians have invaded the
theory of relativity I don't understand it myself any more." Yet
after due reflection, he realized that the traditional three-dimensional space and separate one-dimensional time made such a
complicated frame for relativity that he could not visualize how
to generalize it further, as he wanted to. So he enthusiastically
accepted Minkowski's contribution as just what relativity needed
to synthesize its inspirations into a simpler whole. And, along

with space and time, he let electricity and magnetism have their correspondingly compound dimensions also, which fused these hidden, subjective forces into a new objective, four-dimensional electromagnetic "tensor" permanently embedded in four-dimensional space-time.

And of all the aspects of relativity that made themselves known before World War II, the fourth dimension, as a fresh conception of time, was what most profoundly got under the world's skin. For the fourth dimension not only seemed to ask strange questions but more than hinted at still stranger answers. Plotting out time alongside space as a basically similar dimension, for instance, inevitably led to its division into "past" and "future" and raised the question of the relation between them. This relation seemed to be a causal connection involving all sorts of "forces" that insured a continuous flow from earlier conditions to later ones. Yet a "force," as Bertrand Russell pointed out, is something like a sunrise — just a convenient idea for explaining something. In larger perspective, a "force" no more "forces" anything to happen than the sun literally "rises." To say that one thing causes another almost surely means only that the one thing naturally precedes the other. Spring weather produces eggs in birds' nests. How it does it is not necessarily a causal flow in one continuous direction, because, for all we know, causation works both ways. Your receiving a letter logically "compels" its writer to have written it to you — just as surely as his having written it to you "compels" you to receive it. Perhaps somewhat more so, for I can imagine a letter written without being received more easily than I can imagine a letter received without having been written.

A physicist might try to pin down causation further by experimenting with a causal "force" like gravity, which "causes" the earth to revolve around the sun according to Newton's law of the inverse square of the distance. I have in mind a thought experiment in which the distance acted upon by gravity can be shortened all the way down to zero. But there, at the actual place of contact between mass-point and mass-point, the "force" (gravity) must finally explode, according to the law, for the inverse square of zero is infinity. Does this mean, then, that causation itself must disintegrate in an "infinitistic catastrophe" upon the theoretical meeting of ultimate matter with ultimate matter?

Argue as they would, and testing every available theory, the scientists do not seem to have established much more of an absolute difference between past and future than between right and left or back and forth. Thus they have practically confirmed the reasonableness of the fourth or time dimension — the fourth way in which length can be measured — the path of change — the direction in which Minkowski's *world-points* move along *world-lines* — the natural time track that seems to be just as much relative as any spatial dimension. I mean by this that earlier and later do not necessarily correspond to past and future, for an event may as easily be later as earlier in your past, or as easily sooner as later in my future, and the vastly different tempos of existence in the universe (almost inversely proportional to size) enable worlds as diverse as atoms and grains of sand and stars and galaxies to coexist harmoniously. Also time is something like the sideways continuation of a great wave that breaks and plunges upon a shore, ceasing to exist here, then ceasing there, yet progressively rolling shoreward farther and farther along the beach through its ceaseless unfoldment in the lateral dimension. The remote past in its way appears just as dark as the remote future — possibly darker, as it seems to be going away — yet it is not certain that the two directions are perpetually opposite or, if they are, that they may not change places. In the present century, in a sense, earth time is extending in more than one direction, for the scope and memory of history increase backward as well as forward — particularly where archeologists dig up the past (say, in the upper Nile valley) in desperate competition with politicians just as eagerly shaping the future.

Another kind of time relativity is suggested by the viewpoint of water molecules in a river. To them, one might say, the frothy tumble of a mountain brook represents the past and the broad, salty ocean the future, while time progresses downstream. Yet to a spawning salmon swimming upstream out of his ocean past toward a future brook, the river's time is diametrically reversed. There is a symmetry to time, you see, which — as with motion in space — offers full choice of viewpoints.

Still another example may show how completely mirrorlike time-space can be. Many years ago a Turkish artillery officer, condemned to die, was given the hard choice of jumping off a high tower or being shot out of a huge cannon. Either method would kill him instantly: one by the shock of the abrupt change from high speed to zero speed, the other by the change from zero speed to high speed, these being completely reciprocal. It is said that the officer was actually killed — believe it or not — by *both* methods — which, in the understanding of relativity, are the same — for he managed to jump from the tower in such a way as to land inside the muzzle of the cannon, which killed him just as if he had been shot upward by it in reversed time!

Philosophers have long debated such relativity of time, often confessing with Saint Augustine, "What is time then? If nobody asks me, I know. But if I were desirous to explain it to one that should ask me, plainly I know not."

The most nearly reliable distinction between past and future on Earth has had to await the theories of modern science — in particular, the second law of thermodynamics concerning the natural drift of matter toward relative disorder or entropy (see pages 214, 267). That discovery made it possible at last to define a kind of temporal arrow or general direction to universal time flow so that, if something such as a time-lapse movie film, say, of some strange planet's geological history should ever miraculously appear, scientists could tell its beginning from its end. It would explain why astronomers could not seriously think any creatures who might be living on a withershins moon (such as Saturn's Phoebe) would uneat their food or unbreathe their atmosphere just because their world was revolving oppositely from most of the solar system. It also might suggest why we cannot always calculate the past we have seen, although we can often calculate the future we have not seen. I mean, a tub of lukewarm water *now* tells us very little about the combination of buckets of hot and cold water it was composed from *a minute ago*. Yet if we should mix those same buckets of known temperature *now*, we can easily calculate the temperature they will create *a minute hence*.

Such a way of telling past from future — which takes a thermometer instead of a clock — is not as absolute as it may appear, however. The catch is: it works only in our macrocosmic world, because it depends on entropy. Entropy, in fact, is just the tendency of large numbers of molecules or atoms to shuffle themselves into random disarray. It is a statistical effect, and no single atom can have an entropy state any more than a single bee can swarm. This may explain why modern physicists consider the atom timeless or at least ambiguous in its past-future-past relations. For nothing has been found in the laws of physics to prevent time from running "backward" as well as "forward" in an atom. Nor probably even in a large molecule or a crystal lattice. Macrocosmic vibrations back and forth from state to state, like those of a plucked harp string, of course cannot realistically be called timeless, for we know they do not quite reverse or duplicate themselves. They could be likened to successive equinoxes on Earth which only approximately repeat former equinoctial states — states that are distinguishable enough from one another to be called *events*. Yet there is no evidence that atomic states really are events, any more than that anything else which exactly repeats itself again and again can avoid eventually being considered uneventful.

Thus there may be said to be a lower limit of time, perhaps at the bottom of the macrocosm, just as there must be a lower limit of ordinary heat somewhere below the molecular level of size and motion. And this idea seems to have been corroborated by mathematical physicists such as Eugene P. Wigner, who in 1932 showed how "the reciprocity theorem" can be applied to molecular and atomic collisions — how, for instance, the reaction of two hydrogen molecules ($2H_2$) with an oxygen molecule (O_2), creating two water molecules ($2H_2O$), liberates energy in the form of the two water molecules flying violently apart, while two

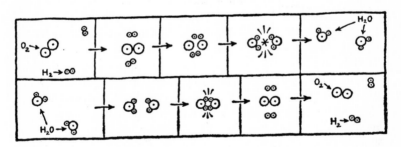

water molecules colliding with that same amount of energy can decompose the water right back into hydrogen and oxygen in exact reciprocity. Nor does such time alternation stop at the atom, for, as you may remember (see page 326), Dirac and Carl D. Anderson discovered a similar reciprocity among elementary particles about the same year. And the phenomenon has since been successfully attributed to nuclear collisions.

Trying to prove time reversal in our macroworld, however, is something else again, and has usually turned out rather like that report in Coeur d'Alene, Idaho, of a mysterious car that for several hours was seen "tearing around the town in reverse." The case was only cleared up when the teen-age girl at the wheel explained to a cop, "My folks let me have the car, and I ran up a little too much mileage. I was just unwinding some of it."

Although we have no indication that any celestial orbit has ever been unwound by a reversal of direction, it appears impossible to prove that our world can *never* return to one of its earlier states, particularly if you consider the universe as enclosed or finite. Some philosophers have even pointed out that a returned state of the world, if complete, would logically include all records, instruments and memories also "returned" to the same state, which would make the return undetectable — so that if such "time loops" are for some unknown reason occurring right now millennially or daily, or on any other frequency, we would have no way of knowing it.

Furthermore, what is the difference between going forward and backward? Of course, one can tell what is "forward" in relation to familiar local events but, once away from the home ground and current contexts, the criterion grows less obvious. Indeed, whichever way the earth turns we naturally name "forward" and so define it. The Phoebeans (if any) would undoubtedly feel their world revolves "forward" — different though their word for it might be. And considering time itself as nothing but the sequential dimension of events, then time also can be made to flow in any "direction" just by events — and its "direction" is, of course, illusory under the relativity principle, being conceivable as "forward" or "backward" only in the sense of "in tune with" or "opposite" what we are used to.

What actually could constitute a backward flow of time through our consciousness anyway? It is worth stopping to think about this. If we began to ungrow and life's processes were reversed, mouths evacuated and rectums fed, and friction and gravity took on the opposite of their present tendencies, would that amount to a reversal of time? We might reasonably assume so, especially if every aspect of life were reversed consistently. But, if anything at all were not reversed, we would likely think there had only been a strange shift in certain laws of nature. If the stars alone continued their motions and rhythms of brightness, for instance, we might conclude that the earth's nature had shifted rather than time itself.

Yet, in the light of the success of the relativity theory and the demotion of NOW, we should realize that earth time is not rigidly geared to star times — that there is a measurable leeway in our celestial relations, making the earth chronologically individual and giving a curious fluid texture to the whole temporal dimension. This is an aspect of, and closely related to, the condition in space known as curvature (which we will soon come to) and which, in combination with distorted time, makes up the characteristic wavy "grain" of space-time.

The theorists have found that the geometry of space-time thus tends toward hyperbolic forms, its basic unit being roughly (and appropriately) representable as an hourglass of which top and bottom spread out indefinitely into the past and future while the narrow middle is the local present, the here-now, laterally encircled by a spatial wedge of elsewhen-elsewhere. On two-dimensional paper it can look like the diagram on the next page and may be worth your serious contemplation.

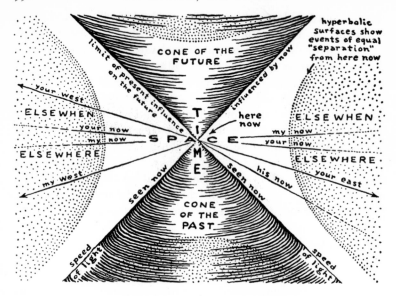

If you are surprised to see that the *past* meets the *future* only *here*, not *elsewhere*, just remember that Einstein has quite thoroughly exploded the myth that simultaneity prevails throughout the universe. And this means that the only definite location of *now* is *here*. In fact, every man's *now* is *here* (the "*here*" meaning "where he is"). While beyond *here*, *now* becomes more and more a matter of viewpoint, of relative motion, as in the case of the train struck by lightning. In terms of simple geometry, *now* can be represented as a line — not necessarily a straight line — of continuous simultaneity. Part of everybody's *now* line touches *here*, where everybody's past and future sometimes meet, but the rest of the *now* lines' lengths stretch out at all possible angles, according to their individual relative velocities, forming the circular wedge of other space that is not *here* and not (for everyone) *now*, nor definitely *past* nor *future*.

The meaning of this weird collar of temporal ambiguity might be clearer to you if you sent a flash of light or radio waves to Mars and it were reflected back to you, arriving, say, half an hour later. For anything that happened to you during that half-hour (from a universal range of viewpoints) could be neither definitely *before* nor definitely *after* nor definitely *simultaneous with* the flash's arrival at Mars. This is not mere theory, either. In the near future there are bound to be lonely ladies on Earth praying for loved ones "out there" on expeditions to Mars and some of them will yearn for the consolation that "he is thinking of me now," presumably at a prearranged moment. Yet "he" will have to think of "her" continuously for a half-hour to be (universally) sure their thoughts mesh as planned. And if he were on Neptune, it would take him a tedious eight hours. If on a nonsolar planet, at least several years. And all because, as Eddington put it, "the *nowness* of an event is like a shadow cast by it into space — and the longer the event the farther will the umbra of the shadow extend."

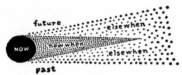

That would seem to limit practical two-way communication, such as a conversation (and possibly any sort of mutual telepathy), to a single planetary neighborhood — for even radio conversations between Earth and moon are annoyingly sluggish with a 2½-second pause before the snappiest possible response to anything said. The basic limitation here, of course, is the speed of light, which is also the maximum rate that any kind of influence can be propagated relative to any material thing in the universe. It is a limitation that not only seems to prevent any sort of a signal or causation from going anywhere except into the future, but also defines the meaning and surface shape of that same future through the presences and absences of those very same causing influences — if you see what I mean. Another way of saying it is that one event is only definitely *before* another if it can influence that other in some way. Thus, to get into somebody's future, you must be moving slower than light in relation to him — which explains why we, who never pass each other as fast as light, are forever getting into each other's futures. It also suggests why light itself is timeless and therefore aloof from the effects of motion (compounded of space and time) as evidenced by its baffling constancy of speed, no matter whether you add or subtract your own speed to (or from) light's by going with or against it. Or you might figure out light's timelessness by the Lorentzian formula of transformation, which says clocks must slow down to zero and stop altogether in relation to anything moving by them at the speed of light.

Is then light an aspect of time itself, since a light beam has no motion through time? No, one cannot quite say that light as light is, properly speaking, an aspect of time. But its speed is. I mean its speed c is the relative speed limit in the material universe and therefore a natural seam of time, "playing the part physically," as Einstein says, "of an infinitely great velocity." Indeed, c holds the secret of the mysterious composition of velocities whose sum can never exceed 186,282 miles a second no matter how many of them there are or how they collate to the velocity of light. So c's constancy truly must be of the essence of time.

Doubtless that is why science holds no hope of our ever being able to overtake a flash of light in this world. However fast we go, the light must still go away from us at 186,282 m.p.s. according to the strictest measurements — even though, paradoxically, the measurements are deceptive. I mean, if a scientific observer could be sent off in a rocket at, say, 161,282 miles per second (earthspeed) in pursuit of a flash of light, the light would seem to witnesses on Earth to be going only 25,000 m.p.s. faster than he was. But he would inevitably measure the difference as 186,282 m.p.s. — because the relative foreshortening of his measuring scale would make his miles only as long as half-miles on Earth, while the retarding of his clocks would turn his seconds into double-seconds of earth time. These two distortions together would stretch his estimate of the light's speed to 100,000 miles a second (really half-miles per double-second). Then by adding on the discrepancy between his *now* line and the earth's *now* line, his different clocks would be warped out of synchronization with each other (from an earthly view) just enough to bring his reading of the light's departure to 186,282 miles a second. Easy, isn't it? And I trust it's twice as clear to you as it is to me!

Anyhow, while you are still quietly digesting this rather sticky conserve of mulled abstractions, may I gently suggest still another curious, and perhaps more helpful, thing about time — that, if any object moves at 186,282 miles a second, the reason it cannot progress through time is that time is essentially a relation between things and themselves — as distinct from space, which is a relation between things and other things — and 186,-282 miles a second of relative speed has the very extraordinary effect of stretching a body's *world-line* out until it is so unbelievably tenuous that the body can no longer have any relation to itself. World-lines, remember, may have *any* kind of shape, depending on how they are regarded and on the motion of the frame you look at them from — so they may seem to be going straight like the light of a star or spiraling like the earth's track around the moving sun or, perhaps, vibrating radially in and out like a throbbing atom or rocking, spinning, tumbling, yawing or even possessing some sort of multidimensional twist not yet imagined.

If this thought does not convey much of a picture of time, it may be only because time is far too abstract for easy visualization, its direction of motion being elusively "perpendicular" to all three dimensions of space at once. Furthermore, time also seems to have its own multiple dimensions or frames of reference, which react upon each other. I mean, a reel of movie film can serve nicely as a model for flowing time. But what is this "time" flowing through? Some framing medium is obviously needed. So the *motion* of the reel constitutes a framing model that reveals a second dimension of time. And the *clock* that times the motion of the reel, a third dimension; the *rotation* of the earth that regulates the clock, a fourth. And so on.

Then there is the curious linkage between time and space which is so familiar we are rarely conscious of it. We use the word "times," for instance, to mean "multiplied by" because time multiplies a three-dimensional amount, such as space, into a four-dimensional product, such as space-time. That is how a hen's daily production of one egg, repeated seven times — or *times seven* — becomes her total product for a week — a nice example of what Aristotle must have meant when he said, "Time is the number of motion."

In a hundred ways thus daily, without thinking of it, we acknowledge our continuum by combining space and time. We write down the *temporal* order of the spoken word in the *spatial* order of visible letters. We inspect the surface of a target to see where bullets passed from their known past into their calculable future. We dive under the sea — holding our breath to a depth as readily measurable in fathoms of space as in seconds of time. And the light-year is a unit, not of time but of distance.

So is it any wonder that mere places evaporate while signals pass between them? That the whole abstraction of *place*, which we once learned to trust, turns out to be nothing but a viewpoint that is different from every side? That, as Einstein declared, "it is neither the point in space, nor the instant in time, at which something happens that has physical reality, but only the event itself"?

I think it was about here in his thinking that Einstein must have realized that Newton's great law of gravitation, for all its beauty and simplicity, needed to be reconsidered —

> That very law which moulds a tear
> And bids it trickle from its source,
> That law that makes the earth a sphere
> And guides the planets in their course.

It was a staggering task, but logically unavoidable. For Newton had neglected putting *time* into his inverse-square equation and, if this world really was the space-time continuum that relativity had already shown it to be, any major force such as gravity acting through *space* simply had to act also through *time*.

This is not to say that Newton was wrong in taking *time* for granted. He was a hundred percent right for the seventeenth century, and much more than ninety-nine percent right even for our own twentieth century. He was as right as anyone could be who assumes that the distance from Earth to moon is a definite distance at any particular instant. And his rightness had been well tested in thousands of working mechanical applications, in practical engineering formulas, in special eighteenth-century expeditions to Lapland and to the equator to measure the gravitational flattening of the earth toward the poles — even in seemingly miraculous astronomical predictions — during three centuries. Yet Newton's caliber of rightness could no longer be quite enough. For a new principle had evolved. Relativity had just demonstrated that space as such cannot be absolutely definite in amount. Not only does it shrink for relatively moving observers but the time at one end of it can no more be the time at the other end of it than the *now* that is *here* can be the *now* that is *there*.

So Einstein set about broadening his relativity theory in the direction of gravitation. He did not see any reason why it could not encompass gravitation if it could be generalized enough. Up to now, he had been dealing only with rather special cases, such as the relative motions of two trains or two measuring sticks, moving at steady, uniform speeds past each other — special cases which had neatly explained Lorentzian transformation and the ether doldrum. He could logically call his conclusions from these cases the Theory of Special Relativity.

But from here on he must consider other motions, more usual and general motions, specifically unsteady and changing ones — in short, *accelerations*. And he would call his findings about their relationships the Theory of General Relativity.

You may wonder at first what all this has to do with gravity. But its appropriateness will become clear if you can visualize Newton's famous apple as it fell to the ground. For apples fall with natural acceleration, and Newton certainly recognized such as the acceleration of gravity, as had Galileo before him.

However, Newton quite reasonably concluded that the apple, in falling, was being *pulled* downward toward the earth. That is, he felt himself standing stationary upon solid ground while the apple approached him. And it evidently never occurred to him to look at things from the apple's point of view.

But Einstein, being a relativist and keenly aware of the importance of nonhuman and exotic viewpoints, wanted to ask the apple what *it* had to say about Newton, the earth and its own motion. And he may have posed his unheard-of question in somewhat this vein: "Tell me, apple, how did Newton look to *you* when you fell toward him?"

"Fell toward him?" retorted the astonished apple, by this time feeling not only bruised but sour. "Fell toward him — nothing! I'll swear it was Newton and that damned earth who fell toward *me!*"

"Well, well," Einstein must have thought, and probably with a grateful twinkle, "I wouldn't be surprised if you've got something there." For why shouldn't the earth fall just like everything else?

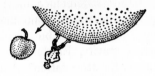

Why could it not be as true to say that the earth falls *up* to meet things in the sky as that things in the sky fall *down* to earth? Is not that simple relativity? Or am I too full of apple juice?

It *is* relativity — yes, he checked himself. But perhaps it is not so very simple. For although the apple is regardable as accelerating downward, can one . . . could one possibly justify a claim that the earth is accelerating upward just as much?

On the face of it, upward terrestrial acceleration would seem quite impossible for more than a very small portion of the earth, since upward, globally speaking, is not *one* direction but *every* direction. In fact, if the earth's surface is accelerating upward all around the earth, the earth as a whole must be exploding. Which it obviously is not. Yet, come to think of it, maybe the earth *is* exploding in a sense. What about its atoms and molecules, gyrating like mad in all directions? Is not that a kind of explosion? Certainly the hammering of molecules against Newton's feet were a more cogent cause for his upward acceleration, even according to his own laws of motion, than anything he could claim as sufficient cause for the apple's acceleration downward.

But perhaps standing on the earth's surface is too special a situation in the universe to be a fair example of universal gravitation — so, as Eddington once suggested, let us consider Newton as standing at the center of the earth, where there should be neither any noticeable gravity nor preponderant molecular pressure pushing him toward the apple that he might see (by subterranean telescope) "falling" toward him from high above. Here the gravitational circumstances of the converging man and apple are equivalent. Neither is being forced by anything visible or tangible toward the other, and each feels *he* is standing still while being fallen upon.

It is a case of two frames of reference, moving relatively — symmetrically — exactly like the freight train and the earth except that here the motion is not constant but accelerating. Could this be the true essence of gravity, Einstein wondered? Is gravity really just another name for acceleration? And if so, why should it attach itself so steadfastly to massive bodies like the earth?

Instinctively, he felt the answer must somehow be bound up with the still cryptic, scarcely emergent nature of space-time, as had been the answer to the riddle of the ether wind. But where to approach it for a real understanding? How to aim one's mental scalpel into the gravitational marrow?

As it turned out, more than ten years were to pass while Einstein struggled with this profound problem — "years," in his own words, "of anxious searching in the dark, with their intense longing, their alternations of confidence and exhaustion" — while around him the most powerful nations of Europe steadily and stealthily aligned themselves into bitter rivalries that eventually ignited the conflagration of World War I.

Sometimes during his unprecedented trial, as the war clouds glowered and later the newspapers were filled with reports of horror and mass destruction, Einstein clutched at dim and fleeting geometric notions of space-time, trying to visualize dimensions and again dimensions. Sometimes he pondered the thoughts of Newton and reviewed the rival gravitational theories of the distorted medieval days — recalling Descartes' celestial vortex of swirling atoms (see page 313) that had been rejected because it contended that things fell only when their surfaces were pushed from above, an argument that did not account for gravity's demonstrable proportionality to the *masses* instead of to the *surfaces* of gravitating objects. The whole vortex idea indeed was about as fantastic as Lorentzian transformation. Yet

Lorentzian transformation had worked out successfully after all, even though for a reason its originator did not foresee. So assuming Lorentzian transformation really was true, Einstein wondered, could it somehow be possible that Descartes' vortex idea was also basically right — although perhaps the hypothetical vortex itself might have to be replaced by some still unsuspected ethereal pressure inherent in the geometry of emptiness?

About at this stage, Einstein happened to look one day at a Mercator map of the earth. You will remember Mercator's projection as the one that spreads all lines of longitude out straight and parallel so that the farther a country is from the equator the more absurdly swollen it must appear in size. And it occurred to Einstein that if anyone who thinks the earth is flat should use such a map he would logically also believe Greenland to be as big as all Europe, because a flat earth is accurately representable on a flat map. But then, if Europeans traveling across Greenland should invariably report that distances there seem to be much shorter than in Europe — that is, "appear" much shorter than they "really" are — the flat-earth believer might well conclude that

Greenland affects people's minds, somehow hypnotizing them so that they do not realize the "true" passage of time, or perhaps actually slowing down their clocks and foreshortening their courses of travel as in the Lorentzian transformation.

Could this not be another analogue of relativity? If so, it would work equally well if Greenlanders drew their own Mercator maps on a different base line, projecting a reciprocal Spain bigger than Greenland — and giving this Spain the mysterious power to transform the space and time of traveling Greenlanders.

It would work in a slightly different way also if two ships steamed side by side across the equator, heading exactly north. If their captains believed the earth were flat, for instance, they would logically assume the two ships could continue parallel to each other along parallel lines of longitude as far as the sea extended. So when, after a few days, they noticed that the ships were gradually coming nearer together and, no matter how perfectly they steered north, that the convergence was steadily accelerating, one of the captains might postulate a mysterious force of attraction to explain it, a force proportional to the inverse square of their distance apart — in short, a law of gravitation hardly distinguishable from that defined by Newton!

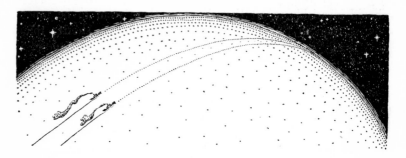

In similar manner did Einstein arrive at his new understanding of gravity, at his revolutionary awareness that the persisting tendency of things to fall is not really a force at all but only an effect of geometry — a nonparallelness of world-lines — an illusion due to the "curvature" of the world. It was a field theory, you might say, for it avoided the "action at a distance" implicit in Newton's old law by attributing falling to the natural response of objects to their immediate or field surroundings. That is, free matter in space literally takes the easiest and most leisurely path, following whatever sort of curve of space-time it finds itself in — a track that has come to be known as a *geodesic*. This, in a sense, is a reversion from Newton back toward Descartes and his vortex pressures. But, much more, it is the discovery of a deeper meaning in the ancient Greek observation that "God always geometrizes."

If this still seems vague and mysterious, at least it can be tested by fairly simple experiments. For it is a remarkable fact that, although no one is known to have suggested it before Einstein, artificial gravity can be created in a small enclosure — say, an airplane or an elevator or this space ship — that is so exactly like natural gravity that no one can tell them apart. This is the basis of the G unit of acceleration (equal to gravity's strength at the earth's surface) that the Air Force now manipulates at will to create gravitational "forces" dozens of times stronger than normal or even to "banish" gravity altogether in a zero-G trajectory for the better part of a minute. This is the reason an airliner in a cloud may bank in a turn so tight its wings point vertically up and down without the passengers becoming aware of it. Few pilots and fewer spacemen can be found to hold brief any longer for the outmoded notion that there is any fundamental difference between gravitation and acceleration. And it is naturally the earthbound folk who cling hardest to the old materialistic concepts of gravity, for they know gravity as something that can be felt, something that never relaxes its relentless tugging-tugging-tugging toward the earth. It is hard for them to remember that the sensation of weight in truth is not gravity itself but only the resistance of the earth to their natural response to it. If they could only get away from the earth somehow and be free of their constant bombardment by the tireless molecules of pavements and floors and chairs and beds, they would be elated at the ethereal liberation of floating at large undisturbed — of *answering* gravity instead of *fighting* it — of conforming gracefully to nature's orbit, drifting in peace upon a world-line, accepting the lovable abstraction of the geodesic.

Suppose, for example, that you were born and brought up (or down) in a falling elevator or, more realistically, in my orbiting space station. In such a vehicle, an apple does not fall and, if you had never heard of the phenomenon of falling, it would take a great effort of imagination to visualize and understand the strange world of a planet's surface where a wholesale molecular bombardment is always pushing "upward" so hard that loose things like apples seem to want to go "downward." It would sound absurd to be told that in fact the only reason your apple inside the vehicle does not "fall" is that the whole vehicle including yourself is already "falling." Yet from outside we know that this is true — at least relatively speaking. We can see at last that the state of falling is the normal state of bodies in the universe — of all free, whole bodies at any rate — and that it is only the denser sub-regions (like a planetary surface) containing tiny captive crumbs (like you) that must undergo the frustration of not being allowed their full response in unhindered falling.

To make the point clearer with an extreme case, consider your space vehicle as orbiting close to the very heavy dwarf star, Sirius B, which, as we shall presently see (page 585), has turned out to be extremely important in relativity theory. Since the density of this body is sixty thousand times greater than that of water, its gravitational field must be of such unbelievable ferocity that, if you could be left standing upright on its solid surface, you would instantaneously collapse in a splash upon the ground. Yet in falling freely through the same gravitational field in your vehicle, even though your acceleration "downward" exceeded what it would be if you were fired from a cannon, whipping you around Sirius B like a feather in a tornado, you would feel no force and would continue

to float in weightless relaxation as if you were a trillion miles away
in utter emptiness.

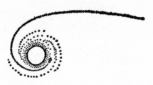

Thus is manifest the outer mystery of gravitation, the paradox
of acceleration — two equivalent aspects of a single phenomenon
as defined in Einstein's now well-known Principle of Equivalence,
a principle in which the "force" (of gravity) that flattens the
standing body on Sirius B is revealed to be identical with the
"force" (of acceleration) that whips the vehicle around it — both
being illusions of geometric space.

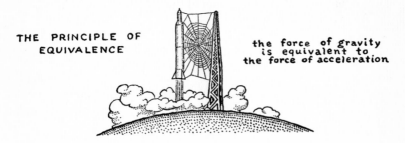

THE PRINCIPLE OF
EQUIVALENCE

the force of gravity
is equivalent to
the force of acceleration

Einstein eventually became quite aware of the shock his free-
ranging concepts would inflict upon unprepared classical minds,
and so he began — at least on one occasion — by begging his eminent predecessor, "Forgive me, Newton," when he introduced his
startling new ideas on gravitation, from there on gently but confidently working into a discussion of the abstruse "geometric
property" that makes things "gravitate." By the time the derivative
called "acceleration" turned up as another face of the same property, however, some of his listeners had been left behind while
others, more discerning, were relatively gaining — among them Sir
Arthur Eddington, Sir James Jeans and, significantly, Bertrand

Russell, who went so far as to denounce acceleration as "a mere mathematical fiction, a number, not a physical fact."

But there remained still another face of the new property to be dealt with: inertia — which, you remember, was defined by Newton as the tendency of a resting body to remain at rest or of a moving body to continue moving uniformly in a straight line at constant speed. Inertia had long been regarded as a rather passive, feminine force with a quiet predilection for complementing the more active, masculine force of gravity, as in the case of the earth's motion around the sun where centrifugal inertia nicely balances solar gravitation. Yet how distinct in fact are these apparently individual forces? And why should they so often merge into one?

After only a little pondering, Einstein got a strong hunch that the two are fundamentally inseparable. He seems to have reached this conclusion under the inspirational aegis of Galileo, who is reputed to have dropped pebbles and cobblestones simultaneously from the leaning tower of Pisa to demonstrate that these weights, no matter how much they vary, will always fall with the same constant acceleration — later determined at 32.2 feet per second per second. How unlike the wind or the sea, which treats heavy stones so differently from light ones, was this curious impartiality of gravity! Its force must act in strict proportion to the criterion of individual mass. But, come to think of it, that is exactly how inertia also acts — a fifty-pound stone requiring ten times as much force to accelerate it or slow it down as a five-pound stone.

It was too much for Einstein to believe that two really independent forces could both obey such an odd rule by pure coincidence, so he began to look for gravity-like influences that might be hidden within inertia — until suddenly he recalled the speculation of Ernst Mach of Austria, that the stars may be mainly responsible for inertia — that the water spreading to the outside of Newton's

famous spinning bucket (see page 521) was probably not so much clinging to "absolute space" as gravitating toward "the masses of the universe," where "all bodies, each in its share, are of importance for the law of inertia."

From here on, Einstein set about the task of incorporating inertia as the *universal* aspect of gravity, along with the reciprocal goal of treating gravity as the *local* aspect of inertia, both being relative geometric properties of the integral space-time continuum — so that the earth no longer need strain centrifugally or schizophrenically against the tension of solar gratitation but instead could float in complete relaxation along her natural track, her private geodesic line through space-time.

Step by step, you see, geometry was growing, maturing, its previously unimaginable abstractions enveloping in turn space, time, motion, acceleration, gravity, and now inertia. Practically all the mechanical sciences had been influenced if not consumed by geometric angles, coordinates and curves. Even electromagnetism, light and the atomic world were apprehensive as to their own approaching days of reckoning. For, amazingly, the metric of space — essence of geometry — seemed able to explain anything.

Eddington, with characteristic lucidity, compared medieval humanity to a race of flat-fish living in an ocean of two dimensions, where fishes in general swam in straight lines except for one area where they all seemed bewitched and could not help going in curves. Some thought

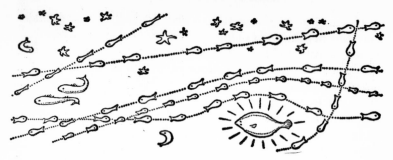

there might be an invisible whirlpool there until a bright fish named Isaac pointed out the "real" cause of the trouble: a very large fish — a sunfish — lying asleep in the middle of the region, who attracted all the other fish in proportion to their sizes. This adequately accounted for most of the peculiar curves, so nobody bothered about the lesser attractions of a small moon-fish circling near by or the great numbers of fixed starfish twinkling in the background. And the only discontentment left was the carping of a few carp who did not see how the sunfish could exert such great influence from such a distance, though they presumed his influence must spread forth somehow through the water.

Then a very unusual fish called Albert got interested in the problem and began analyzing it — studying not only the "forces" involved but, more particularly, the *courses* being swum. And suddenly he arrived at a surprising explanation: there must be a mound where the sunfish lay! Flat-fish could not sense it directly, nor understand it, because they were two-dimensional, but any fish who swam over the slopes of the mound — no matter how straight he aimed — got turned somewhat "inward" toward the mound, just as a piece of cloth over your right shoulder will tend to hang more or less leftward.

Thus there was no longer any need to assume "influence at a distance" in accounting for curvy swimming, since the curves were now built right into the two-dimensional world — even though they were almost impossible for a flat-fish to deduce — thereby making it essentially a three-dimensional world despite the fact that the fish themselves were denied access to the third dimension.

This analogy gives a pretty fair idea, I think, of how a hidden curvature in the world can impart the illusion of an attracting force such as gravity. And of how hard it is to comprehend the curvature while we are enclosed *inside* of the same dimensions it is *outside* of. Our real world, moreover, has mounds not only of space but is teeming with mountain ranges of space-time, not to mention canyons, funnels, gyrating hyperbolas and all manner of indescribable, multidimensional and illusory shapes which are aspects of its grain or structure.

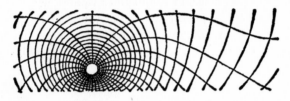

On the subject of shape, I might mention that mere *shape* is always relative and therefore largely illusory — bitter though this may be for the young or beautiful to swallow. It works out that *order* is the intrinsic relation in world geometry, and order is a function of the absolute *interval* that binds the order. But space and time which compose the interval are free to shift and distort, relatively, along with any shapes formed by their dimensions. Thus a square turns into a diamond if you look at it obliquely, and the form of a woman is essentially given her by her observers — which, obviously, I mean not solely in a psychological way.

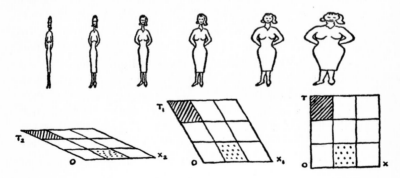

This is why space-time curvature, while very important relatively, must retain the illusory quality that makes it so hard to grasp in the real world. You can visualize a gravitational field around a star or planet, for instance, as a kind of invisible dimple in the skin of space-time, a pucker in the cosmic cloth of at least four dimensions — but that will be an ambiguous picture at best, for it must vary with every frame of observation. Nor is it in any way simple. Indeed even if you knew the G values at hundreds of points around a space-time pucker you could scarcely comprehend its geometry since, in Eddington's words, "what determines the existence of the pucker is not the values of the G's . . . It is the way these values link on to those at other points — the gradient of the G's and, more particularly, the gradient of the gradient."

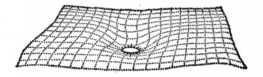

A better way to picture curvature in the cosmos might be to think of space as uniformly studded with floating atoms so that any spatial distance is proportional to the number of atoms it encompasses. A circle in such space could be defined as a curve with a constant minimum number of atoms between any point on it and a central point. Such a circle would have a fixed ratio between the lengths of its diameter and circumference equal to the famous number π or 3.14159265358979323846264338332 79 . . . But now suppose the uniformly floating atoms should become nonuniform, spreading farther apart in some places and crowding into concentrated clots in others, as actually happens in the real world. Then a circle (by the same definition) would no longer keep the ratio of π between its diameter and circumference, nor would it continue to look like a circle, its distortion depending, of course, on the pattern of clots and vacuums among the atoms.

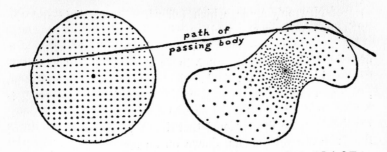

CIRCLES IN UNIFORM AND NON UNIFORM SPACE

Considering this an analogy of actual space, the atom clots representing the regions of stars, now suppose some object should move through the space, penetrating the edge of one of the clots. It would obey the natural law of least resistance, automatically following the path that passes fewest atoms. Although when the space originally was studded *uniformly* with atoms this path was a straight line, now in *nonuniform* space the object naturally must curve around the dense clots, staying far enough away to avoid atom crowds yet not so far that its lengthened route will add unnecessary hermit atoms, either. In this way, the object actually describes a track concave toward stars in proportion to their masses, which makes it appear to be attracted by them — like the flat-fish crossing the sunfish's mound.

But the attraction is not what it seems, for the object is really just drifting along a geodesic, its private line of least resistance, which also (under the influence of Lorentzian transformation) is the track where its time flows fastest, or (which is the same thing) the track that takes the longest time. At least that is what actually happens, according to all the evidence now available. And it explains why gravitation commonly amounts to a repulsion as well as an attraction, sending comets away from the sun about as often as toward it or, teamed with inertia upon a rapidly rotating asteroid, making stones "fall" upward into the sky. It may even suggest how gravitation can be only the effect of looking at things from an accelerated point of view (as from an upward-pushing earth) — or only the effect of the nonparallelness of matter (as in the case of Newton's apple, which fell when its geodesic and the earth's were no longer parallel).

In any case, we cannot go on assuming, as did Newton, that material bodies naturally *want* to go straight. For stars distort space as birds distort air. And straightness is an ideal of almost no practical meaning in the real world, even though *any* track is straight *relative* to *some* frame of reference. By which I mean (as shown in the illustrations) that the supposedly curved orbit of the earth around the sun, drawn on an apparently straight grid of Newtonian rectangular space, can just as well be considered

EARTH'S ORBIT
REPRESENTED
AS A CURVED
LINE ON THE
STRAIGHT GRID
OF NEWTONIAN
SPACE

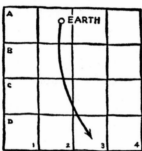

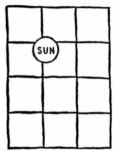

a straight orbit or geodesic, drawn on a curved grid of Einsteinian distorted space. And the latter, newer interpretation is actually a little better suited for interpreting *all* the known facts, as will (I hope) soon be apparent.

An almost obvious test of curvature is the measuring of angles to see if geometric figures come out according to the ideals of

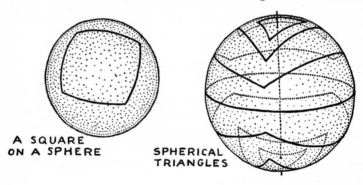

A SQUARE
ON A SPHERE

SPHERICAL
TRIANGLES

Euclid, whom you presumably studied in school. For it is evident that a "square" with sides one foot long, drawn on the surface of a sphere, must contain more than one square foot of area — and that a "triangle" drawn upon earth, with great circles for sides, will have angles that total more than 180° or two right angles, particularly if such a "square" or "triangle" is big in relation to its sphere. The terrestrial "triangle" formed by the Greenwich

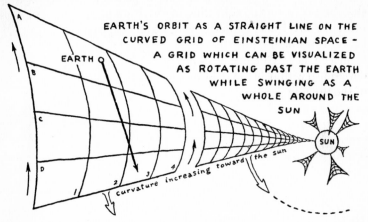

EARTH'S ORBIT AS A STRAIGHT LINE ON THE CURVED GRID OF EINSTEINIAN SPACE — A GRID WHICH CAN BE VISUALIZED AS ROTATING PAST THE EARTH WHILE SWINGING AS A WHOLE AROUND THE SUN

curvature increasing toward (the sun

meridian, the 90° west meridian and the equator, for example, has three right angles. Still bigger "triangles" have still bigger angles — all the way up to a total of six right angles when the "triangle" has stretched out into the form of a continuous great circle. And if you want to push the "triangle" beyond this extreme, in effect turning it inside out, its three angles can approach an ultimate total of 900° or ten right angles!

But this, you may protest, is merely going from plane into solid or three-dimensional geometry, and does not basically conflict with Euclid. Nevertheless what is true of a triangle on the black-board is not necessarily true of a triangle too big for the black-board. For the blackboard represents a straight, flat, two-dimensional ideal that does not exist in nature — a nature where added dimensions turn up apparently willy-nilly and may not be gotten rid of permanently just by sweeping them under the mental rug.

The truth in this seems to have been first realized by Gauss, the prodigious nineteenth-century German mathematician who was seriously questioning the foundations of Euclidean geometry at the age of twelve and a few years later created the "metric theory of surfaces" that described *positive* (spherelike) and *negative* (saddlelike) curves in terms of the angles between their *p* and *q* coordinates resembling latitude and longitude lines. Such a study almost inevitably led him to perform the first space-curvature experiment, consisting of "very accurate geodetic measurements on a triangle formed by three notable peaks: the Brocken in the Harz mountains, the Inselberg in Thuringia and the Hohenhagen near Göttingen" — but in which he could detect no deviation (within his margin of accuracy) from 180° in the sum of the three angles.

However, Gauss's brilliant pupil, Bernhard Riemann, went on to develop a definition of the curvature in a continuum of an indefinite number of dimensions — a feat which half a century later, as if by accident (in the oft-noted way of true history), served Einstein in the development and perfection of his theory of general relativity. For naturally Einstein, having discovered a new *explanation* for gravitation, needed a new *law* of gravitation at least as precise as Newton's inverse-square law which it was to improve on. And this law had to say something about curvature.

The simplest form of spatial curvature, however, was so far beyond normal human experience that it was not really visualizable even to Riemann. The nearest he could do, in fact, was probably to imagine a series of concentric spheres of greater and greater radii — of which, although geometricians used to think their surfaces had to be proportional to the squares of their radii, the surfaces of the outer ones began to be a little less than this criterion called for, then lesser and still lesser (relative to the squares of their radii) until a maximum possible spherical area was attained, beyond which the areas became smaller again until finally they disappeared into a point, the antipode of space — a definite limit that could no more be called a boundary than could the antipodal point opposite you on the surface of the earth.

If that model tried his imagination too hard, Riemann might have chosen some other one such as Jeans's analogy of spindle-shaped bodies, many of whose pointed ends meet at A (as in the illustration), occupying all space surrounding A, but whose other ends (like opposite magnetic poles) can somehow simultaneously stretch and distort themselves into converging, surrounding and meeting at another single point B — thereby demonstrating the spatial curvature between A and B.

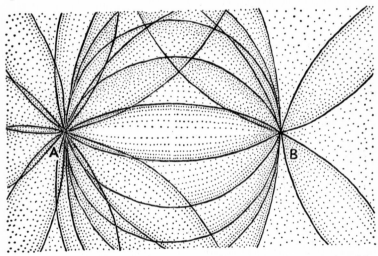

And the curvature of space-time was still more unimaginable than that of space alone, being a four-dimensional manifold embedded in what Eddington describes as "as many dimensions as it can find new ways to twist about in." In reality, as Eddington goes on to say,

a four-dimensional manifold is amazingly ingenious in discovering new kinds of contortion, and its invention is not exhausted until it has been provided with six extra dimensions [three electric and three magnetic ones] making ten dimensions in all. Moreover, twenty distinct measures are required at each point to specify the particular sort and amount of twistiness there. These measures are called coefficients of curvature. Ten of the coefficients stand out more prominently than the other ten.

Einstein's law of gravitation asserts that the ten principal coefficients of curvature are zero in empty space.

If there were no curvature — that is, if *all* the coefficients were zero — there would be no gravitation. Bodies would move uniformly in straight lines. If curvature were unrestricted — that is, if *all* the coefficients had unpredictable values — gravitation would operate arbitrarily and without law. Bodies would move just anyhow. Einstein takes a condition midway between: ten of the coefficients are zero and the other ten are arbitrary. That gives a world containing gravitation limited by a law.

Such a law is as much a generalization of Newtonian law as a hen is a generalization of an egg — and with comparable complications. With subtle and beautiful logic it reaches and influences all matter, all radiation, all world-lines, and all action — action which may be summarized as the curvature of the world.

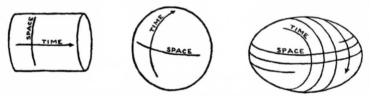

HOW DO SPACE AND TIME COORDINATE ?

Present indications as to the galaxies in our universe (whose numbers seem to be increasing faster with remoteness than do the cubes of their distances away) suggest that cosmic curvature tends to the negative — something like a four-or-more-dimensional saddle, the surface of a doughnut hole or, if you prefer, a negative sphere. Such curvature may, however, exist only in the observable regions of the universe, for there is nothing known to prevent a reversion to positive globular curvature in regions beyond the horizon of present knowability, possibly where matter changes to anti-matter or where some other little-understood seam of symmetry takes dominance over polarity or handedness.

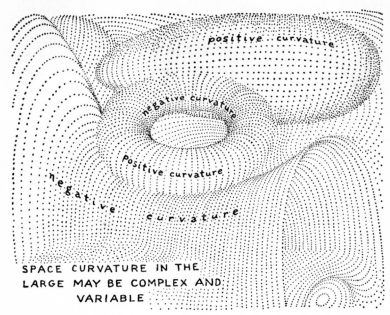

positive curvature

negative curvature

Positive curvature

negative curvature

SPACE CURVATURE IN THE LARGE MAY BE COMPLEX AND VARIABLE

As for the effect of the curvature of space on light and vision, we literally *see* along the gravitating geodesics of light and along the actual orbits of photons without consciously realizing it — in fact, we see around all light's curves and twists. Even though the curvature of light is much too slight to be noticeable to our senses, it has been proven that light actually drops, like other objects on earth, with a constant acceleration that carries it 16 feet in the first second, 48 feet in the next, and so on. And it is only the fact that light also moves forward 186,282 miles during each second that keeps us from noticing the drop.

The direct and very precise measurement of "falling" light on Earth, however, has turned out to be too delicate and ambiguous to be convincing as a proof of general relativity, so Einstein suggested instead "weighing light" on the sun, where gravity is about 27 times stronger than on earth. This could be done by very accurate calibration of star positions just outside the rim of the sun, as seen during a total solar eclipse, then comparing them with the same stars' normal positions to see how much each star beam is bent by the gravitational curvature of solar space.

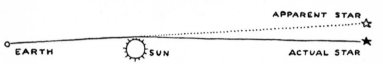

It happens that May 29, when the sun is lined up with the Hyades star cluster, is what Eddington called "the most favorable day of the year for weighing light" and that 1919 was the first year of relative peace after the publication of the General Relativity Theory in 1917 — so it seemed something of a divine happenstance if not a miracle that a total eclipse of the sun "chanced" to occur on May 29, 1919. And on that day several astronomers, including Eddington, substantially confirmed Einstein's prediction that a star beam would be bent by 1.74 seconds of arc in passing the edge of the sun. This amounted to practical proof that the equation for gravity should not be simply Newton's $F = Gm_1m_2/r^2$ but, more specifically, Einstein's $F = Gm_1m_2/r^{2.00000016}$ — which meant that the abstraction of invisible curvature was real.

At this point it would be only reasonable to begin to wonder, since light is bent by space which in turn is bent by gravitational masses, just how massive a star would have to be to bend its own light completely backward against itself. Answering the question, Eddington replied that a star the size of giant Betelgeuse (just about big enough to contain the orbit of Mars), if it were as dense as the sun throughout, would strain space around it so severely that its "light would be unable to escape and any rays shot out would fall back of their own weight." In fact, Eddington ventured, "the curvature would be so great that space would close up round the star, leaving us outside — that is to say *nowhere.*"

Which, if true, would suggest that our existence *somewhere* — yours and mine — is just possibly one of the reasons why Betelgeuse is so vacuous.

A second difference between Newtonian and Einsteinian gravitation is that Newton's laws are based on a planet's orbit's being a simple stationary ellipse, such as Kepler discovered was true in the case of Mars. But under Einstein's theory a planet's orbit works out instead to be a rotating ellipse that does not quite repeat — that precesses like a wobbling top. Part of the reason

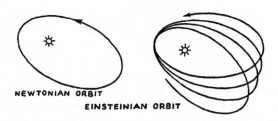

NEWTONIAN ORBIT

EINSTEINIAN ORBIT

for this, as you may have guessed, is that every time the planet nears the sun it must accelerate a little and therefore, by Lorentzian transformation, its mass increases and its track foreshortens, distorting the surrounding space just enough to carry the orbit a tiny way beyond where Newton would have placed it. The difference is so slight that, in the case of the earth's nearly circular orbit, it precesses only 3.8 seconds of arc per century and a whole precessional revolution would take 34 million years. For this reason, planetary precession would have been a difficult phenomenon to prove were it not for the existence of a particular and convenient planet of very elongated orbit and possessed of unusual swiftness: the planet Mercury. Mercury, indeed, had been known for a long time to be precessing at the rate of about 43 seconds of arc per century, and Leverrier, famed for his accurate prediction of Neptune (see page 99), showed in 1845 that this amount of orbital shift could be produced if Mercury were being perturbed by an unknown planet between it and the sun — a planet he felt so sure would be discovered that he named it Vulcan. And it was eagerly looked for and speculated about by astronomers all over the world.

Yet Vulcan never showed up. And the mystery remained unsolved until the general theory of relativity was applied mathematically to test the precession of Mercury and the result turned out — to nearly everyone's relief — to be 43 seconds of arc a century — a proof that has also been found to have its counterpart in the precessing "rosette" orbit of the electron.

The third verification of general relativity has to do with Einstein's prediction that time must flow more slowly not only in a moving frame of reference but logically also in an accelerating frame, which would be equivalent to a field of gravitation. Thus the larger the gravitational mass, the more sluggish its clocks must be, though not necessarily by enough to notice in ordinary life. In fact, Einstein calculated that "a second of time on the sun should correspond to 1.000002 earth seconds."

How could such a slight discrepancy be detected? The answer found was that the discrepancy need not remain so slight, for another star could be used where the time retardation would be much greater than on the sun. The handiest such star turned out to be the well-known dense dwarf Sirius B, with a diameter only a thirtieth of the sun's but a density 25,000 times greater.

Nor would it be necessary to send a clock there, since atoms vibrate reliably enough to regulate the best of clocks, and the spectral colors from the star must clearly reveal the frequencies of its atoms, hence (by comparison), their rate differences from Earth. And so, as very precisely measured in 1925, time on Sirius B was slipping steadily behind earthly time by more than a second every five hours — in accord with general relativity theory.

On the basis of such exotic yet sound evidences of the reality of general relativity, physicists can now describe with considerable confidence the basic time disparities that will appear in a future high-velocity space-ship voyage to some such star as Vega, whether or not it is then still fixed (from an earthly view) in the constellation of the Harp. If the traveling space ship accelerates to a speed close to that of light and uses its motors to reverse its direction fairly quickly at Vega, it may return to Earth in sixty years as recorded by earthly clocks and calendars, yet with only sixty months (of earth time) elapsed upon the space ship itself. I mean of course that an actual disparity in time-flow will have taken place between the space ship and the earth — not just an apparent difference — and that the returning space travelers will find most of their friends and relatives dead and, like as not, some of their own grandchildren already older than themselves.

Whether disparity of this kind is literally possible in any degree has been debated a good deal in this century, with such a noted physicist as Herbert Dingle insisting that two synchronized clocks, no matter how differently or drastically they move through the universe after being separated, will remain symmetrical because "nothing is in question except their relative motion. Hence they cannot show different times on reunion." Yet the leading theorists in general relativity reply that there is an "absolute distinction" between the time of earthly clocks and the time of clocks on space ships that are accelerating through space-time. The distinction lies in the different amounts of acceleration. While the earth merely drifts along on its line of least resistance, on its geodesic of longest time, the space ship, as long as its motors are accelerating or decelerating it (two views of one thing), must inevitably experience a slower passage of time. This was basically established by the Sirius B experiment in 1925, again demonstrated by a tuning experiment between hot and cold crystals of the isotope iron 57 at Harvard in 1960, and is now being conclusively tested by actual clocks in space.

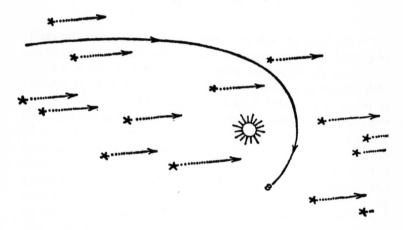

There is also the strange abstraction of gravitational potential, the potential energy created in raising any mass relative to a gravitational field through which it may fall. Every time you go upstairs, for instance, your gravitational potential increases and so does the potential energy of the earth (including you) by the same amount. But the strangest thing about gravitational potential is that it remains directly proportional to the relative slowing of time upon any accelerating object, so that when the space ship swings (under terrific acceleration forces) around Vega at a range giving it vast gravitational potential toward the earth, its clocks and heartbeats are going proportionately slowly as compared to those on Earth. The relative time field of the earth then, you might say, is flowing past the space ship at an alarming rate so that, by the time it returns home, it finds itself some two generations behind.

Such unearthly temporal distortions as these, of course, are way beyond our present intuition. Yet we can deduce that long space journeys to the stars are theoretically possible within reasonable portions of the travelers' expectable lifetimes if we can only achieve velocities close to that of light. If it were possible for a space ship to move exactly as fast as light, freezing the flow of time altogether and foreshortening space down to nothing (in effect making the speed infinite), obviously it would seem to the voyagers to take no time at all, except for the months of acceleration and deceleration at each end. Indeed, the approaches to such a speed might be considered one of the seams of the universe, where the physical and mental worlds meet. At least the speed of light as viewed subjectively, by a mind theoretically keeping up with the light, would equal the speed of thought.

We could go on to such questions of cosmic relativity as "how much of anything must be put into a given volume of space to make it absolutely full?" which is a variation of the basic question: does "to be" necessarily mean "to be somewhere or somewhen?" Or to what extent is existence possible outside space-time? Almost any answer to this question can lead to the curious concept of *space without location or distance* — a seeming, and perhaps semantic, absurdity — a space which, if it really existed, could mean that the distance between things might increase while the things themselves remained at rest relative to one another, as in the case of the fictional fugitive from justice who "puts space between" himself and his pursuers. This is not known to happen literally

on Earth, of course, yet it does make some unearthly and un-
common sense in explaining the constancy of the speed of light
regardless of the approach or recession of its source.

Oddly enough, the time aspect in such unfamiliar considerations is almost always harder to grasp than the space aspect,
perhaps partly because it has higher insulation value in consciousness. I mean by that that the degree of *nowness* in time is apt
to influence our feelings more than the degree of *hereness* in
space. For example, a horrible murder committed right *here* fifty
years ago seems more remote, therefore less shocking, than an
equally horrible murder being committed right *now* fifty miles
away or even fifty thousand miles away — the shock of *nowness*
presumably resulting from our subconscious realization that it
might be possible to fly fifty thousand miles (by rocket) to the
scene of the murder, thereby seeing or interacting with it approximately *now*, while no known vehicle could possibly carry us back
fifty years to become involved in a murder *here* half a century
ago or even a month ago.

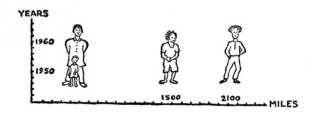

Another curious thing about time is its particular application
to bodies or selves of common identity. For, as I have already
suggested, time seems to be essentially the relationship between
things and things that have common identity — between, say, a
boy and a man grown from that boy — while space is the relationship between things and things without common identity —
as between a man and another man. Thus the deepest time-
space distinction seems to me to be one of identity and, as long
as — and only as long as — identity survives, the time aspect
may be distinguished from that of space. But just as identity may

never have been born inside the time-free atom, so it may die almost anywhere else — because identity is relative, not absolute, and tends to fade into vagueness as perspective recedes, at some level of abstraction ceasing to be determinable at all — even as we saw (page 556) the collar of here-now fading into the aura of elsewhere-elsewhen beyond the hourglass of space-time.

Consider how, when a man is alive, there is an identity between his body (there then) and his body (here now), indicating he exists in time. But after his death, the identity decreases between his body (there then) and his disintegrating body (whenever wherever), indicating that his body at last is loosening its bond with time. His mind also may well escape time before his body — as do abstract (timeless) geometric figures and possibly occurrences inside the atom or outside the galaxy.

I sometimes wonder whether humanity has missed the real point in raising the issue of mortality and immortality — whether perhaps the seemingly limited time span of an earthly life is actually unlimited and eternal — in other words, whether mortality itself may be a finite illusion, being actually immortality and, even though constructed of just a few "years," that those few years are all the time there really is, so that, in fact, they can never cease. Indeed, if time is the relation between things and themselves, how can time end while things exist? Or how can time have ever begun, since either a beginning or an end would logically and almost inevitably frame time in more of itself?

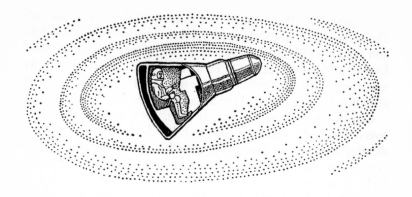

14. the sinews of reality

I T IS ABOUT TIME (Earth time), I think, for me to wind up this volume with some kind of a summary of conclusions as to the nature of the worlds, macro- and microcosmic, as they look from this detached but, I hope, not too dispassioned station. This implies that I should be able to arrive at a decision concerning at least some of the basic laws of nature. Yet I admit that such is, by the same nature, too tall an order for me — and perhaps for any mere man.

The traditional view is that the laws of nature remain constant and more or less hidden, awaiting discovery. But how do we know that the laws of nature are constant? Most things change. Why should laws be an exception? Or, for that matter, what assurance have we that there are any laws of nature at all? Could it possibly be that the men who think they are discovering them are really only thinking them up? This in actual fact was Poincaré's considered view.

It might be helpful here to look at some typical cases in natural law. Before Niccolò Tartaglia's book on ballistics (Venice, 1537), for instance, it had been generally believed that the trajectory of a cannonball consisted of three parts: the straight line of its firing, the curve of its adjusting to gravity and, finally, the vertical straight line of its fall enforced by gravity. While of gravity Leonardo said, "The desire of every heavy body is that its centre may be the centre of the earth."

But soon after Tartaglia and Leonardo, the various laws of nature implied in these beliefs were almost completely swept away before the strong wind of Newton's simpler inverse-square law of gravitation, of which Newton wrote, "The main business of natural philosophy is . . . to deduce causes from effects till we come to the very first cause, which certainly is not mechanical." There is little doubt that Newton had in mind God as his "first cause." And on at least one occasion, he expressed fear that the wheeling planets, moons and swooping comets would in time derange the solar system so badly that nothing short of divine intervention could bring it back into balance.

Then a few years later, Laplace demonstrated mathematically that the perturbations of the planetary bodies upon each other are "not cumulative but periodic" — so the system, after all, must really be capable of self-regulation.

The law that these successively unfolding revelations revealed thus turns out to be a moving, growing thing — a thing even Einstein could not expect to stabilize for very long. And the same may well go for all other laws of nature, it being found generally true that no matter how great the discoverer of anything is, or how small his successors, those successors will inevitably climb upon his high shoulders and from them see farther than he saw.

If this is, in a way, paradoxical, it is also characteristic of nature, which seems almost brimming with paradox — as if her main objective were to baffle our minds or perhaps, as I think more and more, to spark our spirits with wonder. Surely there is wonder in the paradox that, despite the newly proven quantum, nothing is quite sharp or exact in the true world. There is wonder in the facts that the speed of light cannot be determined (even in principle) closer than a few hundred feet per second — that, in any particular case, it has only a probable value; that if you put material into a box, no matter what the material is or what the box is made of, some of the material must escape the box — maybe only a tiny percentage of the elementary particles — but they leap right through it in a ratio of inexorable probability. And there is wonder that the atom is a perpetual motion machine — the very monad that young Democritos had in mind so long ago when he conjectured that "the love and hate of atoms is the cause of unrest in the world."

And, as if that were not enough, matter is both discrete entity and continuous field, at once particle and wave — a wave that is abstract, its illusory nature exemplified in the fact that part of every ocean wave, every sound wave, perhaps every light wave, is always moving backward. Is this also the stuff I am made of and you are made of — the material of life whose very existence is a challenge to the second law of thermodynamics? In speaking of life, of course, we are at the threshold of a whole new subject — but it also impinges on our present discussion and only slightly alters the mixture of our already-rich fuel for thought.

Where does a candle flame go, I might ask, when I blow it out? Is it dead? Is it a hole in nothing? Is it gone forever? Or does it still exist in some other form? The question makes about as much sense as "how fast is the earth moving through space?" It depends on one's viewpoint and various relative factors, including the concepts of identity and continuity. One can logically call a continuous flame "a single flame of one identity," for it is much like a single life. And it is in essence as much an object as the flaming, gaseous sun is an object. Yet, after it is blown out, it is easy enough to light it again if conditions stay about the same — and who can prove the new flame is not the same flame as the old? Thus, in essence and in relativity, death need not end life — not even materially.

This ties in with the basic abstract nature of the world — with opinions such as Jeans's that light waves as such do not really exist — that, when you get right down to it, they are actually only "waves of knowledge." But whatever they really are, the melodies in intelligence are legion when we listen intensively to the world — when we really harken to its inner and outer harmonies!

Since you have probably forgotten most of them, may I briefly review some of the principal kinds of music of the spheres touched upon in this book? First, the harmonic intervals of the 7 notes of the scale explored by Pythagoras, which have certain correspondences to the intervals of the 7 planets of antiquity, and perhaps to the 7 shells of the modern atom, not to mention the 7 octaves of the piano keyboard and the 7 octaves of the Periodic Table of elements — or, in lesser degrees, Bode's Law and Balmer's Ladder, the table of particles, the moon ratios of Jupiter (Io + 2 Ganymede = 3 Europa), the rings of Saturn and the nodes of the Trojan asteroids. Next there are the wave ratios that shape and govern sea waves (group vs. single waves), dunes, snowdrifts, tides, molecules, atoms and other forms of flowing energy — the harmonics and nodes of oscillation in pendulums, springs, and all manner of elastic, chemical, electromagnetic and living bodies. Then the radii of atomic shells, proportioned to the rule of single squares 1, 4, 9, 16, 25 . . . , and

the numbers of electrons in atomic shells to the rule of doubled
squares 2, 8, 18, 32, 50 . . . , the 32 symmetry groupings of
crystals, the 230 distributions of identical objects in space, the
various progressions and means, arithmetic, geometric, harmonic
— and so on . . . and on . . .

The meaning of this seemingly endless music, to me, is that
not only does the atom sing but it sings in tune with the stars
and with its whole surround in space-time, resonating in significant harmonies with other atoms and with all sorts of energies
known and unknown. In truth, reality seems to be a kind of
blossoming limit imposed upon budding possibility by the harmonics of energy in motion — and that limit gives form and value
to all things, gives concreteness to abstraction and actuality to
potentiality.

This is shown in myriad ways almost everywhere I look — in
every field of grass, of stars, of art, science and thought. From
the geometric philosopher, R. Buckminster Fuller, for example,
I learn that the molecular miracle of "synergy" expressible as
$1 + 2 = 4$ is at the bottom of many of his greatest discoveries
in construction engineering. As he himself explains it, "one
equilateral triangle hinged onto 2 others can be folded into a
3-sided tent whose base is a 4th triangle. The inadvertent appearance of this fourth triangle is a demonstration of *synergy*
or the behavior of a system as a whole unpredicted by its parts."

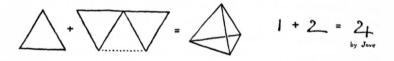

Continuing in similar vein, I consider a folding chair. Does the
chair exist when it is folded up and put away in a closet? Probably

most philosophers would admit that it still exists, even though in a different state — a state of diminished usefulness. If this is so, then, by the same principle, a dismantled watch is still a watch — at least it is a potential watch — and a sperm and an ovum that are capable of meeting and conceiving are, in essence, the creature they will conceivably be. In this sense, you exist before conception and, by the same reasoning, you still exist after decomposition. You ARE, therefore — regardless of time-space. You ARE, I might venture, perhaps partly in the way Jesus meant when he said, "Before Abraham was, I AM."

This is one of the points at which science and religion meet, I think. For if science and religion are opposed at all, they are probably opposed only as a thumb is opposed to fingers. And, as God arranged the hand, a thumb is just the opposition that enables fingers most effectively to grasp things. Furthermore, the *grasp* of things is a kind of created something beyond the members that do the grasping. Which in its turn may help explain why an electron alone is unobservable and therefore, from a practical, objective viewpoint, does not exist as an entity in itself. It is only as united with other particles that the electron, in fact, comes into being for us — that the whole is born of its parts. Thus the abstraction of *addition*, of electron + proton + neutron . . . is what matter IS. It is the abstraction that adds up to and thus creates our world.

In about every important sense, you see, the world is profoundly abstract. And not only the world but also the world's beings are made substantially of abstraction. A being is something like an idea or a song or an organized system. Where was the telephone in A.D. 1800? Where were you and I? None of us had yet been born. All the elements of our future compositions were in the world but not organized into integral systems. And just as the right combination of thoughts and actions produced the telephone and developed it as a system of communication, so did the right combination of motivations and germ cells produce you and me. Thus an organism of life is basically much the same as an organism of systematic ideas — an abstraction, a new combination, a larger reality . . .

This brings up the elusive question of what reality *really* is anyhow — of whether a cubic yard of material taken *out* of a highway is as dangerous or as real (to passing traffic) as a cubic yard heaped *upon* it. If a wonderful world that doesn't exist, for example — say, a mirror world or a thought world — has all the same laws of nature that our "real" world has, how should physicists go about testing it for actuality? Of course, the unreal stars in this unreal world would emit unreal light which could be seen by unreal eyes and recognized in unreal brains. Even the physicists themselves, if they were in such a world, might have to be unreal — but they could still be physicists as distinct from nonphysicists (from, say, sociologists or haberdashers). And there just might be a way for them to test world reality, in a thought experiment, by defining consciousness as reality and somehow determining whether the world in question included consciousness — which, if it was detectable, could (by definition) be real.

Obviously, reality does not need location — which explains how a lens with a focal length of ten feet can be packed in a box only two feet long. And reality does not need to have been experienced — which explains how the shadow of the moon upon Cornwall on August 11, 1999, is already in the world of inference. And reality does not even need to be "true" — which explains how James Watt could build a real and workable steam engine from calculations based on a wrong theory of heat.

Yet reality in some indefinable way does need some degree of existence. I wonder, for instance, about the difficulty of visualizing life on Earth very far beyond one's own birth or death. Could there be a deep reason why one cannot imagine nonexistence? Perhaps the real resolution of such a paradox could be found in the same cosmic positiveness that reveals coldness to be only a reduced heat and darkness but a lesser light. For why should not existence itself, like time and life and love, be relative and capable of infinite range? Who can decide where some degree of being really borders on the not-being? Or, by simple semantics, when the "not-be" will, if ever, begin to not be?

There may even be an uncertainty principle connected with being or reality, as Einstein suggested when he distinguished reality from certainty, saying, "As far as the propositions of mathematics refer to reality they are not certain, and in so far as they are certain they do not refer to reality." In which case, nature probably has a subtler symmetry than most human minds can yet understand — the human mind having hardly yet emerged from the jungle primeval.

As for my own jungle mind, I only hope my mirages turn out to be real mirages, not just picture mirages — and that my mental pictures become real pictures, not merely pictures of pictures. For, as Bertrand Russell once expressed it, how things seem to seem is not enough. We must somehow discover how things really seem.

This of course calls for a certain greatness in perspective. When you look at a small table globe representing the earth, for example, you must never forget that, on the same scale, the "sun" is as big as a barn and a mile away, the "nearest star" as far as the moon, and "other galaxies" way beyond comprehension — even on that small scale. Now if you look out upon the actual sky above your head and beneath your feet, as I do here, you discover it to contain not only much but ultimately everything, not excepting yourself nor all sorts of unbelievable things — not excepting milk from the Milky Way (the earth, incidentally, is part of the Milky Way) — and not excepting much more that is humanly inconceivable, in fact literally all there ever was and is — and perhaps all that might be — entire worlds and galaxies of

worlds and clusters of galaxies of worlds and endless, showering
ebullitions of all these and more, pouring and whirling ever outward into all space — containing among them unnumbered worlds
more enlightened, more beautiful in spirit than our undistin-
guished speck — where ideas unfathomable and joys undream-
able grow and flower and fulfill themselves in actual, breathing
heavens beyond our reach yet, literally, right before our eyes!

Is there nothing then but illusory space-time between us and
Kingdom Come? Naturally, I cannot reach out and touch it with
my hand but I can imagine it someway with my mind and
feel its potentiality in my heart. And I can see beauty and order
there — and most especially the elements of music. I can hear,
in a real sense, the music of the spheres.

Speaking of elements, by the way, one cannot help but be
reminded of the restraint of nature in forming elements on such
a planet as the earth. Suppose that, instead of a hundred chemical elements, there were a hundred million of them. In such a
case, almost every pebble on every beach and every mote of dust
would be of an unknown substance, and it would be next to
impossible to develop any science of chemistry. But that is not the
real way of nature. Nature has a beautiful simplicity of order.
And the intuitions of Pythagoras and Leucippos and some of
Plato's are proving substantially justified.

The world is made of abstraction with sinews of perspective
— and music. Its waves gather knowledge and instruct the universe. Its melody is more than notes, its poetry more than words.
Its stars are as much seeds of distance as earthly acorns are seeds
of time — for if acorns unfold into oak trees after many years,
so may stars "planted" in space be considered spores of mysterious
potency — space seeds that we cannot fathom from here but

which, if the unraveling of space allows, may soon draw near and blossom into our ken.

And as I float — in good company but alone — I must ask once again when is "now"? And where is "here"? As did Sappho while she sang:

> The moon is gone   Time passes on
> And the Pleiads set,   And passes; yet
> Midnight is nigh: Alone I lie.

For this black space has more dimensions than any man can know. It is the page on which I write, the harp on which I play. It is the high vantage out of which I seek new questions for old silences — new presences for old absences.

And I can still remember my youth on the rolling earth and see again the mountains that I saw. And ever must I remind me that when I see those mountains down there, those great and breath-taking mountains of the wrinkled crust, that there are even greater, even stronger, even more beautiful mountains somewhere far behind them — and atom worlds within their atom worlds — and oceans beneath earthly oceans — stars below the stars, constellations beyond the constellations, even "universes" outside "the" universe.

I am obviously still much too small and feeble and young to see all these things clearly. But somehow I know. I know that they are there.

inðex

This full index, made by the author, is especially suited for browsing. It lists hundreds of illustrations and abstract concepts and is liberally crissed and crossed with suggestive and interrelating references.